Prentice Hall
LITERATURE
Timeless Voices, Timeless Themes

D1193438

Selection Support:
Skills Development Workbook
Teacher's Edition

GOLD LEVEL

Prentice
Hall

Upper Saddle River, New Jersey
Glenview, Illinois
Needham, Massachusetts

ISBN 0-13-058355-3

5 6 7 8 9 10   06 05

CONTENTS

UNIT 1: SPINE TINGLERS

UNIT 2: CHALLENGES AND CHOICES

UNIT 4: THE LIGHTER SIDE

UNIT 5: VISIONS OF THE FUTURE

UNIT 9: POETRY

UNIT 10: THE EPIC

"The Cask of Amontillado" by Edgar Allan Poe

Build Vocabulary

Spelling Strategy   When adding an ending that begins with a vowel to a word that ends in a silent letter *e*, the *e* is usually dropped. For example, when adding the suffix *-ing* to the word *subside*, the silent *e* is dropped to form *subsiding*.

Using the Prefix *pre-*

A. DIRECTIONS: Rewrite each sentence, combining the underlined word with the prefix *pre-*.

1. The directions said to <u>condition</u> the fabric before use to avoid permanent stains.

   _____

   _____

2. A select group of patrons was allowed to <u>view</u> the exhibit before the opening.

   _____

   _____

3. Before the <u>flight</u>, the crew gave the airplane a thorough inspection.

   _____

   _____

4. Manufacturers now <u>fabricate</u> whole sections of buildings before delivery to a building site.

   _____

   _____

5. Avoid waiting in line by <u>registering</u> before the semester begins.

   _____

   _____

Using the Word Bank

precluded	retribution	accosted	afflicted
explicit	recoiling	termination	subsided

B. DIRECTIONS: Match each word in the left column with its definition in the right column. Write the letter of the definition on the line next to the word it defines.

____ 1. precluded   a. end

____ 2. explicit   b. greeted, especially in a forward or aggressive way

____ 3. subsided   c. prevented; made impossible in advance

____ 4. retribution   d. clearly stated

____ 5. recoiling   e. settled down; became less active or intense

____ 6. accosted   f. suffering or sickened

____ 7. termination   g. payback; punishment for a misdeed or reward for a good deed

____ 8. afflicted   h. staggering back

"The Cask of Amontillado" by Edgar Allan Poe

Build Grammar Skills: Common and Proper Nouns

Nouns can be divided into two groups: common nouns and proper nouns. A **common noun** names any one of a class of people, places, or things. A **proper noun** names a particular person, place, or thing, and it always begins with a capital letter. In proper nouns of more than one word, the first word, the last word, and all other important words are capitalized.

The following sentence from "The Cask of Amontillado" contains both common and proper nouns. Notice that *sherry*, a common noun, names a class of wine; *Amontillado*, a proper noun, names a particular wine.

And as for Luchesi, he can't distinguish sherry from Amontillado.

A. Practice: Correct the capitalization errors in the following sentences by writing the words correctly on the line that follows each sentence.

1. In the Short Story "The cask of amontillado," Fortunato is eager to accompany montresor into the wine vaults.

   _____

2. As they descend into the Catacombs, Montresor pretends to be concerned about fortunato's health.

   _____

3. When fortunato hears Montresor's Family Motto, he seems unaware of the irony in the latin words.

   _____

4. In this story, Montresor and Fortunato are the Main Characters, and Montresor is the Narrator.

   _____

5. Edgar allan poe, whose parents were both Actors, was a Poet and a Critic as well as a short-story writer.

   _____

B. Writing Application: Choose one of the following groups of common nouns. Write two or three sentences based on these words. Include at least one proper noun for each category.

   Common Nouns: team, school, athlete

   Example: My swim team, the Flying Fish, won a meet last night at Provincetown High School. Mike Jameson and three other swimmers qualified for the district relay team.

1. movie, actors, theater

2. holiday, family members, location

3. sporting event, participants, location

4. concert, musician, recordings

   _____

   _____

   _____

   _____

"**The Cask of Amontillado**" by Edgar Allan Poe

Reading Strategy: Breaking Down Confusing Sentences

Good readers use a variety of strategies to monitor and increase their literal comprehension, or their ability to understand the basic meaning of a writer's words. One strategy is to **break down confusing sentences.**

You can break down a sentence by reading it in meaningful sections rather than word by word. Doing so will help you to identify exactly where the meaning is unclear. Be sure to note any unfamiliar words and clarify their meanings.

You can also break down a confusing sentence by locating its subject. After you have done that, look for words or phrases that tell something about the subject. Sometimes you may need to rearrange the parts of a sentence, or move some parts out of the way, in order to find the main idea.

DIRECTIONS: Read the following passages from "The Cask of Amontillado." Practice breaking down the sentences by reading them in meaningful sections and locating the subjects. Rewrite the sentences in your own words, placing the subjects first.

> **Example:** It must be understood that neither by word nor deed had I given Fortunato cause to doubt my good will.
>
> **Sample Answer:** I had given Fortunato no cause to doubt my good will, neither by word nor deed.

1. In painting and gemmary, Fortunato, like his countrymen, was a quack.

   _____

   _____

2. It was about dusk, one evening during the supreme madness of the carnival season, that I encountered my friend.

   _____

   _____

3. Thus speaking, Fortunato possessed himself of my arm; and putting on a mask of black silk and drawing a roquelaure closely about my person, I suffered him to hurry me to my palazzo.

   _____

   _____

4. In an instant he had reached the extremity of the niche, and finding his progress arrested by the rock, stood stupidly bewildered.

   _____

   _____

5. But to these words I hearkened in vain for a reply.

   _____

   _____

Name _____ Date _____

"The Cask of Amontillado" by Edgar Allan Poe

Literary Analysis: Mood

Mood is the emotion evoked in the reader by a piece of writing. When reading "The Cask of Amontillado," you can identify mood from the descriptive details Poe uses. Notice how the italicized details in the following excerpt from Poe's story create an eerie mood:

"The niter!" I said; "see, it *increases*. It *hangs like moss upon the vaults.* We are below the river's bed. *The drops of moisture trickle among the bones.*"

Descriptive details can help you identify the specific mood of a passage or piece of writing. Consider the sentence "We walked down the hallway." This sentence does not create an atmosphere or mood. Now consider the sentence "We crept down the long, dark hallway." You can identify a suspenseful mood by the vivid verb *crept* and the descriptive detail *long, dark hallway.*

DIRECTIONS: Read the following passages from "The Cask of Amontillado." Identify the mood of each passage. List the descriptive details that help create the mood.

1. I took from their sconces two flambeaux, and giving one to Fortunato . . . I passed down a long and winding staircase, requesting him to be cautious as he followed. We came at length to the foot of the descent, and stood together upon the damp ground of the catacombs of the Montresors.

   Descriptive details:_____

   _____

   Mood: _____

2. We passed through a range of low arches, descended, passed on, and descending again, arrived at a deep crypt, in which the foulness of the air caused our flambeaux rather to glow than flame.

   Descriptive details:_____

   _____

   Mood: _____

3. "Pass your hand," I said, "over the wall; . . . it is *very* damp. Once more let me *implore* you to return. No? Then I must positively leave you. . . ."

   Descriptive details:_____

   _____

   Mood: _____

4. A succession of loud and shrill screams, bursting suddenly from the throat of the chained form, seemed to thrust me violently back. For a brief moment I hesitated, I trembled.

   Descriptive details:_____

   _____

   Mood: _____

"The Most Dangerous Game" by Richard Connell

Build Vocabulary

Spelling Strategy   When suffixes beginning with a vowel are added to words ending in e, the e may be retained or displaced by another letter.

Retained: courage + -ous = courageous; advantage + -ous = advantageous
Displaced: sense + -ous = sensuous; scruple + -ous = scrupulous

Using Forms of *scruples*

A. DIRECTIONS: Use the correct form of *scruples* to fit each of the following sentences:

1. Rainsford had _____ when it came to hunting human beings as prey.

2. He took _____ care to conceal signs of his traps from his hunters.

3. General Zaroff's _____ actions would have earned him capital punishment in most courts of law.

Using the Word Bank

palpable	indolently	bizarre	naive
scruples	blandly	grotesque	futile

B. DIRECTIONS: Match each word in the left column with its definition in the right column. Write the letter of the definition on the line next to the word it defines.

_____ 1. palpable   a. misgivings about one's behavior

_____ 2. indolently   b. in a mild, dull way

_____ 3. naive   c. fantastic; strange

_____ 4. scruples   d. easily perceived by the senses

_____ 5. blandly   e. useless, vain

_____ 6. grotesque   f. in a lazy way

_____ 7. futile   g. distorted in manner or appearance

_____ 8. bizarre   h. artless or unsophisticated

C. DIRECTIONS: Read each series of words. Write the word from the Word Bank that best fits with the other words. Use a word only once.

1. weird, strange, eerie, _____

2. morals, doubts, feelings, _____

3. vain, unsuccessful, silly, _____

4. ugly, gruesome, macabre, _____

"The Most Dangerous Game" by Richard Connell

Build Grammar Skills: Pronouns and Antecedents

Pronouns take the place of nouns. The noun to which a pronoun refers is called its **antecedent**. A pronoun may appear before its antecedent, after it, or even in another sentence. Some common pronouns are *I, you, he, she, it, we, they, his,* and *hers.* Pronouns should agree in number and gender with their antecedents. In the following examples, the pronouns are underlined, and the antecedents are in italics.

> **Examples:** *Rainsford*, reclining in a steamer chair, indolently puffed on his favorite brier.
> Rainsford remembered the *shots*. They had come from the right.

The pronoun *his* refers to its singular antecedent, *Rainsford*. The pronoun *They* refers to its plural antecedent, *shots*.

A. Practice: On the line below each sentence from "The Most Dangerous Game," write the antecedent of the underlined pronouns.

1. "Don't talk rot, Whitney," said Rainsford. "You're a big-game hunter, not a philosopher."

   _____

2. "Nonsense," laughed Rainsford. "This hot weather is making you soft, Whitney."

   _____

3. Rainsford heard a sound. It came out of the darkness, a high screaming sound, the sound of an animal in an extremity of anguish and terror.

   _____

4. The man's only answer was to raise the hammer of his revolver with his thumb.

   _____

5. "Ivan is an incredibly strong fellow," remarked the general, "but he has the misfortune to be deaf and dumb."

   _____

6. The general laughed with entire good nature. He regarded Rainsford quizzically.

   _____

7. "If my quarry eludes me for three whole days, he wins the game. If I find him"—the general smiled—"he loses."

   _____

B. Writing Application: Write a pronoun that agrees with the underlined antecedents in each sentence.

1. As Whitney and Rainsford sail near Ship-Trap Island, _____ discuss superstitions about it.

2. After Rainsford had slept, _____ felt renewed.

3. Each of the men spoke confidently about _____ hunting experience.

4. The dogs' barking grew louder as _____ neared _____ prey.

5. It seemed unlikely that the men who became stranded on Ship-Trap Island would escape with _____ lives.

"The Most Dangerous Game" by Richard Connell

Reading Strategy: Using Context Clues

You can often determine the meaning of an unfamiliar word from its **context**—the words, phrases, and sentences that surround it. Sometimes a writer will define or restate the meaning of an unfamiliar word. More often, you have to look for less obvious clues. For example, you may wonder about the meaning of the word *anguish* in the following sentence: "It came out of the darkness, a high screaming sound, the sound of an animal in an extremity of anguish and terror." By noting the words *screaming* and *terror*, you can figure out that *anguish* must mean "a condition of great suffering or pain."

DIRECTIONS: Read these sentences from "The Most Dangerous Game." Use context clues to determine the meaning of each underlined word. Circle the clues you use to help determine the word's meaning. Write your definition on the line under each sentence and then check your definition against the definition in a dictionary.

1. Rainsford, reclining in a steamer chair, indolently puffed on his favorite <u>brier</u>.

   _____

2. Rainsford remembered the shots. They had come from the right, and <u>doggedly</u> he swam in that direction, swimming with slow, deliberate strokes, conserving his strength.

   _____

3. But as he forged along he saw to his great astonishment that all the lights were in one enormous building—a <u>lofty</u> structure with pointed towers plunging upward into the gloom.

   _____

4. The revolver pointed as <u>rigidly</u> as if the giant were a statue.

5. When I shot some of his prize turkeys with it, he did not punish me; he complimented me on my <u>marksmanship</u>.

   _____

6. If my quarry <u>eludes</u> me for three whole days, he wins the game.

   _____

7. He filled Rainsford's glass with <u>venerable</u> Chablis from a dusty bottle.

   _____

8. An <u>apprehensive</u> night crawled slowly by like a wounded snake, and sleep did not visit Rainsford, although the silence of a dead world was on the jungle.

   _____

9. The <u>pent-up</u> air burst hotly from Rainsford's lungs.

   _____

10. Then, as he stepped forward, his foot sank into the <u>ooze</u>.

    _____

"The Most Dangerous Game" by Richard Connell

Literary Analysis: Suspense

Suspense is the quality in a work of literature that makes us continue to read to see what will happen next. Writers create suspense with details that arouse curiosity in the reader by foreshadowing, or hinting at, what is to come. See how Richard Connell builds suspense in this sentence from "The Most Dangerous Game."

The baying of the hounds grew nearer, then still nearer, nearer, ever nearer.

Note how the repeated use of the word *nearer* helps bring to life the character's terror of being pursued by the hounds. Will the hounds overtake their prey?

A. DIRECTIONS: Read the following passage, and watch for details the author uses to create suspense. Circle the words in the passage that make you curious about the outcome.

On a ridge Rainsford climbed a tree. Down a watercourse, not a mile away, he could see the bush moving. Straining his eyes, he saw the lean figure of General Zaroff; just ahead of him Rainsford made out another figure whose wide shoulders surged through the tall jungle weeds; it was the giant Ivan, and he seemed pulled forward by some unseen force.
Rainsford knew that Ivan must be holding the pack in leash.

B. DIRECTIONS: Study the following list of details. Which of these might be used to create suspense? Which would not be useful in arousing curiosity? Circle the details that you think could help create suspense, and use them to help you write an opening paragraph for a suspenseful story.

an abandoned movie theater

late at night

in a small town in Pennsylvania

cobwebs hanging from the rotting red velvet curtains that cover the screen

the place is called the Davenport Theater

a large clock stopped at five minutes past twelve

a burnt-out electric exit sign, broken and hanging crooked

first floor is flooded two feet deep with river water

mist lies low over the water on the floor

the floor of the balcony wobbles, with boards missing in places

_____

_____

_____

_____

_____

_____

_____

"Casey at the Bat" by Ernest Lawrence Thayer

Build Vocabulary

Spelling Strategy Adding the suffix -ous may require changing other letters, depending on the spelling of the base word.

> **Examples:** *dangerous* (add to root word)
> *tumultuous* (add *u* before suffix)
> *religious* (keep *i*; drop -*on*)

Using Forms of *tumult*

Recognizing different forms of a word can help expand your vocabulary. If you recognize the word *tumult*, meaning "a noisy commotion," you may be able to figure out the word *tumultuous*, an adjective meaning "wild and noisy."

A. Directions: Use the given form of *tumult* in a sentence of your own.

1. tumult:_____

   _____

2. tumultuous: _____

   _____

Using the Word Bank

pallor	wreathed	writhing	tumult

B. Directions: Each of the following questions consists of a related pair of words in CAPITAL LETTERS, followed by three lettered pairs of words. Choose the pair that best expresses a relationship similar to the one expressed in the pair in CAPITAL LETTERS.

____ 1. WRITHING : WRIGGLING ::
        a. tugboat : ship
        b. run : walk
        c. hop : jump

____ 2. PALLOR : RED ::
        a. paper : book
        b. sweet : candy
        c. flush : white

____ 3. WREATHED : ENCIRCLED ::
        a. youthful : aged
        b. hard : difficult
        c. fast : race

____ 4. TUMULT : PEACE ::
        a. uproar : calm
        b. loud : din
        c. turbine : jet

C. Directions: Choose the word that is most similar in meaning to the numbered word.

____ 1. pallor
        a. paleness
        b. darkness
        c. temper

____ 2. wreathed
        a. straight
        b. curled
        c. hanging

____ 3. writhing
        a. twisting
        b. screaming
        c. crawling

____ 4. tumult
        a. jump
        b. noise
        c. crowd

"Casey at the Bat" by Ernest Lawrence Thayer

Build Grammar Skills: Possessive Nouns

When writers want to indicate ownership or relationship, they use the **possessive** form of a noun. In the following example, the possessive form *Casey's* shows that the eye and the lip belong to Casey.

Defiance glanced in Casey's eye, a sneer curled Casey's lip.

Following are several rules for forming possessive nouns.

Rules	Examples
For a singular noun, add an apostrophe and *s*.	• the shoe's heel • the man's laughter • the actress's role
For a plural noun that ends in *s*, add only an apostrophe.	• the shoes' heels • the Thompsons' house • his stories' details
For a plural noun that does *not* end in *s*, add an apostrophe and *s*.	• the men's laughter • the mice's nest • children's books

A. Practice: Write the singular and plural possessive forms of each noun.

Noun	Singular Possessive	Plural Possessive
1. body	_____	_____
2. woman	_____	_____
3. fox	_____	_____
4. igloo	_____	_____
5. class	_____	_____

B. Writing Application: In the following sentences, the underlined words express possession. Revise each group of underlined words so that it uses a possessive noun to express the same relationship.

1. When Casey went up to bat, the <u>cheers of the crowd</u> could be heard near and far.

_____

2. The <u>chances of the team</u> of winning were not looking good.

_____

3. Casey smiled at the <u>anticipation of the fans</u>.

_____

4. It seems that Casey underestimated the <u>skill of the pitcher</u>.

_____

Name _____ Date _____

"Casey at the Bat" by Ernest Lawrence Thayer

Reading Strategy: Summarizing

It is often useful to pause when reading to summarize—briefly restate—what is happening. Repeating the key events of the action can help you understand and enjoy the work.

A. DIRECTIONS: On the line at the left, write the letter of the phrase that best summarizes the stanza from "Casey at the Bat."

_____ 1. Then from the gladdened multitude went up a joyous yell—
It rumbled in the mountaintops, it rattled in the dell;
It struck upon the hillside and rebounded on the flat;
For Casey, mighty Casey, was advancing to the bat.

    a. Distant thunder sounded and everyone was startled.
    b. Casey, the hero, made a lot of noise approaching his turn at bat.
    c. The crowd reacted wildly as Casey approached the plate.
    d. There was whispering and laughing among the crowd when Casey appeared.

_____ 2. Ten thousand eyes were on him as he rubbed his hands with dirt,
Five thousand tongues applauded when he wiped them on his shirt;
Then when the writhing pitcher ground the ball into his hip,
Defiance glanced in Casey's eye, a sneer curled Casey's lip.

    a. Someone threw an object onto the field.
    b. Casey tensely awaited the pitcher's throw.
    c. Casey became interested in the style of the stitching on the leather ball.
    d. The umpire went on strike when Casey refused to do what he was supposed to do.

_____ 3. From the benches, black with people, there went up a muffled roar,
Like the beating of the storm waves on the stern and distant shore.
"Kill him! kill the umpire!" shouted someone on the stand;
And it's likely they'd have killed him had not Casey raised his hand.

    a. The crowd was strongly displeased with the umpire's judgment.
    b. The crowd got nervous as a storm seemed to be approaching.
    c. The umpire was known to the crowd, which planned to murder him.
    d. Casey raised his hand to threaten the umpire.

B. DIRECTIONS: Write a one-sentence summary of each of the following stanzas:

1. But Flynn preceded Casey, and likewise so did Blake,
And the former was a pudd'n, and the latter was a fake.
So on that stricken multitude a deathlike silence sat;
For there seemed but little chance of Casey's getting to the bat.

_____

_____

2. With a smile of Christian charity great Casey's visage shone;
He stilled the rising tumult, he made the game go on;
He signaled to the pitcher, and once more the spheroid flew;
But Casey still ignored it, and the umpire said, "Strike two."

_____

_____

"Casey at the Bat" by Ernest Lawrence Thayer

Literary Analysis: Climax and Anticlimax

When you reach the point in a story or a narrative poem at which you learn how the conflict will be resolved, you've finally reached the **climax.** If the outcome is a downward turn of events, and one that you hadn't expected, it is called an **anticlimax.**

In "Casey at the Bat," the turning point is reached when Casey fails at the plate. We've heard that Casey was "mighty" so we are surprised at the outcome. The turning point is an anticlimax.

DIRECTIONS: Review in your mind a recent story you have read or a movie or television program you have viewed. Analyze how the author or director made use of climax or anticlimax. How was the story similar to or different from "Casey at the Bat"? Complete your analysis by filling in the chart below.

Story/Program: _____

Author/Director: _____

_____

Plot Summary: _____

_____

_____

_____

_____

Climax/Anticlimax: _____

_____

_____

_____

_____

_____

Comparison to "Casey at the Bat": _____

_____

_____

_____

_____

_____

_____

"The Birds" by Daphne du Maurier

Build Vocabulary

Spelling Strategy   Most words ending in silent *e* keep the *e* before a suffix beginning with a consonant. Examples: *furtive + ly = furtively; sure + ly = surely; cute + ness = cuteness.*

Using the Suffix *-ful*

The suffix *-ful* has a number of meanings. Examples: "having the quality of"—*masterful*; "having the quantity that would fill"—*teaspoonful*; "full of"—*fretful.*

A. DIRECTIONS: Read the following sentences. Then write a related sentence, adding the suffix *-ful* to the italicized word in the original sentence.

1. He began to *fret* as the storm approached.

   _____

   _____

2. The child's eyes filled with *wonder* at the new-fallen snow.

   _____

   _____

3. The farmer filled a *bucket* with feed for the sheep.

   _____

   _____

Using the Word Bank

placid	garish	recounted	sullen
furtively	imperative	reconnaissance	fretful

B. DIRECTIONS: Match each word in the left column with its definition in the right column. Write the letter of the definition on the line next to the word it defines.

____ 1. placid   a. absolutely necessary; urgent

____ 2. recounted   b. irritable and discontented

____ 3. imperative   c. tranquil; calm

____ 4. fretful   d. stealthily, so as to avoid being heard

____ 5. reconnaissance e. too bright or gaudy

____ 6. furtively   f. told in detail

____ 7. sullen   g. gloomy; dismal

____ 8. garish   h. exploratory in nature; as when examining or observing to seek
                            information

"The Birds" by Daphne du Maurier

Build Grammar Skills: Reflexive and Intensive Pronouns

Pronouns that end in -*self* or –*selves* are either reflexive or intensive pronouns. A **reflexive pronoun** indicates that someone or something performs an action to, for, or upon itself. A reflexive pronoun points back to a noun or pronoun earlier in the sentence. In the following example, the reflexive pronoun *himself* points back to *uncle*.

My uncle considers *himself* a gourmet cook.

An **intensive pronoun** simply adds emphasis to a noun or pronoun in the same sentence. In the following example, the intensive pronoun *herself* adds emphasis to *president*.

The president *herself* visited the new school.

A. Practice: Read each of the following sentences. Indicate whether the italicized pronoun is reflexive or intensive.

1. Nat thought that the birds *themselves* must get a message that winter is coming.

   _____

2. Jill squeezed *herself* into the crowded car.

   _____

3. Nat was careful to check the food supply *himself.*

   _____

4. They made *themselves* dinner and waited for a radio report.

   _____

B. Writing Application: Rewrite each of the following sentences using the pronoun provided as reflexive or intensive, as directed.

1. The villagers prepared for more bird attacks. (*themselves*, reflexive)

   _____

2. Nat wanted to finish the work. (*himself*, intensive)

   _____

3. Nat's wife tried to keep calm by doing routine tasks. (*herself*, reflexive)

   _____

4. In order to reach people, the birds would destroy the house. (*themselves*, intensive)

   _____

5. Nat prepared for the worst. (*himself*, reflexive)

   _____

"The Birds" by Daphne du Maurier

Reading Strategy: Predicting

Writers often provide details that enable you to **predict** what will happen next in a story. Predicting keeps you actively involved in your reading. As you read, revise your predictions based on new details.

DIRECTIONS: Use the following chart to keep track of your predictions as you read "The Birds." After reading the passage in the first column, make a prediction about what you think will happen next. After you read on, use the third column to note the accuracy of your prediction.

Story Event	Make a Prediction	Assess Your Prediction
The birds had been more restless than ever this fall of the year, the agitation more marked because the days were still. . . . There were many more than usual; Nat was sure of this.		
Suddenly a frightened cry came from the room across the passage where the children slept.		
He could see the gulls now, circling the fields, coming in toward land. Still silent. Still no sound. "Look, Dad, look over there, look at all the gulls." "Yes. Hurry, now."		
The cows were lowing, moving restlessly in the yard, and he could see a gap in the fence where the sheep had knocked their way through, to roam unchecked in the front garden before the farmhouse. No smoke came from the chimneys. He was filled with misgiving. He did not want his wife or the children to go down to the farm.		

"The Birds" by Daphne du Maurier

Literary Analysis: Foreshadowing

Foreshadowing is a writer's use of hints to suggest events that have yet to occur in a story. Often, writers use this technique to create suspense. Read this passage from "The Birds" in which Nat has a conversation with the farmer, Mr. Trigg.

"Have you boarded your windows?" asked Nat.
"No. Lot of nonsense. They like to scare you on the wireless. I've had more to do today than to go round boarding up my windows."
"I'd board them now, if I were you."

What events in the story are foreshadowed here? When you read this passage, did you feel that something bad would happen to the Triggs? Why? Daphne du Maurier's use of foreshadowing in "The Birds" adds to the suspense in the story, keeping us on the edge of our seats as we read.

A. DIRECTIONS: Read the following passages from "The Birds." On the lines that follow, describe what is being foreshadowed and explain the hints that contributed to your reasoning.

1. Presently the tapping came again, this time more forceful, more insistent, and now his wife woke at the sound and, turning in bed, said to him, "See to the window, Nat, it's rattling."

   _____

   _____

2. They had not learned yet how to cling to a shoulder, how to rip clothing, how to dive in mass upon the head, upon the body.

   _____

   _____

B. DIRECTIONS: Imagine that you are writing a story about a cruise ship that runs into a fierce storm. The danger of the situation is increased because the operators of the ship have cut corners on safety preparations. List some details that you might put into your story that will foreshadow the trouble to come. Then sketch out a plot that will incorporate the details you listed.

_____

_____

_____

_____

_____

_____

_____

_____

_____

_____

_____

"The Red-headed League" by Sir Arthur Conan Doyle

Build Vocabulary

Spelling Strategy   When a prefix is added to a word or root, the spelling of the word or root is not changed. Common prefixes include *un-* (not) as in *unneeded*; *re-* (again) as in *replay*; *intro-* (into) as in *introspective*; *mis-* (wrong, bad) as in *misrule*.

Using the Root *-spec-*

Knowing the meaning of a root can help you figure out the meaning of unfamiliar words. The root *-spec-* means "look" or "see." Think about how *-spec-* provides a clue to the meaning of each of the following words: *introspective* ("causing one to look into one's own feelings"); *perspective* ("point of view"); *spectator* ("viewer").

A. DIRECTIONS: Use a word from the box to complete each of the sentences that follow.

spectacular	spectator	inspector	spectacle

1. The criminals were planning a _____ bank robbery.

2. It was quite a _____ to witness Holmes capturing the criminals.

3. The _____ returned to his office at Scotland Yard.

4. Doctor Watson was mostly a _____ during the capture.

Using the Word Bank

singular	avail	hoax	introspective
vex	conundrums	astuteness	formidable

B. DIRECTIONS: Match each word in the left column with its definition in the right column. Write the letter of the definition on the line next to the word it defines.

____ 1. singular a. causing one to look into one's own thoughts and feelings

____ 2. avail b. annoy

____ 3. hoax c. extraordinary; rare

____ 4. introspective d. puzzling questions or problems

____ 5. vex e. shrewdness

____ 6. conundrums f. be of use

____ 7. astuteness g. awe-inspiring

____ 8. formidable h. a deceitful trick

C. DIRECTIONS: For each numbered word, choose the word or phrase that is most nearly the same in meaning.

____ 1. singular
   a. special b. many c. varied d. colorful

____ 2. astuteness
   a. inability b. likeness c. temperature d. cleverness

"The Red-headed League" by Sir Arthur Conan Doyle

Build Grammar Skills: Coordinate Adjectives

Sir Arthur Conan Doyle uses numerous adjectives to bring vivid details to his writing. **Coordinate adjectives** are adjectives of equal rank that separately modify the noun they precede. They are separated by commas. They are not coordinate if the final adjective is thought of as part of the noun. For example:

> **Coordinate:** It was instantly opened by a *bright-looking, clean-shaven* young fellow, who asked him to step in.
>
> **Not Coordinate:** Altogether, look as I would, there was nothing remarkable about the man save his *blazing red* head.

A. Practice: Read the following sentences, paying careful attention to the italicized adjectives. On the line that follows each sentence, identify the adjectives as coordinate or not coordinate.

1. No one paid any attention to the *short, quiet* man.

   _____

2. Inspector Fargo was struck by the man's *jet black* mustache.

   _____

3. His *quick, eager* mind racing, Fargo searched his memory for where he had seen that face before.

   _____

4. Suddenly he recalled a *mysterious, unsolved* robbery from years ago.

   _____

B. Writing Application: Rewrite the following sentences, adding two or more adjectives, coordinate or not coordinate as indicated before the italicized word.

1. The tracks on the wall posed a (coordinate) *mystery.*

   _____

   _____

2. The (not coordinate) *tracks* didn't belong to any animal we had ever seen.

   _____

   _____

3. We began to suspect we were the victims of a (coordinate) *hoax.*

   _____

   _____

4. The investigation soon uncovered a (coordinate) *scheme.*

   _____

   _____

"The Red-headed League" by Sir Arthur Conan Doyle

Reading Strategy: Using Key Details

While it's important to note key details when reading any piece of fiction, it is especially important when reading a mystery. By taking note of important details, the careful reader tries to solve the crime along with the detective. Sometimes you might even be able to solve it *before* the detective!

DIRECTIONS: As you read, take note of key details about the mystery as it unfolds. Put yourself in Sherlock Holmes's shoes, paying attention to—and analyzing—every detail. Use the graphic organizer below to help you in *your* analysis.

Key Details in "The Red-headed League"

Who	What	When	Where
assistant	works for half pay		pawn shop

"The Red-headed League" by Sir Arthur Conan Doyle

Literary Analysis: The Mystery

The mystery is one of the most popular genres of fiction. Some of the most enduring and popular characters in literature are fictional detectives such as Sherlock Holmes, who may be the most famous fictional detective of them all.

A mystery is a story of suspense that usually contains the following elements: a crime, a crime-solver, suspects, a criminal, and key details such as clues, alibis, and characters' motives.

DIRECTIONS: Use what you've learned about mysteries to plan your own mystery story. Fill in the chart below with your ideas.

Crime: _____

_____

_____

Crime-solver: _____

_____

_____

Suspects: _____

_____

_____

Suspects' motives: _____

_____

_____

Suspects' alibis: _____

_____

_____

Clues: _____

_____

_____

Solution: _____

_____

_____

"The Listeners" by Walter de la Mare
"Beware: Do Not Read This Poem" by Ishmael Reed
"Echo" by Henriqueta Lisboa

Build Vocabulary

Spelling Strategy When adding a suffix that begins with a vowel to a word that ends in a consonant, the spelling of the word does not change. For example, adding the suffix -ary to the word *legend* forms the new word *legendary*.

Using Poetic License and Vocabulary in Poems

Poets sometimes use poetic license—changing the spelling of words or abbreviating words in a poem—to add meaning to a poem.

A. Directions: Read the following draft for a poem. Then use poetic license to add meaning and expression to the poem by altering spelling or changing or adding words.

The ancient tune floated from the stage

Fluid it flowed upward forever _____

Violins surrounded me _____

Then came the piccolo staccato— _____

Its notes were very short _____
_____

Using the Word Bank

perplexed	thronging	legendary	strafing

B. Directions: Match each word in the left column with its definition in the right column. Write the letter of the definition on the line next to the word it defines.

____ 1. perplexed   a. crowding into

____ 2. thronging   b. puzzled

____ 3. legendary   c. attacking with machine-gun fire

____ 4. strafing   d. based on stories handed down for generations

Using the Suffix -ary

The word *legendary* is formed by adding the suffix -ary to the word *legend*. The suffix -ary means "of or connected with." Adding the suffix -ary changes a noun to an adjective.

> **legend** *n.* : A story handed down among a group of people
> **legendary** *adj.* : Something related to or connected with a legend

C. Directions: Define each of the following words. Add the suffix -ary to each word. Then write the meaning of the word with the -ary suffix.

1. parliament _____

2. budget _____

"The Listeners" by Walter de la Mare
"Beware: Do Not Read This Poem" by Ishmael Reed
"Echo" by Henriqueta Lisboa

Build Grammar Skills: Types of Adjectives

An **adjective** is a word used to describe a noun or pronoun or to give a noun or pronoun a more specific meaning. Adjectives modify nouns and pronouns by answering the questions *What kind? Which one? How Many?* or *How much?* Sometimes a noun, pronoun, or verb may serve as an adjective. Look at the following examples of adjectives taken from the selections in this grouping.

> **Adjective:** *Green* parrot
>
> **Noun as adjective:** By the lonely *Traveler's* call
>
> **Pronoun as adjective:** one day the villagers broke / into *her* house
>
> **Verb as adjective:** When the *plunging* hoofs were gone

A. Practice: In the following sentences, the underlined words serve as adjectives. As what other part of speech (noun, pronoun, or verb) might each one serve? Write your answers on the line following each sentence.

1. The only <u>night</u> sounds the Traveler heard were <u>his</u> own loud knockings.

_____

2. The hungry poem gobbled up thousands of its <u>unsuspecting</u> readers.

_____

3. The wild <u>parrot</u> screams pierced the air.

_____

B. Writing Application: Write sentences using each of the following words as adjectives.

1. morning

_____

_____

2. whispering

_____

_____

3. her

_____

_____

"The Listeners" by Walter de la Mare
"Beware: Do Not Read This Poem" by Ishmael Reed
"Echo" by Henriqueta Lisboa

Reading Strategy: Using Your Senses

The poets de la Mare, Reed, and Lisboa use words that help you create pictures as you read their poems. As you read these poems, what **senses** do you use to experience the images? Do you *hear* the sound of the Traveler's knocking? Can you *feel* his knuckles on the door?

DIRECTIONS: As you read each poem, note the words and phrases that appeal to your senses. In the following table, write each word or phrase in the appropriate section. Because an image can appeal to more than one sense, you may enter a word or phrase more than once.

Senses	"The Listeners"	"Beware: Do Not Read This Poem	"Echo"
Touch			
Taste			
Smell			
Hearing			
Sight			

"The Listeners" by Walter de la Mare
"Beware: Do Not Read This Poem" by Ishmael Reed
"Echo" by Henriqueta Lisboa

Literary Analysis: Imagery

Poets use **imagery**—words and phrases that appeal to a reader's senses—to convey vivid impressions with just a few words.

DIRECTIONS: Read the poems and find the following phrases. Consider each phrase in the context of the poem. Then write a complete description of the image that the phrase conveys.

> **Example:** the moonlit door
> **Answer:** The door is heavy and wooden. The moonlight makes shadows in the cracks and crevices in the door. It has a solid but empty sound when the Traveler knocks.

"The Listeners"

1. the dark stair,/That goes down to the empty hall

_____

_____

_____

"Beware: Do Not Read This Poem"

2. she was too swift/for them. she disappeared/into a mirror

_____

_____

_____

3. it is a greedy mirror/you are into this poem. from/the waist down

_____

_____

_____

"Echo"

4. A great uproar/invaded the forest

_____

_____

5. steely screams rained/and rained down

_____

_____

"Caucasian Mummies Mystify Chinese" by Keay Davidson

Build Vocabulary

Spelling Strategy In words that end in *y* preceded by a consonant, the *y* is usually changed to *i* when a suffix is added. Examples: *archaeology/archaeologist; body/bodily; rely/reliable; merry/merrily.*

Using the Suffix -*ist*

The suffix -*ist* means "one who practices." The selection word *archaeologist* means "one who practices archaeology." Other examples of words with the suffix -*ist* are *pessimist, violinist,* and *druggist.* Note that, as in the word *pessimist,* the suffix -*ist* is not always used to construct a word for a profession or career.

A. DIRECTIONS: For each item below, write an -*ist* word that matches the definition.

1. one who practices pharmacy: _____

2. one who believes in anarchy: _____

3. one who studies science: _____

4. one who writes novels: _____

5. one who studies the economy: _____

Using the Word Bank

dogmas	parched	archaeologist
imperialist	subjugation	reconcile

B. DIRECTIONS: Match each word in the left column with its definition in the right column. Write the letter of the definition on the line next to the word it defines.

____ 1. dogmas

____ 2. parched

____ 3. archaeologist

____ 4. imperialist

____ 5. subjugation

____ 6. reconcile

a. a person from a country that seeks to dominate weaker countries

b. bring into agreement

c. firmly held beliefs or doctrines

d. enslavement

e. a person who practices the scientific study of the remains of ancient ways of life

f. dried up by heat

C. DIRECTIONS: Each of the following questions consists of a related pair of words in CAPITAL LETTERS, followed by three lettered pairs of words. Choose the pair that best expresses a relationship similar to that expressed in the pair in CAPITAL LETTERS.

____ 1. PARCHED : HEAT ::
    a. warmth : coolness
    b. shivering : cold
    c. dry : wet

____ 2. DOGMAS : BELIEFS ::
    a. thoughts : ideas
    b. bears : cubs
    c. temperature : elevation

"Caucasian Mummies Mystify Chinese" by Keay Davidson

Build Grammar Skills: Proper and Compound Adjectives

A **proper adjective** is a proper noun used as an adjective or an adjective formed from a proper noun. For example:

> a *Detroit* car company
>
> an *Idaho* ranch
>
> *European* art

Compound adjectives are adjectives that are made up of more than one word. They are either hyphenated or written as combined words. Consult a dictionary whenever you are unsure of the spelling of a compound adjective. For example:

> a *full-time* employee
>
> the *lionhearted* warrior
>
> a *four-year* college

A. Practice: Identify the proper and compound adjectives in the following sentences.

1. I enjoyed the article on the Caucasian mummies very much.

   _____

2. It must have been exciting to discover the well-preserved mummies who seemed to be of European descent.

   _____

3. I asked the Bedrock High School librarian, Mr. Holt, if he could find more well-written articles by science reporters.

   _____

4. I think the Davidson article will have a far-reaching effect on the topic of Chinese history.

   _____

B. Writing Application: Write five sentences. Use at least one of the following words as a proper or compound adjective in each sentence. Underline the words you use.

Proper adjectives: United States; Glacier National Park; Asia; Canadian; Pacific

Compound adjectives: three-hour, far-flung, wind-blown, red-haired; lighthearted

1. _____

2. _____

3. _____

4. _____

5. _____

"Caucasian Mummies Mystify Chinese" by Keay Davidson

Reading Strategy: Finding the Main Idea

The **main idea** of a piece of writing is the most important point. Sometimes the main idea is not obvious. One easy way to focus on the main idea as you read is to look for answers to these questions: *Who? What? When? Where? Why? How?*

DIRECTIONS: As you read "Caucasian Mummies Mystify Chinese," jot down your answers to these questions in this five W's and H graphic organizer.

Who?	
What?	
When?	
Where?	
Why?	
How?	

"Caucasian Mummies Mystify Chinese" by Keay Davidson

Literary Analysis: News Article

The purpose of a **news article** is to inform the reader about the subject of the article by answering six basic questions, known as the five W's and H: *Who? What? When? Where? Why? How?* The opening sentences of a news article are called the *lead.* The lead is written to capture your attention, to summarize the article's main points, and to begin providing answers to the six questions. The paragraphs that follow the lead provide further answers in the form of details and expert opinions.

Look at the following chart that summarizes a news article.

Who: team of astronomers
What: new method of tracking asteroids and comets
When: over next few months
Where: at observatory
Why: concerns that planet may be vulnerable to asteroid/comet
How: with more powerful radio telescopes

DIRECTIONS: Choose a news article from a recent edition of your local newspaper or a newsmagazine. After reading the article, answer the questions below.

Who is the article about? _____

What is the article about? _____

When did the events take place? _____

Where did the events take place? _____

Why did the events happen as they did? _____

_____

_____

How did the events happen? _____

_____

_____

from *A Lincoln Preface* by Carl Sandburg

Build Vocabulary

Spelling Strategy Words ending in two consonants retain the final consonants when adding an ending starting with a vowel. For example, when *slouch* takes an ending, the *ch* spelling remains the same: *slouch* + *ing* = *slouching*, *slouch* + *es* = *slouches*, *slouch* + *ed* = *slouched*.

Using the Suffix *-ic*

Knowing the meaning of a suffix can help you figure out the meaning of words formed with that suffix. For instance, Sandburg describes Lincoln as a man "clothed with *despotic* power." If you know that *-ic* means "like" or "pertaining to," then you can figure out that *despotic* means "like a despot or an absolute ruler."

A. DIRECTIONS: Define each of the following words. Then write the meaning of the word formed with the suffix *-ic*.

1. hero _____

   heroic _____

2. calorie _____

   caloric _____

3. optimist _____

   optimistic _____

4. sulfur _____

   sulfuric _____

5. athlete _____

   athletic _____

Using the Word Bank

despotic	chattel	cipher	slouching
censure	gaunt	droll	

B. DIRECTIONS: Match each word in the left column with its definition in the right column. Write the letter of the definition on the line next to the word it defines.

____ 1. despotic   a. comic and amusing in an odd way

____ 2. chattel   b. code

____ 3. cipher   c. thin and bony

____ 4. slouching   d. like an absolute ruler or tyrant

____ 5. censure   e. drooping

____ 6. gaunt   f. strong disapproval

____ 7. droll   g. a movable item of personal property

A Lincoln Preface   **29**

from *A Lincoln Preface* by Carl Sandburg

Build Grammar Skills: Transitive and Intransitive Verbs

Action verbs can be **transitive** or **intransitive**. An action verb is transitive if it directs action toward someone or something named in the same sentence. The receiver of the action of a transitive verb is called the object of the verb.

Transitive: Joe read a *book* about the Civil War.

An action verb is intransitive if it does not direct action toward someone or something named in the sentence. Intransitive verbs do not have objects.

Intransitive: Joe reads during summer vacation.

In the first example, the verb *read* directs action toward *book;* therefore, *read* is a transitive verb and *book* is its object. In the second example, the verb *reads* does not direct action toward anything in the sentence; therefore, *reads* is an intransitive verb and it has no object.

A. Practice: The underlined verbs in the following passages from the selection are either transitive or intransitive. Write *T* if the verb is transitive and *I* if it is intransitive.

_____ 1. He instructed a messenger to the Secretary of the Treasury, "Tell him not to bother himself about the Constitution."

_____ 2. He asked his Cabinet to vote on the high military command. . . .

_____ 3. The telegrams varied oddly at times. . . .

_____ 4. The enemy was violating the Constitution to destroy the Union.

_____ 5. His life, mind, and heart ran in contrasts.

B. Writing Application: Rewrite the following sentences. Add the words in parentheses to change the intransitive verbs to transitive verbs.

Example: President Lincoln explained patiently. (the problem)

Answer: President Lincoln explained the problem patiently.

1. Lincoln won for the first time. (an election)

_____

2. The politicians argued for a week. (their positions)

_____

3. He chose carefully. (his allies)

_____

4. President Lincoln wrote on his own. (his speeches)

_____

from *A Lincoln Preface* by Carl Sandburg

Reading Strategy: Establishing a Purpose for Reading

Before you begin to read a selection, **establish a purpose** for your reading. Sometimes you read purely for your own enjoyment, and other times you may read to gather information about a topic or to learn how to do something. Establishing a purpose for reading helps you focus your attention on the most important material in the text. It also helps you to comprehend the material.

After you complete the exercise below, consider your purpose for reading the excerpt from Carl Sandburg's *A Lincoln Preface*.

DIRECTIONS: Read the following list of various reading materials. After each item, briefly describe a purpose you might have for reading it.

Example: magazine article

Sample Answer: to learn more about a topic; for entertainment

1. newspaper article

_____

_____

2. short story

_____

_____

3. comic strip

_____

_____

4. biography

_____

_____

5. a "how-to" book

_____

_____

6. a children's picture book

_____

_____

Unit 2: Challenges and Choices

from *A Lincoln Preface* by Carl Sandburg

Literary Analysis: Anecdote

An **anecdote** is a brief story about an interesting, amusing, or strange event. Sandburg uses many anecdotes, both interesting and amusing, to give readers a sense of the person Lincoln was.

Understanding Anecdotes

A. DIRECTIONS: Describe what each of the following anecdotes reveals about Lincoln's personality.

1. He asked his Cabinet to vote on the high military command, and after the vote, told them the appointment had already been made. . . .

   _____

   _____

2. While the war drums beat, he liked best of all the stories told of him, one of two Quaker-esses heard talking in a railway car. "I think that Jefferson will succeed." "Why does thee think so?" "Because Jefferson is a praying man." "And so is Abraham a praying man." "Yes, but the Lord will think Abraham is joking."

   _____

   _____

3. An enemy general, Longstreet, after the war, declared him to have been "the one matchless man in forty millions of people," while one of his private secretaries, Hay, declared his life to have been the most perfect in its relationships and adjustments since that of Christ.

   _____

   _____

Using Anecdotes

Sandburg's biography uses anecdotes effectively to paint a vibrant portrait of a famous person. Anecdotes can enhance many, but not all, forms of writing.

B. DIRECTIONS: Explain why an anecdote would or would not work in each of the following types of writing.

1. A letter to a friend _____

   _____

2. A business letter _____

   _____

3. A news report about flood victims _____

   _____

4. A report for biology class _____

   _____

"**I Have a Dream**" by Martin Luther King, Jr.
from *Rosa Parks: My Story* by Rosa Parks with Jim Haskins
"**There Is a Longing . . .**" by Chief Dan George
"**I Hear America Singing**" by Walt Whitman

Build Vocabulary

Spelling Strategy   Before adding a suffix beginning with a vowel to a word that ends in a silent e, you usually drop the e. For example, when adding the suffix -ance to endure, the silent e is dropped and the word becomes endurance.

Using the Word Root *-cred-*

The word root *-cred-* comes to us from Latin. The Latin word means "to believe or trust." When people who spoke Latin expressed their beliefs, the first word they used was *credo*, meaning "I believe." The English word *creed* and its meaning come from that use of the Latin word.

A. DIRECTIONS: Explain how the meaning of each of the following English words is tied to "believing" or "trusting" as the root *-cred-* implies. An example has been done for you.

Example: discredit   make someone or something not believable

1. credence _____

2. credit _____

3. incredible _____

4. credential _____

Using the Word Bank

creed	oppression	oasis	exalted	prodigious
hamlet	complied	manhandled	determination	endurance

B. DIRECTIONS: Match each word in the left column with its definition in the right column. Write the letter of the definition on the line next to the word it defines.

____ 1. creed   a. of great size

____ 2. oppression   b. lifted up

____ 3. oasis   c. ability to withstand difficulties

____ 4. exalted   d. altered one's actions according to someone else's wishes or to a rule

____ 5. prodigious   e. the act of deciding definitely and firmly

____ 6. hamlet   f. fertile place in the desert

____ 7. complied   g. set of beliefs

____ 8. manhandled   h. unjust or cruel use of power or authority

____ 9. determination i. very small village

____ 10. endurance   j. treated roughly

"I Have a Dream" by Martin Luther King, Jr.
from *Rosa Parks: My Story* by Rosa Parks with Jim Haskins
"There Is a Longing . . ." by Chief Dan George
"I Hear America Singing" by Walt Whitman

Build Grammar Skills: Action Verbs and Linking Verbs

Verbs fall into two main categories. An **action verb** tells what action someone or something is performing, such as *run, work, say,* and *choose.* A **linking verb** connects a word at or near the beginning of a sentence with a word at or near the end. The most common linking verbs are forms of the verb *to be,* such as those listed below.

am	is	are	was
were	be	being	been

The following verbs may also be used as linking verbs when they help words at the end of sentences name or describe words at the beginning.

seem	look	appear	smell
taste	feel	sound	become

However, these verbs are action verbs when they describe an action that someone or something is performing.

Linking: The candidate *grew* sad when he heard the election results.

Action: The farmer <u>grew</u> peas and beans.

A. Practice: Circle the verbs in each of these sentences from the selections. Write *A* on the line if the verb is an action verb. Write *L* if it is a linking verb.

_____ 1. I have a dream today.

_____ 2. It is a dream deeply rooted in the American dream.

_____ 3. This is our hope.

_____ 4. He was still tall and heavy, with red, rough-looking skin.

_____ 5. I saw a vacant seat in the middle section of the bus and took it.

B. Writing Application: Follow the instructions for writing sentences that contain action and linking verbs.

Example: Use *was* as a linking verb in a sentence about the speaking style of Martin Luther King, Jr.

Sample Answer: Martin Luther King, Jr., was a very powerful speaker.

1. Use *felt* as a linking verb in a sentence about Martin Luther King, Jr.

_____

2. Use *describes* as an action verb in a sentence about King's dreams.

_____

3. Use *was* as a linking verb in a sentence about the life of Rosa Parks.

_____

4. Use *is* as a linking verb in a sentence about the speaker's hopes in "There Is a Longing. . . ."

_____

"I Have a Dream" by Martin Luther King, Jr.
from *Rosa Parks: My Story* by Rosa Parks with Jim Haskins
"There Is a Longing . . ." by Chief Dan George
"I Hear America Singing" by Walt Whitman

Reading Strategy: Responding

When you pause occasionally to respond to and reflect on what you have read, you can increase your understanding of a piece of literature.

DIRECTIONS: Read these passages from "I Have a Dream." Then answer the questions that follow to help you respond to, reflect on, and understand Dr. King's speech.

A. . . . I have a dream. It is a dream deeply rooted in the American dream. . . . that one day this nation will rise up and live out the true meaning of its creed: "We hold these truths to be self-evident; that all men are created equal.". . . I have a dream that my four little children will one day live in a nation where they will not be judged by the color of their skin but by the content of their character.

1. What does Dr. King mean by "the American dream"?

_____

2. What do *you* think of when you think about "the American dream"?

_____

_____

3. What does Dr. King mean by judging people "by the content of their character"?

_____

4. Do *you* judge people by the content of their character? How? Why or why not?

_____

_____

B. I have a dream that . . . every hill and mountain shall be made low, the rough places will be made plains, and the crooked places will be made straight . . . . This is our hope. . . . With this faith we will be able to work together, to pray together, to struggle together, to go to jail together, to stand up for freedom together, knowing that we will be free one day.

1. What powerful words does Dr. King use in this section?

_____

2. How do those words make you feel?

_____

_____

C. When we let freedom ring . . . [we] will be able to join hands and sing . . . "Free at last! Free at last! Thank God almighty, we are free at last!"

1. How might this closing paragraph have affected Dr. King's audience?

_____

2. How does this closing paragraph make *you* feel?

_____

_____

"I Have a Dream" by Martin Luther King, Jr.
from *Rosa Parks: My Story* by Rosa Parks with Jim Haskins
"There Is a Longing . . ." by Chief Dan George
"I Hear America Singing" by Walt Whitman

Literary Analysis: Author's Purpose

Any time a writer creates a poem, essay, or speech, he or she has a purpose—a reason for writing. Figuring out the author's purpose enhances your understanding of the work.

DIRECTIONS: Following are excerpts from and references to "There Is a Longing . . ." by Chief Dan George. Answer the questions about the content and style of the passage to find clues to the author's purpose.

1.
>   There is a longing in the heart of my people
>   to reach out and grasp that which is needed
>   for our survival. There is a longing among
>   the young of my nation to secure for them-
>   5   selves and their people the skills that will
>   provide them with a sense of worth and
>   purpose. . . .

What main point does the author make in these opening lines of the poem?

_____

_____

2.
>   I am a chief, but my power to make war
>   is gone, and the only weapon left to me
>   is speech. It is only with tongue and speech
>   that I can fight my people's war.
>   20   Oh, Great Spirit! Give me back the courage
>   of the olden Chiefs. Let me wrestle with
>   my surroundings. . . .

What connection does the author establish between the past and present in these lines?

_____

_____

3. Line 20 begins like a prayer with "Oh, Great Spirit!" Why might the author have wanted to make this part sound like a prayer?

_____

_____

4. Would you describe the feeling of "There Is a Longing . . ." as light or serious? Explain your answer.

_____

_____

5. Based on the content and style of "There Is a Longing . . .", what do you think Chief Dan George's purpose was for writing it?

_____

_____

"The Golden Kite, the Silver Wind" by Ray Bradbury

Build Vocabulary

Spelling Strategy   When adding certain prefixes to a word, the final consonant of the prefix changes to match the first letter of the word to which it is attached. The result is a doubled consonant. For example, the prefix *ad-* changes to *ac-* when attached to the word *claim* to form *acclaim*. The prefix *in-* becomes *ir-* in *irregular*, and *ad-* becomes *as-* in *assign*.

Using the Word Root *-claim-*

The word root *-claim-* means "to call out" or "to shout." The prefix *ad-* means "to" or "toward." When the two are joined in *acclaim*, the new word means "to call out toward."

A. DIRECTIONS: Here are some other words with the word root *-claim-*. Look up the meanings of the prefixes and suffixes in a dictionary if you need to. Then use what you already know about the root to determine the meaning of each word.

1. reclaim _____

2. proclaim _____

3. exclaim _____

Using the Word Bank

portents	vile	ravenous
acclaimed	pandemonium	spurn

B. DIRECTIONS: Circle the letter of the best synonym for each numbered word.

1. portents
   a. events   b. omens   c. shapes

2. vile
   a. wicked   b. rugged   c. unclean

3. ravenous
   a. damaging   b. hungry   c. maddened

4. acclaimed
   a. criticized   b. roared   c. praised

5. pandemonium
   a. rejoicing   b. violence   c. uproar

6. spurn
   a. reject   b. cancel   c. ignore

© Prentice-Hall, Inc.

Unit 2: Challenges and Choices

"The Golden Kite, the Silver Wind" by Ray Bradbury

Build Grammar Skills: Compound Verbs

A **compound verb** is two or more verbs that have the same subject and are joined by a conjunction such as *and* or *or*.

The people *talked* and *laughed* at the party.

We can either *walk* to the store or *run* to the bus stop.

The various animals *trotted, loped, scampered,* and *flew* to the water.

A. Practice: The following sentences are taken from "The Golden Kite, the Silver Wind." For each one, write the verbs that make up the compound verb.

1. Here the stonemasons groaned and wept.

   _____

2. "And so," said the whisper, said the Mandarin, "you raisers of walls must go bearing trowels and rocks and change the shape of *our* city!"

   _____

3. "And with this lake of water," said the whisper and the old man, "we will quench the fire and put it out forever."

   _____

4. They ran to the walls and built them near to their new vision. . . .

   _____

5. The wind will beautify the kite and carry it to wondrous heights.

   _____

B. Writing Application: Use a compound verb to combine each pair of sentences into one sentence.

1. The Mandarin heard about the neighboring town's wall. He worried about its shape.

   _____

   _____

2. The Mandarin's daughter listened to her father's concerns. She suggested a solution.

   _____

   _____

3. One Mandarin saw the other's new wall. He rebuilt his own.

   _____

4. The people couldn't hunt anymore. They couldn't fish anymore.

   _____

5. The two Mandarins could work together. Or, the two Mandarins could grow even weaker.

   _____

   _____

"The Golden Kite, the Silver Wind" by Ray Bradbury

Reading Strategy: Predicting Consequences Based on Actions

The two cities in "The Golden Kite, the Silver Wind" seem to be locked in a contest of cleverness. The events of the story seem to pile up on one another.

DIRECTIONS: As you read, fill in the blanks in the Series of Events graphic organizer. Following each section of the graphic organizer, predict what the consequences of those events might be. What do you think will happen next? Then read on.

1.

| Kwan-Si builds wall in shape of pig | → | | → | Mandarin's daughter volunteers to help | → | Mandarin builds wall in shape of _____ |

Predict the consequences of these events: _____
_____

2.

Kwan-Si builds wall in shape of bonfire → [ ] → People in city begin to get weaker and poorer → [ ] → Mandarin builds wall in shape of needle

Predict the consequences of these events: _____
_____

3.

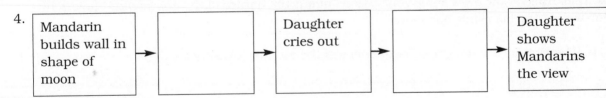

[ ] → Mandarin builds wall in shape of scabbard → Kwan-Si builds wall in shape of lightning → [ ] → Funerals begin

Predict the consequences of these events: _____
_____

4.

Mandarin builds wall in shape of moon → [ ] → Daughter cries out → [ ] → Daughter shows Mandarins the view

Predict the events: _____
_____

5.

Daughter suggests shapes of wind and kite for city walls → [ ] → [ ]

Predict the consequences of these events: _____
_____

Unit 2: Challenges and Choices

"The Golden Kite, the Silver Wind" by Ray Bradbury

Literary Analysis: Fable

Examining Characters' Actions

Unlike most fables, "The Golden Kite, the Silver Wind" does not include a briefly stated moral at the end. Ray Bradbury leaves it up to his readers to discover the moral by reading carefully, examining the characters' actions, and drawing conclusions.

Examining a character's actions—and the consequences of those actions—can help you determine the unstated moral of a fable such as "The Golden Kite, the Silver Wind."

A. Directions: Complete the chart with information about the consequences of the characters' actions.

Character's Actions	Consequences
1. The Mandarin chooses to respond to the new shape of Kwan-Si's wall, over and over again.	1.
2. The Mandarin chooses to listen to his daughter.	2.
3. Kwan-Si chooses to respond to the new shape of the first Mandarin's wall, over and over again.	3.
4. The daughter advises her father to send for Kwan-Si.	4.
5. The daughter suggests the plan for the final shape of each wall.	5.

Drawing Conclusions

B. Directions: Now draw some conclusions about the nature of the characters' choices by answering the following questions.

1. In general, what are the consequences of the Mandarin's actions?

   _____

2. What consequences did Kwan-Si's actions bring about?

   _____

3. What consequences did the daughter's actions bring about?

   _____

4. How does examining the positive and negative consequences of the characters' actions lead you to the unstated moral of this fable?

   _____

"The Road Not Taken" by Robert Frost
"New Directions" by Maya Angelou
"To be of use" by Marge Piercy

Build Vocabulary

Spelling Strategy   Do not double the letters *w, h, x,* or *y* at the end of a word before adding an ending such as *-ing* or *-ed*. For example, adding *-ed* to the word *box* forms the word *boxed*.

Using the Suffix *-ly*

The suffix *-ly* is often used to turn adjectives into adverbs that describe "how or in what manner." For example, the word *meticulous* means "very careful or thorough," so the word *meticulously* means "in a very careful or thorough manner."

A. DIRECTIONS: Define the italicized words using your understanding of the suffix *-ly* as well as clues provided in the sentences.

1. Rough waves splashed *repeatedly* into our small boat.

_____

2. The tiger snarled *savagely* at the explorers in the jungle.

_____

3. When he had missed his bus every morning, we asked why he was *habitually* late.

_____

4. The music was *excessively* loud, so we left the auditorium.

_____

Using the Word Bank

diverged	amicably	meticulously	specters	ominous
unpalatable	dallying	submerged	harness	

B. DIRECTIONS: Match each word in the left column with its definition in the right column. Write the letter of the definition on the line next to the word it defines.

____ 1. submerged   a. branched out in different directions

____ 2. specters   b. agreeably

____ 3. unpalatable   c. threatening

____ 4. harness   d. wasting time

____ 5. diverged   e. underwater

____ 6. ominous   f. very carefully

____ 7. amicably   g. attach, as with straps

____ 8. dallying   h. distasteful

____ 9. meticulously   i. phantoms

Unit 2: Challenges and Choices

"The Road Not Taken" by Robert Frost
"New Directions" by Maya Angelou
"To be of use" by Marge Piercy

Build Grammar Skills: Regular Verbs

Most verbs in the English language are regular. The past and past participle of a **regular verb** are formed by adding *-ed* or *-d* to the present form. The chart below shows the principal parts of three regular verbs.

PRINCIPAL PARTS OF REGULAR VERBS

Present	Present Participle	Past	Past Participle
walk	(is) walking	walked	(has) walked
start	(is) starting	started	(has) started
cure	(is) curing	cured	(has) cured

A. Practice: Indicate the principal part of each underlined verb.

1. The traveler is <u>looking</u> down each road.

   _____

2. In "The Road Not Taken," the speaker may or may not have <u>enjoyed</u> his choice.

   _____

3. After Annie's husband left, she <u>decided</u> not to work as a domestic.

   _____

4. We learn that she is <u>working</u> hard to prepare food for the next day.

   _____

5. In "To be of use," the speaker <u>admires</u> people who work hard.

   _____

B. Writing Application: Write sentences using the indicated principal part of each of the following verbs.

1. pour (past)

   _____

2. chew (past participle)

   _____

3. amble (present)

   _____

4. whisper (present participle)

   _____

"The Road Not Taken" by Robert Frost
"New Directions" by Maya Angelou
"To be of use" by Marge Piercy

Reading Strategy: Generating Questions

Asking and answering questions as you read a selection will help you to understand and appreciate what you are reading. Begin by using common question words such as *Who? What? Where? When? Why?* and *How?*

DIRECTIONS: Answer the following questions to guide your understanding of "The Road Not Taken," "New Directions," and "To be of use."

"The Road Not Taken"

1. *What* decision does the speaker face in the opening lines of the poem?

_____

2. *Why* does the speaker feel sorry?

_____

3. *How* does he feel about his decision?

_____

"New Directions"

1. *What* jobs are not acceptable to Annie Johnson?

_____

2. *Why* are these jobs not acceptable?

_____

3. *How* does Annie's business grow and change?

_____

"To be of use"

1. *Who* are the people the speaker loves the best?

_____

2. *Why* does the speaker love these people best?

_____

3. *What* are some of the activities the speaker describes?

_____

Unit 2: Challenges and Choices

"The Road Not Taken" by Robert Frost
"New Directions" by Maya Angelou
"To be of use" by Marge Piercy

Literary Analysis: Figurative Language

Writers Frost, Angelou, and Piercy use figurative language—language that implies more than its literal, word-for-word meaning. Figurative language makes writing more interesting for readers because it connects an abstract idea—such as the value of meaningful work—to a concrete image—such as the image of an ox pulling a cart through mud.

DIRECTIONS: Consider the following lines in the context of each work. Then, in your own words, describe the abstract and concrete ideas that are being compared in each passage.

"The Road Not Taken"

Example: Two roads diverged in a wood, and I—/I took the one less traveled by,/And that has made all the difference.

Concrete Image: two roads that separate in the woods

Comparison: The writer compares two roads in the woods and the choice a traveler makes between them to an important decision a person makes and the life he or she has led as a result.

"The Road Not Taken"

1. Oh, I kept the first for another day!/Yet knowing how way leads on to way,/I doubted if I should ever come back.

   Concrete image: _____

   Comparison: _____

   _____

"To be of use"

2. The work of the world is common as mud./Botched, it smears the hands, crumbles to dust./But the thing worth doing well done/has a shape that satisfies, clean and evident.

   Concrete image: _____

   Comparison: _____

   _____

"New Directions"

3. In her words, "I looked up the road I was going and back the way I come, and since I wasn't satisfied, I decided to step off the road and cut me a new path."

   Concrete image: _____

   Comparison: _____

   _____

"Old Man of the Temple" by R. K. Narayan

Build Vocabulary

Spelling Strategy When spelling a word that contains a *j* sound before an *e*, the word is usually spelled with a *g*. For example, the *j* sound in the word *longevity* is spelled with a *g*. Other examples include *cage*, *page*, *courageous*, *generous*, and *stooge*. Exceptions include *subject*, *majesty*, and *conjecture*.

Using the Suffix -*ity*

The suffix -*ity* means "the state or condition of." In the word *longevity*, you will recognize the base word *long* and the suffix -*ity*. Therefore, you can determine that the word *longevity* means "the condition of having a long life."

A. DIRECTIONS: Complete each sentence so that the meaning of the italicized word is clear. Use precise details in each sentence.

1. The *brutality* of the king's laws caused _____

_____

2. The old man attributed his *longevity* to _____

_____

3. Known for her selfless *generosity*, the volunteer _____

_____

4. To assure his *sobriety*, the designated driver _____

_____

5. Serena expresses her *individuality* by _____

_____

6. The *severity* of the winter created _____

_____

Using the Word Bank

sobriety	awry	literally
longevity	imperative	venture

B. DIRECTIONS: Match each word in the left column with its definition in the right column. Write the letter of the definition on the line next to the word it defines.

____ 1. sobriety   a. actually, in fact

____ 2. awry   b. a chance

____ 3. literally   c. absolutely necessary; urgent

____ 4. imperative   d. the length or duration of a life

____ 5. venture   e. moderation, especially in the use of alcoholic beverages

____ 6. longevity   f. not straight; askew

"Old Man of the Temple" by R. K. Narayan

Build Grammar Skills: Adverbs

An **adverb** is a word that adds extra meaning to other words. An adverb modifies a verb, an adjective, or another adverb. It answers the questions *Where? When? In what way?* or *To what extent?* Look at the adverbs in the following sentences.

The dog ate his food *noisily*.

The children played in the snow *quite happily* for several hours.

The elevator lurched *downward*.

The adverb *noisily* modifies *ate*. The adverb *happily* modifies *played*, and *quite* modifies *happily*. The adverb *downward* modifies *lurched*.

A. Practice: Underline the adverbs in the following sentences from "Old Man of the Temple." Draw an arrow to the word each adverb modifies.

1. It has always mystified me.

2. The stars overhead sparkled brightly.

3. I looked at him anxiously.

4. He coughed uncontrollably.

5. Why doesn't the king ever come this way?

6. He constantly interrupted me, but considered deeply what I said.

7. He drew himself up, made a dash forward, and fell down in a heap.

8. I banged on the door violently.

B. Writing Application: Rewrite the sentences using the adverb in parentheses to add meaning.

1. The distance between Kumbum and Malgudi was far to walk. (too)

_____

2. The driver drove the taxi. (smoothly)

_____

3. It was dark outside, but Doss was certain that he saw someone. (very, quite)

_____

4. Doss's hands trembled, and he spoke in a high voice. (uncontrollably, unusually)

_____

_____

5. The man had been attacked by robbers. (violently)

_____

6. The people in the cottage had heard knocking, but never found anyone at the door. (often)

_____

_____

"**Old Man of the Temple**" by R. K. Narayan

Reading Strategy: Distinguishing Fantasy From Reality

In "Old Man of the Temple," elements of reality and fantasy intertwine to make the fantasy more believable.

DIRECTIONS: To help you distinguish what is real from what is not, complete the chart below as you read. Write elements of reality in the "Real" column and elements of fantasy in the "Fantastic" column.

Real	Fantastic
Example: The narrator is riding down a rural road late at night in a taxi driven by a man named Doss.	Doss sees an old man walking toward the car, but the narrator does not see anyone.
1.	2.
3.	4.
5.	6.
7.	8.
9.	10.

© Prentice-Hall, Inc.

Unit 2: Challenges and Choices

Name _____ Date _____

"**Old Man of the Temple**" by R. K. Narayan

Literary Analysis: Fantasy

A **fantasy** can contain improbable characters, events, and places that could not be found in real life. An author uses a great deal of imagination when writing a fantasy. Fantasy often involves either the supernatural or magic.

DIRECTIONS: The following passages are from "Old Man of the Temple." Read each passage and think about it in the context of the whole story. Then write a brief phrase or statement that identifies the element of fantasy conveyed by the passage.

1. "What has happened to your voice? You sound like someone else," I said.
"Nothing. My voice is as good as it was. When a man is eighty he is bound to feel a few changes coming on."

_____

_____

2. "Don't feel hurt; I say you shouldn't be here anymore because you are dead."
"Dead! Dead!" he said. "Don't talk nonsense. How can I be dead when you see me before you now? If I am dead how can I be saying this and that?"
"I don't know all that," I said.

_____

_____

_____

_____

3. "See here," I said. "It is imperative you should go away from here. If she comes and calls you, will you go?"
"How can she when I tell you that she is dead?"
I thought for a moment. Presently I found myself saying, "Think of her, and only of her, for a while and see what happens. What was her name?"
"Seetha, A wonderful girl. . ."
"Come on, think of her." He remained in deep thought for a while. He suddenly screamed, "Seetha is coming! Am I dreaming or what? I will go with her. . ." He stood up, very erect; he appeared to have lost all the humps and twists he had on his body. He drew himself up, made a dash forward, and fell down in a heap.

_____

_____

_____

_____

4. When I passed that way again months later I was told that the bullocks passing the temple after dusk never shied away now and no knocking on the doors was heard at night. So I felt that the old fellow had really gone away with his good wife.

_____

_____

_____

_____

"**Perseus**" by Edith Hamilton

Build Vocabulary

Spelling Strategy   When adding an ending beginning with a vowel to a word of more than one syllable that ends in a consonant preceded by a vowel, you usually don't double the final consonant. For example, *cancel + ed* becomes *canceled*, and *waver + ing* becomes *wavering*. If the word's stress is on the final syllable, however, you generally double the consonant. *Compel + ing* becomes *compelling*, and *prefer + ed* becomes *preferred*.

Using the Word Root *-mort-*

In Edith Hamilton's account, Perseus is extremely embarrassed, or mortified, by his lack of a gift for the King. The word root *-mort-* comes from the Latin word for death.

A. DIRECTIONS: Other English words also use the word root *-mort-*. Use what you have learned about the root *-mort-* to identify meanings of the following words and phrases. Write your answers on the lines provided.

1. mortuary _____

2. mortal wound _____

3. immortal legend _____

Using the Word Bank

kindred	mortified	despair	wavering
revelry	deity	reconciled	

B. DIRECTIONS: Complete each sentence by writing the correct word from the Word Bank in the blank. Use each word only once.

1. Locked in the dark chest, adrift on the ocean, Danaë must have felt _____ at the chances of survival for her and her son.

2. Sharing a similar mythology, the Romans and Greeks used different names, Mercury and Hermes, for the same _____.

3. Many people, like Perseus, are _____ in social situations for which they feel they lack the right possessions.

4. Perseus kept going, showing no signs of _____ in his resolve, despite seemingly impossible odds.

5. The difference between Medusa and her _____ Gorgons was that the other two sisters were immortal and could not be killed.

6. After the tyrant Polydectes turned to stone, it's easy to imagine the joyous _____ by the freed islanders, with music, feasting, and speeches.

7. Perseus and Acrisius probably never could have _____, given the actions of Acrisius toward his grandson.

"**Perseus**" by Edith Hamilton

Build Grammar Skills: Active Voice and Passive Voice

A verb is in the **active voice** if its subject performs the action. A verb is in the **passive voice** if its action is performed upon the subject. Good writers use both the active and passive voices, depending on their purpose and what they want to emphasize. The following examples are taken from "Perseus."

> **Active voice:** Then he aimed a stroke down at Medusa's throat and Athena guided his hand.

> **Passive voice:** Then it was taken out to sea and cast into the water.

A. Practice: Read the following sentences from "Perseus." Write *A* if the sentence is written in the active voice and *P* if it is written in the passive voice. Some sentences may contain more than one subject-verb pair.

_____   1. So Apollo's oracle was again proved true.

_____   2. Danaë attracted his attention.

_____   3. Perseus had been led by his angry pride into making an empty boast.

_____   4. . . . He met a strange and beautiful person.

_____   5. . . . at the sight one and all, the cruel King and his servile courtiers, were turned into stone.

_____   6. . . . one day the little boy—his name was Perseus—was discovered by his grandfather.

B. Writing Application: Revise each sentence by changing the passive voice to the active voice, or the active voice to the passive voice.

> **Example:** Danaë was asked by King Acrisius to name her son's father.

> **Answer:** King Acrisius asked Danaë to name her son's father.

1. Days in the underground house were filled by Danaë with watching clouds.

_____

_____

2. The wild sea tossed, rolled, and lifted the chest.

_____

3. Perseus was helped by Hermes and Pallas Athena to slay the monster Medusa.

_____

_____

4. King Acrisius was fatally wounded by Perseus's flying discus.

_____

5. The day Perseus stole their shared eye will probably be remembered by the Gorgons.

_____

_____

"Perseus" by Edith Hamilton

Reading Strategy: Predicting

DIRECTIONS: Use this graphic organizer *as you read* to help you analyze characters' actions and their consequences. When a situation or problem occurs in "Perseus" that you think will need to be resolved, note it in the first column, "Situation." Then, in the second column, "Possible Outcomes," list several things that might happen. In the third column, "Reasons," write why you think a possible outcome could happen. Finally, in the fourth column, "Actual Outcome," write what actually happens in the story as you read. After you finish reading "Perseus," assess your predictions, outcomes, and reasons.

Situation	Possible Outcomes	Reasons for Prediction	Actual Outcome

Unit 2: Challenges and Choices

"Perseus" by Edith Hamilton

Literary Analysis: Hero in a Myth

The mythic hero lives in a world of natural and supernatural beings, ordinary and extraordinary feelings, and realistic and unrealistic events. As you read "Perseus," you probably recognized that some characters and actions could not exist in the real world. Nevertheless, for thousands of years readers and listeners have hoped Perseus could overcome his challenges, just as they hope they can overcome their own.

DIRECTIONS: In the first column of the following chart, under the heading "Natural," write qualities of Perseus that seem natural or possible—the ways in which he is like any of us. In the next column, write characteristics of Perseus that seem beyond those of the natural world.

Next, select other characters in the story, and write their names in one category or the other, or in both.

Finally, list some of the story's natural and supernatural events in the appropriate columns. What events could have taken place? What events could never happen?

	Natural	Supernatural
Perseus		
Other Characters		
Events		

"Slam, Dunk, & Hook" by Yusef Komunyakaa
"The Spearthrower" by Lillian Morrison
"Shoulders" by Naomi Shihab Nye

Build Vocabulary

Spelling Strategy   Remember the long *a* sound in *neighbor* and *weigh* to help you determine the placement of *i*'s and *e*'s. The rule is "Place *i* before *e* except after *c* or when sounded like *a* as in *neighbor* and *weigh*." The easiest test is to listen for the long *a* sound. Thus, in *feint, sleigh, reign, freight, deign, feign, weight,* and *eight,* the *e* comes before the *i*. *Friend* does not pass the long *a* test, so the *i* comes before the *e*.

Using Sports Jargon

The special vocabulary associated with a sport, an occupation, or industry is called **jargon**. Jargon is a sort of verbal shorthand that intends to communicate efficiently—and often colorfully—to people in the same field. Often jargon enters common use, sometimes combining in unusual ways. A sportscaster uses television jargon, "primetime," to refer to athletes who are at their best at the most important moment. Thus the sportscaster uses one form of jargon to create another when he refers to a "prime-time player."

A. DIRECTIONS: The following words and phrases started out as sports jargon and then entered common use. Identify the source of each word or phrase, and then give its common usage.

	Source	Common Usage
1. sidelined		
2. strike out		
3. Monday-morning quarterback		
4. game plan		
5. get in gear		
6. aced the exam		

Using the Word Bank

metaphysical	jibed	feint	surge

B. DIRECTIONS: Match each word in the left column with its definition in the right column. Write the letter of the definition on the line next to the word it defines.

_____ 1. metaphysical   a. pretend move to trick opponent

_____ 2. jibed   b. increase suddenly; speed up

_____ 3. feint   c. jerked from side to side

_____ 4. surge   d. spiritual; beyond the body

Slam/Spearthrower/Shoulders   **53**

Unit 2:   Challenges and Choices

"Slam, Dunk, & Hook" by Yusef Komunyakaa
"The Spearthrower" by Lillian Morrison
"Shoulders" by Naomi Shihab Nye

Build Grammar Skills: Irregular Verbs

Verb tenses are formed from a verb's four principal parts and helping verbs. The formation of two of those principal parts—the past and past participle—determine whether a verb is regular or irregular. A verb is an **irregular verb** if the past and past participle are *not* formed by adding *-ed* or *-d* to the present form. The chart below shows some of the past and present participles of irregular verbs.

PRINCIPAL PARTS OF IRREGULAR VERBS

Present	Present Participle	Past	Past Participle
sit	sitting	sat	(have) sat
win	winning	won	(have) won
run	running	ran	(have) run
take	taking	took	(have) taken

A. Practice: Circle the correct form of the verb in parentheses. Look back at the poems to see how the verbs are used.

1. After the spider (has spun, has spinned) its web, it waits for flies to be caught in it.

2. The girl (knowed, knew) the answer, so she raised her hand.

3. Before the horse (ran, runned) the race, the rider spent time warming up.

4. We watched admiringly as the eagle (flew, flied) in graceful circles.

5. As my brother (has sayed, has said) many times before, he loves to play football.

6. The ringmaster announced, "The acrobats (have fallen, have fell), but they aren't hurt."

B. Writing Application: Write sentences using the indicated principal part of each of the following verbs. If you are not sure of a verb's principal part, you may check a dictionary.

1. begin (past participle) _____

2. catch (past)_____

3. find (past) _____

4. come (present participle) _____

5. go (past participle) _____

Name _____ Date _____

Reading Strategy: Forming Mental Images

Poets use descriptive language to help you "experience" their poetry. Komunyakaa wants you to "see" and "feel" the basketball players spinning and "corkscrewing." He wants you to smell the sweat on the players' bodies. When you use your senses to form mental images as you read, you will feel a part of the poem.

DIRECTIONS: Use the spider maps on this page to help you develop in your mind the images in "Slam, Dunk, & Hook," "The Spearthrower," and "Shoulders." Use all of your senses. Think about how it feels, smells, and looks to carry a sleeping child or to shoot a basket. Write on the arms of the spider maps words or phrases that describe the images in your mind.

1.
His ear fills up with breathing.
He hears the hum of a boy's dream
deep inside him.
from "Shoulders"

2.
that the vaulter soar,
clear the highest bar,
from "The Spearthrower"

3.
A high note hung there
A long second. Off
The rim.
from "Slam, Dunk, & Hook"

4.
. . . Bug-eyed, lanky,
All hands & feet . . . sprung
rhythm.
from "Slam, Dunk, & Hook"

"Slam, Dunk, & Hook" by Yusef Komunyakaa
"The Spearthrower" by Lillian Morrison
"Shoulders" by Naomi Shihab Nye

Literary Analysis: Theme in Poetry

Accumulation

A poem's central idea, its **theme**, comes to us from the way the poem's figurative language unfolds as we read. Sometimes a poet provides a theme by giving repeated examples. In "Slam, Dunk, & Hook," Komunyakaa implies very early that his poem is about more than basketball. He then makes many references to issues outside the realm of sport. This accumulation of language reinforces the theme.

A. DIRECTIONS: Find references that imply that the theme of "Slam, Dunk, & Hook" is more than the pleasure of playing basketball. List those references in the first column. Give reasons for your choices in the second column.

Theme References   **Reasons**

1. _____   _____

2. _____   _____

3. _____   _____

4. _____   _____

5. _____   _____

Modification

Sometimes a poem begins with one idea and moves to another. Lillian Morrison's "The Spearthrower" begins with one woman walking "alone" in the "bullying dark" and ends with a joyous invitation to all to praise pure athleticism in women as well as men while "great crowds cry/to their heroines/Come on!" The theme of the poem changes focus as the reader continues. By modifying early negative language with positive language that celebrates feelings of athletic accomplishment, Morrison moves the poem past complaint into the larger world of human exultation.

B. DIRECTIONS: Morrison's "The Spearthrower" begins with two dark images, and then modifies them by using language that uplifts. Find examples of figurative language that modifies the dark images of the poem's beginning so that the theme of the poem becomes more encouraging as it progresses. List those references in the first column. Give reasons for your choices in the second.

Theme References   **Reasons**

1. _____   _____

2. _____   _____

3. _____   _____

4. _____   _____

5. _____   _____

"Children in the Woods" by Barry Lopez

Build Vocabulary

Spelling Strategy When adding an ending that begins with a vowel to a word that ends in a silent *e*, drop the *e* before you add the ending. For example, *charge + ed* is *charged*, *make + ing* is *making*, and *observe + ant* is *observant*.

Using the Prefix *extra-*

A. Directions: The prefix *extra-* means "outside" or "beyond." Following are the definitions of some words. Determine what word is being defined and write it in the space provided. Apply the prefix *extra-* to the word, and write the meaning of this new word.

Example: having to do with the physical body ____corporeal_____

extracorporeal—being outside the physical body

1. having to do with the senses _____

_____

2. something not at all unusual _____

_____

3. having to do with laws and justice _____

_____

Using the Word Bank

charged	acutely	elucidate	extrapolation	detritus
effervesce	myriad	insidious	ineffable	

B. Directions: Replace the italicized words in each sentence, with the appropriate word from the Word Bank.

1. Chipmunks are harmless, but I often think of them as *treacherous* invaders in my garden.

_____

2. Observe the seed closely as I *explain* the germination process. _____

3. The view from the mountain top was *overwhelming*. _____

4. The deer were *sharply* attentive to signs of danger. _____

5. Only after examining the facts can there be any *conclusion drawing*. _____

6. In spite of their age, my grandparents continue to *be lively*. _____

7. With the storm gathering, it was a *tensely expectant* afternoon. _____

8. *Countless* geese and ducks begged for food from the visitors. _____

9. The rotten log had collected leaves, seeds, and other *debris*. _____

Unit 3: Moments of Discovery

"Children in the Woods" by Barry Lopez

Build Grammar Skills: Prepositions

A **preposition** is a word that relates a noun or pronoun that appears with it to another word in the sentence. Some examples of prepositions are *about, above, according to, at, because of, below, by, during, in, in front of, near, next to, of, on, over, past, through, to, under, upon,* and *with*. Notice that, though most prepositions are single words, some are made up of two or three words. These are compound prepositions.

James jumped *over* the fence.

The car veered *off* the road.

The girl *next to* the door is my sister.

The preposition *over* relates *fence* to *jumped*. The preposition *off* relates *road* to *veered*. The preposition *next to* relates *door* to *sister*.

A. Practice: Underline the prepositions in these sentences from "Children in the Woods." There may be more than one preposition in a sentence.

1. The sensation of movement from a rural area into an urban one was sharp.

2. I have never forgotten the texture of this incident.

3. They always like venturing into the woods.

4. In the beginning, I think I said too much.

5. I remember once finding a fragment of a raccoon's jaw in an alder thicket.

6. The teeth told by their shape and placement what this animal ate.

7. Whenever I walk with a child, I think how much I have seen disappear in my own life.

8. We were on our knees, making handprints beside the footprints.

B. Writing Application: Rewrite the paragraph, and insert appropriate prepositions from the list. You may use a preposition more than once.

beside	about	into	through
with	among	in	on

Barry Lopez knows a lot _____ nature _____ the Oregon forest. He enjoys taking

curious children _____ nature walks _____ the woods and talking _____ them

_____ the things they find there. As he wanders _____ the woods, Lopez's curiosity prob-

ably leads him to inspect everything _____ the streams and _____ the leaves.

"**Children in the Woods**" by Barry Lopez

Reading Strategy: Relating Generalizations and Evidence

One strategy good readers use to construct meaning from text is making **generalizations** about the writer's main ideas. To arrive at a generalization, a reader must gather details of **evidence** that support it. For example, if you read about a boy who has taken piano lessons for five years, plays piano with the school orchestra, and buys piano recordings, you can make the generalization that this boy is quite serious about the piano. As you read, take note of key details that may become evidence to support generalizations you make about the writer's ideas. A graphic organizer like the one below can help you organize and remember what you read.

DIRECTIONS: Complete the chart based on "Children in the Woods." Use appropriate evidence to support the generalization given, or make a generalization based on the stated evidence.

Generalization	Evidence
	1. As a child, Lopez noticed a pattern of sunlight on a windowpane. 2. Lopez describes many details of his surroundings in Oregon. 3. He notices the many ways children learn.
Barry Lopez takes an extraordinary interest in helping children learn.	
	1. Lopez ties the discovery of the jaw bone to other encounters during the walk. 2. When Lopez walks in the forest with children, he reflects on his own life. 3. Lopez and a child compare their own handprints with a heron's footprints.

Unit 3: Moments of Discovery

"Children in the Woods" by Barry Lopez

Literary Analysis: Reflective Essay

An **essay** is a short piece of nonfiction in which a writer expresses a personal view on a topic. In a **reflective essay,** the writer shares one or more personal experiences and includes his or her reflections on the significance of the experience.

As you read a reflective essay, you will need to identify both the experience and the writer's reactions to the experience. In some cases, you will also be able to relate your own experience to what has happened to the writer. While this can make reading the essay even more enjoyable, it is not necessary to identify with either the writer's experience or his or her reaction to understand and appreciate what the writer learned from the experience.

DIRECTIONS: Find specific details in "Children in the Woods" that identify two or three different experiences or incidents, then identify the reactions or feelings that the author seems to emphasize in his reflections on each experience.

Experience	Reflection

"Rules of the Game" by Amy Tan

Build Vocabulary

Spelling Strategy   The English word *prodigy* is one of only four words in common usage that are *not* spelled with an *o* before the *-gy* ending. The other three words are *effigy*, *elegy*, and *strategy*. Many other words end in *-ogy*, such as *apology* and *gemology*.

Using Words From French

"Rules of the Game" includes some English words that have been "borrowed" from the French language, such as *café*. Other English words have "evolved" from French words. In a dictionary, the abbreviations *F*, *MF*, or *OF*, in the etymology or word origin portion of each word entry, indicate that a word has evolved from "French," "Middle French," or "Old French."

A. DIRECTIONS: Look up the following words in a dictionary. Circle each word that has a French origin. Then write whether it comes from French, Middle French, or Old French. If a word does *not* have a French origin, indicate what language the word does come from.

1. restaurant _____   5. torture _____

2. alley _____   6. sign _____

3. trace _____   7. costume _____

4. pungent _____   8. menu _____

Using the Word Bank

pungent	benevolently	retort
prodigy	malodorous	concessions

B. DIRECTIONS: Match each word in the left column with its definition in the right column. Write the letter of the definition on the line next to the word it defines.

_____   1. pungent   a. sharp or clever reply

_____   2. benevolently   b. things given or granted, as privileges

_____   3. retort   c. producing a sharp sensation of smell

_____   4. prodigy   d. having a bad smell

_____   5. malodorous   e. in a kind and well-meaning way

_____   6. concessions   f. a person who is amazingly talented

Recognizing Antonyms

C. DIRECTIONS: Circle the word or phrase that is most nearly *opposite* in meaning to the Word Bank word.

1. benevolently
   a. not cleverly
   b. violently
   c. well-wishing
   d. unkindly

2. malodorous
   a. without an odor
   b. fragrant
   c. flower-scented
   d. strong-smelling

Rules of the Game   **61**

Name _____ Date _____

"Rules of the Game" by Amy Tan

Build Grammar Skills: Prepositional Phrases

A **prepositional phrase** is made up of a preposition plus a noun or pronoun, called the object of the preposition, and any other words that come between the preposition and the object of the preposition. In the sentences below, the prepositional phrases are italicized, the prepositions are underlined, and the objects of the prepositions are circled.

The bright, red car looked odd _in the nearly deserted street._

The cat came slowly _toward them._

A lamp was hung _above a large, colorful painting._

A. Practice: Locate the prepositional phrases in these sentences from "Rules of the Game." Write each phrase, then underline the preposition once and circle its object.

1. I was six when my mother taught me the art of invisible strength.

   _____

2. Farther down the street was Ping Yuen Fish Market.

   _____

3. My brothers and I believed that the bad people emerged from this door at night.

   _____

4. I watched Vincent and Winston play during Christmas week.

   _____

5. I ran home and grabbed Vincent's chess set, which was bound in a cardboard box with rubber bands.

   _____

6. His face widened with surprise and he grinned as he looked at the box under my arm.

   _____

7. Oranges and tin cans careened down the sidewalk.

   _____

B. Writing Application: Form prepositional phrases using the following prepositions. Then use each prepositional phrase in a sentence.

   Example: among _____   among good friends

   We like being among good friends.

1. before _____   _____

2. until _____   _____

3. at _____   _____

4. during _____   _____

5. according to _____   _____

Name _____ Date _____

"Rules of the Game" by Amy Tan

Reading Strategy: Contrasting Characters

As you read "Rules of the Game," notice the conflict between Waverly and her mother. This conflict adds interest and tension to the story. The conflict arises because of the differences between the two main characters. Keeping track of those differences will help you understand the conflict more fully.

DIRECTIONS: As you read, note the differences and similarities in background, personality, and point of view between Waverly and her mother, Mrs. Jong. Fill in the Venn diagram with examples of these differences and similarities. Then use the examples you have noted to answer the questions that follow.

Waverly	Waverly and Mrs. Jong	Mrs. Jong

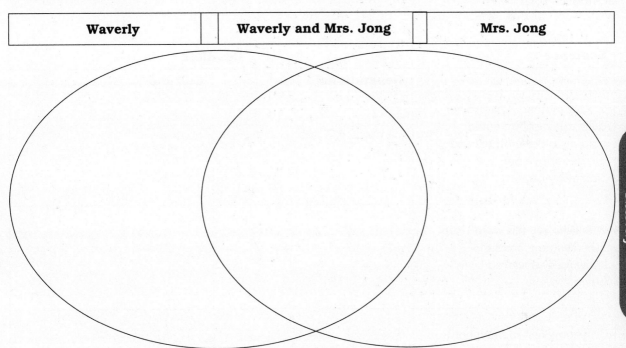

Unit 3: Moments of Discovery

1. What difference in cultural background separates Waverly and her mother?

_____

_____

2. How do personality differences and similarities cause conflict between Waverly and her mother?

_____

_____

3. How do Waverly and her mother react differently to Waverly's chess success?

_____

4. In what ways do Waverly and her mother differ over their hopes and dreams for Waverly's future?

_____

_____

"Rules of the Game" by Amy Tan

Literary Analysis: Generational Conflict

Generational conflicts are common between parents and their offspring, that is, between one generation and another. Sometimes, however, generations are also separated by cultural differences, as when parents and their children are born in different countries. For instance, Waverly (Meimei) and her mother, Mrs. Jong, experience typical generational conflicts, but they also experience cultural conflicts because Mrs. Jong was born in China and Waverly (Meimei) in the United States.

DIRECTIONS: The following sentences from "Rules of the Game" illustrate both generational and cultural conflicts. Under the appropriate headings, identify the specific conflicts to which these sentences refer.

Sentence	Conflicts	
	Generational	**Cultural**
1. "My mother imparted her daily truths so she could help my older brothers and me rise above our circumstances."		
2. " 'Who say this word?' she asked without a trace of knowing how wicked I was being."		
3. "[At my first tournament, when my name was called], my mother unwrapped a small tablet of red jade and tucked it into my pocket."		
4. "As my mother wiped each chess piece with a soft cloth, she said, 'Next time win more, lose less.' "		
5. " 'Ma, I can't practice when you stand there like that,' I said one day. She retreated to the kitchen and made loud noises with the pots and pans."		

"**Checkouts**" by Cynthia Rylant
"**Fifteen**" by William Stafford

Build Vocabulary

Spelling Strategy   When you add an ending to words ending in *y* preceded by a consonant, change the *y* to *i*, unless the ending begins with an *i*. The Word Bank word *harried*, for example, comes from the verb *harry*, "to harass or bother." To add an -*ed*, change the *y* to *i*, and add the ending: harry = *harri + ed*.

Using the Suffix -*ment*

The suffix -*ment* indicates "the state of or condition of." The suffix is usually added to a verb to create a noun that names the condition defined by the verb. For example, the state defined by the verb *excite* is *excitement*.

A. Directions: Determine the verb used to create the italicized word in each of the following sentences. Define the verb, and use its definition and your knowledge of the -*ment* suffix to define the italicized word. Write your answers in the spaces provided.

1. In 1963, Jacqueline Kennedy's *bereavement* was shared by the entire nation.

   Verb _____ Definition _____

   Bereavement: _____

2. Sarah's offer of *atonement* for the missed classes was extra homework.

   Verb _____ Definition _____

   Atonement: _____

Using the Word Bank

intuition	reverie	shard	harried	brazen
dishevelment	perverse	articulate	lingered	demure

B. Directions: For each of the following words, circle the letter of the word most nearly *opposite* in meaning.

1. brazen
   a. clamorous
   b. silent
   c. timid
   d. optimistic

2. perverse
   a. forward
   b. compliant
   c. stubborn
   d. kind

3. demure
   a. brazen
   b. awkward
   c. accept
   d. incline

4. lingered
   a. touched
   b. expelled
   c. dropped
   d. departed

5. dishevelment
   a. confusion
   b. bravery
   c. order
   d. embarrassment

6. articulate
   a. indistinct
   b. silent
   c. clear
   d. well-spoken

"Checkouts" by Cynthia Rylant
"Fifteen" by William Stafford

Build Grammar Skills: Prepositional Phrases as Modifiers

Prepositional phrases describe or add information to words in a sentence. That is, they act as modifiers. Prepositional phrases function either as adjectives, modifying nouns and pronouns (other than the nouns and pronouns within the phrase), or as adverbs, modifying verbs, adjectives, and other adverbs.

The girl *in the house* was lonely.

The prepositional phrase *in the house* acts as an adjective, modifying girl; it tells which girl was lonely.

. . . When one is moving *off the bus* . . .

The prepositional phrase *off the bus* acts as an adverb, modifying the verb *is moving*; it tells *where* one is moving.

A. Practice: Underline each prepositional phrase in the sentences, or extracts from sentences, from "Checkouts" and "Fifteen." Draw an arrow to the word each prepositional phrase modifies.

1. Then one day the bag boy dropped her jar of mayonnaise . . .

2. And he, too, knew the instant she came through the door . . .

3. Some months later the bag boy and the girl with the orange bow again crossed paths . . .

4. He had blood on his hand . . .

5. I helped him walk to his machine . . .

B. Writing Application: Rewrite the following sentences about the selections. Use the preposition in parentheses to complete the sentence with a prepositional phrase.

> **Example:** The girl's family moves _____. (to)
> The girl's family moves to Cincinnati.

1. For a month, the girl stays _____. (in)

   _____

2. The girl first sees the bag boy _____. (in)

   _____

3. The girl and the bag boy kept thinking _____. (about)

   _____

4. At the movie theater, they stood in line _____. (with)

   _____

5. The speaker in the poem "Fifteen" finds a motorcycle _____. (near)

   _____

6. The motorcycle's owner had flipped _____. (over)

   _____

"Checkouts" by Cynthia Rylant
"Fifteen" by William Stafford

Reading Strategy: Relating to Personal Experience

Good writers know that they can depend upon readers to bring their own lives with them when they sit down to read. Even though a writer may be presenting a totally new experience, readers will relate their personal experience to it as best they can. At some level, this process may be as simple as the sensory image created by a single word. When you see the word *bridge*, do you imagine a span over a river, part of a guitar, or a piece of dental work? The answer may vary, depending upon whether you're an engineer, a musician, or a dentist. Your reactions would probably be influenced by your experiences.

At another level, writers depend upon their readers to use personal experience in large ways. You may never have been to Cincinnati, but you probably have been to a supermarket. When the author of "Checkouts" sets her story in a supermarket, she doesn't have to describe the place in detail. She knows that you know a lot about supermarkets, what they look like, how they're lighted, where the checkout stands are—even the way customers eye each other and pretend not to. The author counts on readers to understand this part of the story, and because we do, we understand and identify with her characters. Because we understand, the writing makes an even stronger connection with us. Look for connections as you read.

DIRECTIONS: Use the graphic organizer to help you identify connections in the selections while you read. In the first column, note an event, detail, feeling of a character, or sensory image as you read. In the second column, describe the way the event, detail, feeling, or image relates to your own experience. One example from "Checkouts" appears. Work from either selection.

Event, detail, feeling, image	My related experience
large house with beveled glass windows and several porches	My grandparents' house on Pennsylvania Ave. seemed so formal and huge.

Checkouts/Fifteen **67**

Unit 3: Moments of Discovery

"Checkouts" by Cynthia Rylant
"Fifteen" by William Stafford

Literary Analysis: Irony

The word *irony* comes from an ancient Greek word meaning "dissembler in speech." To "dissemble" is to evade, misrepresent, or hide the truth. **Irony** in literature occurs when the description of an event, situation, or person doesn't match what one might conventionally expect. Writers use irony as a deliberate technique to call attention to the mismatch. The effect of irony sharpens the sense of expression, for readers relate to irony. For example, it's ironic that on the only cloudy day you remember your umbrella, it doesn't rain.

There is something ironic in "Checkouts" when the author describes a thoroughly American girl in a thoroughly American supermarket shopping in a thoroughly American way as "a Tibetan monk." Look for irony to add meaning as you read the selections.

DIRECTIONS: For each of the following excerpts from "Checkouts" and "Fifteen," place an *I* in the space provided if the excerpt is ironic and an *N* if it is not. Briefly explain why or why not on the lines following each excerpt.

_____ 1. But it is difficult work, suffering, and in its own way a kind of art, and finally she didn't have the energy for it anymore.

_____

_____

_____ 2. She interested him because her hair was red and thick, and in it she had placed a huge orange bow, nearly the size of a small hat.

_____

_____

_____ 3. The bag boy seemed a wonderful contrast to the perfectly beautiful house she had been forced to accept as her home, to the *history* she had become used to . . .

_____

_____ 4. It is reason enough to be alive, the hope you may see again some face which has meant something to you.

_____

_____

_____ 5. I admired all that pulsing gleam/the shiny flanks, the demure headlights/fringed where it lay.

_____

_____

_____ 6. He ran his hand/over it, called me a good man, roared away.

_____

_____

"Sympathy" by Paul Laurence Dunbar
"Caged Bird" by Maya Angelou
"We never know how high we are" by Emily Dickinson
from *In My Place* by Charlayne Hunter-Gault

Build Vocabulary

Spelling Strategy   Never double the final consonant when a word ends in more than one consonant. For example, when you add the ending *-ed* to *warp*, the final consonant *p* is not doubled: *warp* + *-ed* = *warped*.

Using Levels of Diction

Different levels of diction, or choice of words, help writers achieve specific purposes, reach a particular audience, and create different moods.

A. DIRECTIONS: Write answers to each of the following questions.

1. What is one purpose of the writer's elevated diction in the following excerpt from *In My Place*?

   And we . . . were now imbued with an unshakable determination to take control of our destiny and force the South to abandon the wretched Jim Crow laws . . . .

   _____

2. What feeling is created by the use of the words *bruised, sore,* and *beats* in the following lines from "Sympathy"?

   When his wing is bruised and his bosom sore,—/ When he beats his bars and he would be free;

   _____

Using the Word Bank

keener	warp	epithets	effigies
disperse	imbued	perpetuated	

B. DIRECTIONS: Complete each sentence with a word or words from the Word Bank. Use each word only once.

1. Demonstrators carried _____ and shouted hateful _____.

2. The commencement speaker _____ the graduating students with lofty goals.

3. After viewing the debate, many voters had a _____ understanding of the issues.

4. The unethical politician set out to _____ the public's perception of his opponent.

5. Racism is _____ by ignorance, hatred, and fear.

6. Huge crowds at the rally did not _____ until well after midnight.

"Sympathy" by Paul Laurence Dunbar
"Caged Bird" by Maya Angelou
"We never know how high we are" by Emily Dickinson
from *In My Place* by Charlayne Hunter-Gault

Build Grammar Skills: Preposition or Adverb?

Many words that act as prepositions can also act as adverbs, depending on how they are used. For a word to act as a preposition, it must have an object and be part of a prepositional phrase. Adverbs do not have objects.

Preposition: The cat leaped *over* the chair.   **Adverb:** Can you come *over*?

A. Practice: Label each underlined word *preposition* or *adverb*.

1. The speaker feels trapped like a bird <u>in</u> a cage.

   _____

2. The bird appears to be eager to go <u>outside</u>.

   _____

3. In "Caged Bird," a free bird flies <u>up</u> and floats <u>on</u> the wind.

   _____

4. The speaker in "We never know how high we are" believes people can rise <u>to</u> a challenge.

   _____

5. The writer of *In My Place* made history when she walked <u>onto</u> the college campus, because

   there had never been a black student at the school <u>before</u>.

   _____

B. Writing Application: Identify the adverb in each sentence below, and then write a prepositional phrase using the word as the preposition. The prepositional phrase does not have to relate to the original sentence.

   Example: The bird escaped its cage and flew around.
   around the world

1. We're falling behind.

   _____

2. The strong current pulled him under.

   _____

3. The shopkeeper said, "run along."

   _____

4. I wanted the movie to be over.

   _____

5. It's time to go in.

   _____

6. She fell down.

   _____

"Sympathy" by Paul Laurence Dunbar
"Caged Bird" by Maya Angelou
"We never know how high we are" by Emily Dickinson
from *In My Place* by Charlayne Hunter-Gault

Reading Strategy: Drawing Conclusions

When you draw a conclusion, you come to an opinion about something based on evidence you can point to. As you read, look for evidence that can help you form your own opinions about what you've read. Each of these selections invites you to draw a particular conclusion about the value of dreaming and reaching for a goal. Analyzing the structure and language of the selections in this unit can help you identify evidence for your conclusions.

DIRECTIONS: Provide specific examples from the selections to answer the following questions.

1. What conclusion can you draw from these lines from "Caged Bird"?

    The caged bird sings/with a fearful trill/of things unknown/but longed for still/and his tune is heard on the distant hill/for the caged bird/sings of freedom.

    _____
    _____
    _____

2. What is the speaker's point of view in these lines from "Sympathy"?

    "I know what the caged bird feels, alas!" "I know why the caged bird beats his wing," and "I know why the caged bird sings, ah me,"

    _____
    _____
    _____

3. What does the transition word *but* suggest in the following passages from "Caged Bird"?

    "But a bird that stalks/down his narrow cage/can seldom see through his bars of rage" and "The caged bird sings/with a fearful trill/of things unknown but longed for still"

    _____
    _____
    _____

4. What conclusions about the speaker's attitude toward dreaming can you draw from the following lines from "We never know how high we are"?

    "We never know how high we are/Till we are asked to rise/And then if we are true to plan/Our statures touch the skies -"

    _____
    _____
    _____

"Sympathy" by Paul Laurence Dunbar
"Caged Bird" by Maya Angelou
"We never know how high we are" by Emily Dickinson
from *In My Place* by Charlayne Hunter-Gault

Literary Analysis: Symbols

A **symbol** is an object, person, event, or action that represents something beyond itself. In the hands of writers, particularly poets, ordinary words assume more than their literal, or defined, meaning. Symbols are succinct and powerful ways of strengthening an idea, creating a mood, or emphasizing a theme.

Identifying Symbols

A. DIRECTIONS: Match each symbol in the left column with the idea it symbolizes in the right column. Write the letter of the idea in the blank next to the appropriate item number.

____ 1. child	a.	corruption
____ 2. dark cloud	b.	joy
____ 3. weeds	c.	knowledge
____ 4. encyclopedia	d.	possibilities
____ 5. horizon	e.	doom
____ 6. leaping	f.	innocence

Understanding Symbols

B. DIRECTIONS: Write the definition of each word. Then suggest what the word might symbolize.

1. scales

   definition: _____

   symbolic meaning: _____

2. fog

   definition: _____

   symbolic meaning: _____

3. hourglass

   definition: _____

   symbolic meaning: _____

4. fire

   definition: _____

   symbolic meaning: _____

"The Interlopers" by Saki (H. H. Munro)

Build Vocabulary

Spelling Strategy For words that end in *y* preceded by a vowel, do not change the *y* when adding an ending. For example, *-s* added to the Word Bank word *medley*, forms the word *medleys*. Likewise, *-s* added to the word *monkey* forms the word *monkeys*, and *-ed* added to the word *journey* forms the word *journeyed*.

Using the Root *-dol-*

In "The Interlopers," Ulrich claims that Georg will be left to die beneath the beech tree and adds, "Only as you will have met your death poaching on my lands I don't think I can decently send any message of **condolence** to your family." The word *condolence* contains the root *-dol-*, which means "pain." *Condolence* literally means "a feeling of pain with another" or "an expression of sympathy with a grieving person."

A. Directions: Read the following sentences and define the italicized words using your understanding of the root *-dol* as well as clues provided in the sentences.

1. She was not selected to play on the team and walked home with a *doleful* expression on her face.

   _____

2. The poet writes of the *dolor* people feel upon the loss of a loved one.

   _____

3. The *dolorous* song made many people cry.

   _____

4. Most employers will not tolerate *indolent* workers.

   _____

Using the Word Bank

precipitous	marauders	medley
condolence	languor	succor

B. Directions: Match each word in the left column with its definition in the right column. Write the letter of the definition on the line next to the word it defines.

____ 1. precipitous   a. weakness

____ 2. marauders   b. a mixture of things not usually found together

____ 3. medley   c. steep; sheer

____ 4. condolence   d. help; relief

____ 5. languor   e. an expression of sympathy with a grieving person

____ 6. succor   f. raiders; people who take goods by force

"The Interlopers" by Saki (H. H. Munro)

Build Grammar Skills: Different Kinds of Conjunctions

A **conjunction** is a word used to connect other words or groups of words. The three main kinds of conjunctions are **coordinating**, **correlative**, and **subordinating**. The coordinating conjunctions are *and, but, for, nor, or, so,* and *yet.* They connect similar kinds of words or similar groups of words.

> **Example:** All of Judy's cats *and* dogs get along well.

Correlative conjunctions always appear in pairs. Some correlative conjunctions are *both . . . and, either . . . or,* and *not only . . . but also.*

> **Example:** Luke plays *not only* piano, but also saxophone.

Subordinating conjunctions connect two complete ideas by making one idea subordinate (lower in rank or importance) to the other idea. Some subordinating conjunctions are *after, although, because, so that, unless,* and *whenever.*

> **Example:** Adam finishes his homework on Saturday *so that* he has Sunday free.

A. Practice: Identify the underlined conjunctions in the following excerpts from "The Interlopers" as *coordinating, correlative,* or *subordinating.*

1. . . . a man stood one winter night watching <u>and</u> listening, <u>as though</u> he waited for some beast of the woods to come within the range of his vision, <u>and</u>, later, of his rifle.

   _____

2. Ulrich had banded together his foresters to watch the dark forest, <u>not</u> in quest of four-footed quarry, <u>but</u> to keep a lookout for the prowling thieves . . .

   _____

3. I have men, too, in the forest, close behind me, <u>and</u> they will be here first <u>and</u> do the releasing.

   _____

4. <u>When</u> they drag me out from under these branches it won't need much clumsiness on their part to roll this mass of trunk right over on the top of you.

   _____

B. Writing Application: Combine the sentence pairs, using the type of conjunction specified.

1. I'm going to the bookstore. I need something to read. (subordinating)

   _____

   _____

2. A book on history interests me. A book on science interests me. (correlative)

   _____

   _____

3. The store sells paperback books. It also sells hardcover books. (coordinating)

   _____

   _____

"The Interlopers" by Saki (H. H. Munro)

Reading Strategy: Identifying Causes and Effects

Most conflicts have **causes**, or reasons, and **effects**, or results. In "The Interlopers," a dispute over land is the cause of the story's central conflict between two families. The effect of this conflict is a hatred between the two families that has lasted for generations. "The Interlopers" is filled with other causes and effects that drive the story toward an unexpected conclusion.

DIRECTIONS: Use the cause-and-effect chart below to keep track of events in "The Interlopers" as you read. Whenever you notice a conflict arising in the story, identify the cause of the conflict and the effect of that conflict.

Cause	Effect
Land dispute	Lifelong feud between two families

"The Interlopers" by Saki (H. H. Munro)

Literary Analysis: Conflict

Conflict is the ground upon which a plot is built. The conflict between opposing forces determines which actions the characters will take and the sequence in which those actions will occur. Stories rarely involve a single conflict. More often, several conflicts of different types are intermingled, challenging the characters in a variety of ways. An **internal conflict** occurs within a character's mind. An **external conflict** takes place between the characters or between characters and the forces of nature. A fight-to-the-end contest between two enemies in an adventure story is an example of a physical external conflict; however, external conflicts need not be physical or violent. A quiet disagreement between two friends is also an external conflict.

A. DIRECTIONS: "The Interlopers" is a brief story, but it involves more than one type of conflict. On the lines below, briefly describe the story situations that illustrate the type of conflict named.

1. external conflict/person against nature

_____

_____

_____

2. external conflict/person against person

_____

_____

_____

3. internal conflict/person against himself

_____

_____

_____

B. DIRECTIONS: Although the ending of the story is resolved based on the external conflict of man against nature, the author clearly focused on another type of conflict throughout the story. Identify the type of conflict you consider most central to the story and explain why you think it is the most important in the story.

_____

_____

_____

_____

_____

_____

_____

_____

_____

Name _____ Date _____

Build Vocabulary

Spelling Strategy   For words that end with two consonants, retain both consonants when adding an ending. For example, the ending -ed added to the word *encompass* forms the Word Bank word *encompassed*.

Using the Root -vis-

The Latin root -*vis*- means "see." You can find this root in the Word Bank word *improvised*, which refers to something arranged quickly, with little preparation. In the case of *improvised*, -*vis* is preceded by the prefixes *im*- and *pro*-, which mean "not" and "before," respectively. So, the literal meaning of *improvised* is "unforeseen."

A. DIRECTIONS: The words in the following list all contain the root -*vis*-. Read the sentences below and fill in each blank with the most appropriate word from the list.

vista	visible	visit	visionary

1. Tourists enjoyed the stunning _____ from the picture window in the hotel lobby.

2. The philosopher's ideas were at first seen as _____ .

3. We hope to _____ our friends again soon.

4. The road was barely _____ through the dense fog.

Using the Word Bank

improvised	laden	encompassed	impose	ingeniously

B. DIRECTIONS: Match each word in the left column with its definition in the right column. Write the letter of the definition on the line next to the word it defines.

____ 1. laden   a. put to some trouble

____ 2. ingeniously   b. surrounded, encircled

____ 3. impose   c. arranged or put together quickly

____ 4. improvised   d. burdened

____ 5. encompassed   e. cleverly

C. DIRECTIONS: Each of the following sentences has a blank space, indicating that a word has been omitted. Following the sentence are four lettered words. Choose the letter of the word that best completes the meaning of the sentence as a whole.

1. We quickly _____ a dinner for our unexpected guests.
   a. encompassed
   b. imposed
   c. entered
   d. improvised

2. The librarian's arms were _____ with heavy books.
   a. encompassed
   b. enlightened
   c. laden
   d. lifted

"The Rug Merchant" by James A. Michener

Build Grammar Skills: Interjections

An **interjection** is a word that expresses feeling or emotion. Interjections are unrelated to any other words in the sentence, so punctuation is used to set them apart. Though interjections should be used sparingly in writing, they can draw attention to a particular incident, help define a character's personality, or create a particular mood. Some common interjections are *aha, bravo, great, hurray, oh, oops, ouch, well,* and *whew*.

> *Wow!* That's an amazing trick.
>
> Can you, *uh*, help me with this?
>
> *Oh no!* I've lost my keys.

A. Practice: In these sentences from "The Rug Merchant," note the use of interjections (underlined). In a word or two, describe the feeling or emotion expressed by each.

1. "No! No! No rugs!"

   _____

2. "Ah, Michener-sahib, you have fine eye."

   _____

3. "Well, I've invested so much in it already, I may as well risk a little more."

   _____

4. Alas, shortly thereafter the rugs were stolen, but I remember them vividly and with longing.

   _____

B. Writing Application: Write each sentence, adding an appropriate interjection to each.

1. That pan is hot!

   _____

2. You did a great job!

   _____

3. I didn't mean to do it that way.

   _____

4. That looks awful.

   _____

"The Rug Merchant" by James A. Michener

Reading Strategy: Making Inferences About Characters

As a reader, think of the details a writer gives about the words and actions of characters as clues that will help you to have a better understanding of the story. These clues allow you to make **inferences,** or draw your own conclusions, about characters.

DIRECTIONS: As you read, note in the following chart details of appearance, words, and actions that allow you to make inferences about characters. After each detail, write in parentheses the inference you have made. An example of each type of detail and its corresponding inference is shown below.

Appearance (inference)	Words (inference)	Actions (inference)
Zaqir: thin, long hair (might be poor)	Zaqir: "I leave here. You study. You learn to like." (Persistent; he knows a potential customer when he sees one.)	Michener: continues to talk to Zaqir, even though he says he doesn't want rugs. (There is something about Zaqir he likes.)

"The Rug Merchant" by James A. Michener

Literary Analysis: Characterization in Essays

Characterization is the act of creating and developing a character. Just as fiction writers use methods of characterization to create a vivid portrait of a fictional character, essay writers use the same methods of characterization to create a vivid portrait of a real-life person. These methods include describing a character's thoughts, words, and actions, as well as what others say and think about the character.

DIRECTIONS: Answer the following questions about the characters in "The Rug Merchant."

1. What kind of salesperson is Zaqir?

   _____

   _____

2. Which of Zaqir's words and actions create the vivid portrait of him?

   _____

   _____

   _____

3. Why do you think the author is finally persuaded to buy a rug from Zaqir?

   _____

   _____

   _____

4. What does Zaqir's willingness to give the author the rugs and wait for payment reveal about his character?

   _____

   _____

   _____

5. What do you learn about Michener's character through his storytelling?

   _____

   _____

   _____

"**Combing**" by Gladys Cardiff
"**Women**" by Alice Walker
"**maggie and milly and molly and may**" by E. E. Cummings
"**Astonishment**" by Wisława Szymborska

Build Vocabulary

Spelling Strategy When you are adding an ending beginning with a vowel to a word that ends in one consonant after two vowels, do not double the final consonant. For example, *plait* + *-ing* becomes *plaiting*. *Ghoul* + *-ish* becomes *ghoulish*, *deal* + *-er* becomes *dealer*, and *feel* + *-ing* becomes *feeling*.

Using Words With Multiple Meanings

A poet's goal is to make you see, feel, and think as much as possible in the short time it takes you to read a poem. For this reason, poets often charge their language with power by choosing words with more than one meaning. Consider these lines:

Noon in the steel mill,
Lunchboxes open under heavy arms

Here, *heavy* can describe the bulk of the workers' arms, or imply fatigue. Both meanings become part of our understanding.

A. DIRECTIONS: In each of the following sentences, choose the word with multiple meanings from the pair in parentheses. Then, in the space provided, explain why the choice you made has more impact.

1. It was his (way/fashion) to dress as expensively as possible.

_____

2. Her eyes were (sharp/searching) as she questioned where I'd been.

_____

3. He (spoke/performed) convincingly explaining the lost homework.

_____

4. That small (group/stand) of trees is the last remnant of the original forest.

_____

Using the Word Bank

intent	stout	plaiting	languid

B. DIRECTIONS: Match each word in the left column with its definition in the right column. Write the letter of the definition on the line next to the word it defines.

_____ 1. intent   a. drooping, weak

_____ 2. plaiting   b. sturdy, forceful

_____ 3. languid   c. firmly fixed, concentrated

_____ 4. stout   d. braiding

"Combing" by Gladys Cardiff
"Women" by Alice Walker
"maggie and milly and molly and may" by E. E. Cummings
"Astonishment" by Wisława Szymborska

Build Grammar Skills: Parenthetical Expression

A **parenthetical expression** is a word or phrase that interrupts the general flow of a sentence and is grammatically unrelated to the rest of the sentence. Names of people being addressed, common expressions (of course, in my opinion, on the other hand), conjunctive adverbs (also, besides, however, nevertheless), and contrasting expressions (not that one, not there) are the most common parenthetical expressions. Parenthetical expressions are always set off from the sentence, most commonly with commas, but also with parentheses or dashes, which add more emphasis.

> Tell us, John, what you think of the new senator.
>
> She didn't say, by the way, how long she would be gone.
>
> I looked outside (there's a window near my desk) and noticed that it was raining.
>
> The sun looked pale—it was mid-winter, after all—and it made me feel colder.

A. Practice: Identify the parenthetical expressions in these sentences, and set them off with the punctuation specified at the end of each item.

1. Gladys Cardiff a poet whose work I enjoy wrote "Combing." (dashes)

2. It was this poem not that one that I liked better. (commas)

3. The women in these poems they remind me of people I know seem strong. (parentheses)

4. Alice Walker by the way writes a lot about the strong women who influenced her. (commas)

5. E. E. Cummings his poetry is always interesting is famous for his creative misuse of grammar conventions. (parentheses)

6. Wisława Szymborska however uses questions to catch the reader's attention. (commas)

B. Writing Application: Write a sentence using each parenthetical expression and punctuating it appropriately. If you wish, you may write about the topic in parentheses.

1. in my opinion (poetry versus short stories)

   _____

   _____

2. otherwise (driving safety)

   _____

   _____

3. not that one (games)

   _____

   _____

4. there are certainly a lot of opportunities (volunteering)

   _____

   _____

"Combing" by Gladys Cardiff
"Women" by Alice Walker
"maggie and milly and molly and may" by E. E. Cummings
"Astonishment" by Wisława Szymborska

Reading Strategy: Interpreting Meaning

These poems all bring moments of insight to readers, as the poets take us through their thoughts to new understanding. To be ready for those insights, readers interpret meaning as they read through the poems. What do we see, hear, feel, and think as we read each line? Do we get a picture that reminds us of something from our own lives? In the ten simple lines of "maggie and milly and molly and may," the poet gives us four distinct personalities. How does he do that? Poets depend on readers to think along and interpret as they read.

DIRECTIONS: Use the graphic organizer to help you think about connections between words, the world of the poem, and your world. In the innermost circle, write words or phrases from one of the poems which give you a sensory image. In the next circle outward, describe the picture or sense that the image gives you. What is going on in the world of the poem? What do you see? Finally, in the outer circle, write what that image reminds you of in your own life. If necessary, use the back of this worksheet to describe more fully the connection between the words of the poem and your life.

The World of the Poem

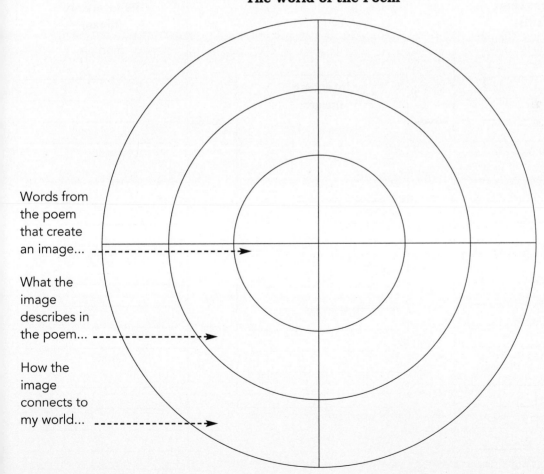

Words from the poem that create an image...

What the image describes in the poem...

How the image connects to my world...

"Combing" by Gladys Cardiff
"Women" by Alice Walker
"maggie and milly and molly and may" by E. E. Cummings
"Astonishment" by Wisɫawa Szymborska

Literary Analysis: Moment of Insight

These poems provide moments of insight, which help us see something in a new way, or present new ideas based on what happens in a poem. Interpreting images as we read helps us prepare for the insight. Often, when the moment of insight occurs, it causes us to go back and re-think what we read in the poem. We discover the insight, and consider or reconsider the poem differently as a result. This moment of insight becomes a new lens through which we see the world.

In "maggie and milly and molly and may" by E. E. Cummings, four girls go to the beach. Use the chart on this page to discover how insight changes our understanding about each girl—and the world.

DIRECTIONS: In the first column, interpret the stanza about each girl. Write what you think is happening in the world of the poem. In the second column, interpret the final stanza. What is the insight Cummings offers? In the third column, write what you think the insight means about the personality of each girl. How does the insight change your understanding of each girl?

Interpretation and Insight

Interpret Lines (Events)	Interpret Insight	Re-Interpret (Ideas)
maggie (lines 3–4)	(lines 11–12)	maggie
milly (lines 5–6)		milly
molly (lines 7–8)		molly
may (lines 9–10)		may

"The Secret Life of Walter Mitty" by James Thurber

Build Vocabulary

Spelling Strategy For words that end in silent *e*, the *e* usually drops out before adding an ending that begins with a vowel. So *cannonade + ing* becomes *cannonading*, *rake + ish* is *rakish*, and *cure + able* is *curable*. If the final silent *e* is preceded by a *g*, however, the *e* does not drop, as in *knowledgeable* and *manageable*.

Using the Root -scrut-

A. DIRECTIONS: These words contain the root *-scrut-*, meaning "to search or examine." Use what you know about the root to match these words with their definitions. Write the letter of the appropriate meaning next to the word.

____ 1. scrutable   a. searching, examining

____ 2. scrutator   b. can be understood by examining

____ 3. scrutatory   c. in a closely searching manner

____ 4. scrutinously   d. one who examines or investigates

Using the Word Bank

rakishly	hurtling	distraught	haggard	insolent
insinuatingly	cur	cannonading	derisive	inscrutable

B. DIRECTIONS: Replace the italicized word or words in each sentence with the appropriate word from the Word Bank. Rewrite the sentence.

1. The people waiting at the emergency veterinary clinic all looked *extremely troubled*.

   _____

2. Crowds outside the government building chanted *contemptuous* slogans.

   _____

3. On occasion, Ms. Mason gave *not easily understood* answers to our questions.

   _____

4. The meteorite was *moving swiftly and forcefully* through space toward Earth.

   _____

5. Last night's *continuous firing of artillery* took its toll on the factories on the edge of town.

   _____

6. The *boldly disrespectful* way in which the child looked at me made me uncomfortable.

   _____

7. She always wore her hats *with a casual, dashing look*, as if she hadn't a care in the world.

   _____

8. The fact that she looked at me *in an indirectly suggestive manner* made me angry.

   _____

Unit 4 The Lighter Side

"The Secret Life of Walter Mitty" by James Thurber

Build Grammar Skills: Complete Subjects and Predicates

Every sentence has two main parts, a **complete subject** and a **complete predicate**. Together, these parts express a complete thought. The complete subject always includes a noun or pronoun that names the person, place, or thing the sentence is about. The complete predicate always includes a verb that tells something about the complete subject. The following examples are taken from "The Secret Life of Walter Mitty."

> A newsboy | went by shouting something about the Waterbury trial.

> A woman who was passing | laughed.

Note that the complete subject or predicate can contain one word or several words.

A. Practice: Draw a vertical line between the complete subject and the complete predicate.

1. Walter Mitty has a lively imagination.

2. Mitty faces a tense situation in each of his daydreams.

3. Mrs. Mitty wonders why her husband is so absentminded.

4. Mitty tried to take his tire chains off.

5. One daydream occurs in a hospital operating room.

6. Dr. Remington and Dr. Pritchard-Mitford recognize Walter Mitty as a famous physician.

7. Some passersby were amused at Mitty's comment.

8. He can't remember things on his shopping list.

9. An old magazine triggers another daydream.

10. His wife wants to take his temperature.

B. Writing Application: Add a complete subject or a complete predicate to each item.

1. My favorite vacation spot

   _____

2. The most interesting school club

   _____

3. likes to sky dive

   _____

4. set a new record in the long jump

   _____

5. The two old friends

   _____

"The Secret Life of Walter Mitty" by James Thurber

Reading Strategy: Reading Back and Reading Ahead

While reading a text, we sometimes encounter places where the meaning is unclear. This may happen because the topic is difficult, a word is new, or our attention wanders. All readers sometimes have these experiences. Good readers use the strategy of **reading back and reading ahead** when they don't understand something.

Sometimes just rereading a passage, or reading a few lines ahead, will clarify its meaning. If not, this strategy will help you pinpoint the area that is causing difficulty. You may need to look up a word's meaning in the dictionary or paraphrase a sentence. Also remember to ask questions as you read. By interacting with the text in these ways, you will stay focused and improve your comprehension.

DIRECTIONS: Read the following passage from "The Secret Life of Walter Mitty." Then locate the passage in your text. By reading back and reading ahead, find details that help you clarify its meaning. Use the graphic organizer below to record the information you find. Then answer the questions.

> . . . "The cannonading has got the wind up in young Raleigh, sir," said the sergeant. Captain Mitty looked up at him through tousled hair. "Get him to bed," he said wearily. "With the others. I'll fly alone." "But you can't, sir," said the sergeant anxiously. "It takes two men to handle that bomber . . . "

"Reading-Back Details"	**"Reading-Ahead Details"**

1. What is *cannonading*?

_____

2. What triggers Mitty's daydream about being a fighter pilot?

_____

3. What rouses him from his daydream?

_____

Name _____ Date _____

Literary Analysis: Point of View

The **point of view,** or perspective from which a story is told, determines what kind of information the reader is given. In "The Secret Life of Walter Mitty," Thurber writes from Walter Mitty's point of view. The story presents Mitty's thoughts and actions and his account of his encounters with the other characters. If Thurber had written the story from the point of view of another character, the content of the story would be quite different. For example, if the story had been told from Mrs. Mitty's point of view, the reader would not learn the details of Mitty's daydreams and thus might not feel sympathy toward him.

DIRECTIONS: Following are the names of minor characters from "The Secret Life of Walter Mitty." On the lines provided, describe each character's involvement in the story. Then explain how the reader's understanding of Walter Mitty would be different if the episode had been written from that character's point of view.

1. The woman on the sidewalk

_____

_____

_____

_____

_____

_____

2. The parking-lot attendant

_____

_____

_____

_____

_____

_____

3. Mrs. Mitty

_____

_____

_____

_____

_____

_____

_____

"The Inspector-General" by Anton Chekhov

Build Vocabulary

Spelling Strategy   When adding a suffix that begins with a vowel to a word that ends in a consonant, the spelling of the word does not change. For example, when adding the suffix *-or* to the word *inspect,* the spelling of the word *inspect* does not change to form the new word *inspector.*

Using the Word Root *-nym-*

The word root *-nym-* means "name." The word *anonymous* contains the root *-nym-* and means "without a known name."

A. DIRECTIONS: Each of the following sentences contains an italicized word that is formed with the root *-nym-*. Use context clues and the meaning of the prefix to determine the meaning of the word. Write the definition of the word on the blank line.

1. An appropriate *synonym* to describe the inspector-general's creeping actions might be "secretive" or "deceptive." *(syn-* = "together")

   _____

2. In some of his early short stories, Chekhov used the *pseudonym* Antosha Chekhonte. *(pseudo-* = "false")

   _____

3. In the Russian language, a *patronymic* is formed by adding "-ich" to the father's name, such as in "Pavlovich." *(patro-* = "father")

   _____

Using the Word Bank

incognito	anonymous	trundle	valet	buffet

B. DIRECTIONS: Match each word in the left column with its definition in the right column. Write the letter of the definition on the line next to the word it defines.

____ 1. anonymous   a. with true identity unrevealed or disguised

____ 2. buffet   b. a man's personal servant who takes care of the man's clothes

____ 3. incognito   c. a restaurant with a counter where refreshments are served

____ 4. trundle   d. without a known or acknowledged name

____ 5. valet   e. to roll along; to rotate

C. DIRECTIONS: Choose the word or phrase that is most nearly *opposite* in meaning to the numbered word. Write the letter of the word in the blank.

____ 1. incognito
   a. revealed b. disguised c. identical d. anonymous

____ 2. anonymous
   a. unknown b. camouflaged c. famous d. nameless

Unit 4: The Lighter Side

"The Inspector-General" by Anton Chekhov

Build Grammar Skills: Compound Verbs and Compound Subjects

When a sentence has two or more subjects, it has a **compound subject**. When a sentence has two or more verbs, it has a **compound verb**. Compound subjects and verbs are joined by conjunctions such as *and* or *or*. The following examples are taken from "The Inspector-General."

> **Compound Subject:** The *valet* and the *coachman* have got tongues in their heads.

> **Compound Verb:** The driver *turns* and *looks* at the traveler. . . .

A. Practice: Underline the compound subject or the compound verb in the sentences.

1. The Inspector-General usually eats and drinks well.

2. The driver's questions and answers are very clever.

3. The traveler plots and plans his surprise appearance.

4. The driver and his friends know the Inspector-General's tricks.

5. The traveler shouts and gestures for the driver to turn the cart around.

B. Writing Application: Write sentences by adding either a compound subject or a compound verb to the subject or predicate.

> **Example:** The eagle
> The eagle soared and dived in the sky.

1. The noisy neighborhood children

   _____

2. snuffled in their cages

   _____

3. The linebackers

   _____

4. lifted the heavy table

   _____

5. The sleek racing boats

   _____

"The Inspector-General" by Anton Chekhov

Reading Strategy: Reading Between the Lines

When you draw general conclusions about a character or situation from specific evidence provided by a writer, you are **reading between the lines.** Sometimes a writer withholds key details to keep you guessing or to make you uncertain about a story's outcome. In his play "The Inspector-General," Chekhov withholds an essential piece of information: the identity of the traveler. Use the details Chekhov provides to read between the lines and find out who the traveler is.

DIRECTIONS: As you read "The Inspector-General," use the following chart to gather information and draw conclusions about the traveler's identity. Then use the evidence you have gathered to answer the questions that follow the chart.

Evidence of the traveler's appearance and of what he says and does:	What the evidence suggests:
Example: The traveler wears dark glasses and a long overcoat with its collar turned up.	**Example:** He is traveling incognito and does not want his identity to be known.
1.	
2.	
3.	
4.	
5.	

6. Who is the traveler?

_____

7. What is his reason for traveling incognito?

_____

8. What conclusion can you draw about the traveler's attitude toward his work?

_____

9. What does the evidence suggest about the traveler's expectations?

_____

10. What conclusions can you draw about the traveler's character?

_____

The Inspector-General **91**

"The Inspector-General" by Anton Chekhov

Literary Analysis: Irony

In a literary work, **irony** is created when a contrast occurs between an expected outcome and an actual outcome. There are three types of irony: verbal irony, dramatic irony, and irony of situation. In **verbal irony,** a word or phrase is used to suggest the opposite of its usual meaning. In **dramatic irony,** a contradiction occurs between what a character thinks and what the reader or audience knows is true. In **irony of situation,** an event occurs that contradicts the expectations of the characters, of the reader, or of the audience. In Chekhov's play, all three types of irony are used.

DIRECTIONS: Read each of the following passages or descriptions of events from the play. Identify which type of irony is used in each passage or description. Then briefly explain the contrast or contradiction that occurs in each passage.

1. **TRAVELER.** So, what do you reckon? Any good, is he? (*The* DRIVER *turns around.*)
   DRIVER. Oh, yes, he's a good one, this one.

   Type of irony: _____

   Contrast: _____

   _____

2. He hops on a train just like anyone else, just like you or me. When he gets off, he don't go jumping into a cab or nothing fancy. Oh, no. He wraps himself up from head to toe so you can't see his face, and he wheezes away like an old dog so no one can recognize his voice.

   Type of irony: _____

   Contrast: _____

   _____

3. **TRAVELER.** Very cunning, you were saying.

   Type of irony: _____

   Contrast: _____

   _____

4. **TRAVELER.** And then he pounces, yes? I should think some people must get the surprise of their life, mustn't they?

   Type of irony: _____

   Contrast: _____

   _____

5. **DRIVER.** So there's the inspector-general, all muffled up like a roll of carpet, going secretly along in a cart somewhere, and when he gets there, nothing to be seen but vodka and cold salmon!
   TRAVELER. (shouts). Turn around!

   Type of irony: _____

   Contrast: _____

   _____

"Go Deep to the Sewer" by Bill Cosby
"Fly Away" by Ralph Helfer

Build Vocabulary

Spelling Strategy When adding -ly to a word ending with a short vowel followed by an l, double the final l. Thus *lateral* becomes *laterally*, *civil* becomes *civilly*, and *thoughtful* becomes *thoughtfully*.

Using Sports Jargon

The special vocabulary associated with a sport, occupation, or industry is called **jargon.** Jargon is a sort of verbal shorthand that communicates efficiently—and often colorfully—to make a point or express an idea. When Bill Cosby is "sweeping to glory" along the curb in Philadelphia, we know in his imagination he is running one of football's fundamental plays in heroic fashion. In sports-loving America, the jargon of the playing field frequently finds its way into daily life.

A. DIRECTIONS: Explain the meaning of each italicized word or phrase in the following sentences. Explain the relationship of each to sports.

1. Junior's not knowing the word "decoy" *threw a curve* into Cosby's plan.

_____

2. When Helfer realized he could control the flies with a tranquilizer, he knew he was *in the home stretch.*

_____

3. After he said he could do the job in two days, Helfer wondered if he'd *jumped the gun.*

_____

Using the Word Bank

lateral	yearned	decoy	interpretation	skeptical

B. DIRECTIONS: Each item consists of a related pair of words in CAPITAL LETTERS, followed by four lettered pairs of words. Choose the pair that best expresses a relationship similar to that expressed in the pair in capital letters. Circle the letter of your choice.

____ 1. LATERAL : FORWARD ::
    a. back : front
    b. vertical : sideways
    c. behind : around
    d. sideways : ahead

____ 2. YEARNED : WANTED ::
    a. appetite : food
    b. longed : wished
    c. grew : aged
    d. thought : hoped

____ 3. DECOY : TRAPPED ::
    a. lie : silence
    b. trick : attack
    c. lure : snared
    d. bait : fool

____ 4. INTERPRETATION : ANALYSIS ::
    a. explanation : study
    b. fact : opinion
    c. learning : predicting
    d. guess : examination

Unit 4: The Lighter Side

"Go Deep to the Sewer" by Bill Cosby
"Fly Away" by Ralph Helfer

Build Grammar Skills: Direct Objects

A **direct object** is a noun or pronoun that receives the action of a transitive action verb. It completes the meaning of the predicate of a sentence. To help determine whether a word is a direct object, ask the questions *Whom?* or *What?* after an action verb. Note these examples.

The snow covered the frozen *ground.*

> **Ask:** Covered what? **Answer:** ground

The clown entertained the delighted *audience* inside the circus tent.

> **Ask:** Entertained whom? **Answer:** audience

A. Practice: Underline the direct objects in the sentences, or extracts from sentences, from "Go Deep to the Sewer" and "Fly Away."

1. The quarterback held this position not because he was the best passer. . . .

2. Suppose I start a fly pattern to the bakery. . . .

3. "Cause I can't see the ball."

4. See if you can shake your man before you hit. . . .

5. I will never forget one particular play from those days. . . .

6. The director wants thousands of flies to be crawling. . . .

7. The next day I visited a good friend of mine. . . .

8. Inside I could see massive swarms of maggots. . . .

9. With everything set, I opened the small door of the fly house.

10. Well, actually, I've recently trained 432 flies to form a chorus line. . . .

B. Writing Application: Write your own sentences using the subject and direct object given. You might begin by thinking of an appropriate action verb.

> **Example:** sister/pie
> My sister baked a pie.

1. dog/bone

_____

2. carpenter/desk

_____

3. brother/dishes

_____

"Go Deep to the Sewer" by Bill Cosby
"Fly Away" by Ralph Helfer

Reading Strategy: Recognizing Situational Humor

One of the hardest things to do is to describe why something is funny. Different types of things make us laugh, and what one person finds hilarious may leave another cold. Some humor, like a knock-knock joke, is verbal. Other humor, like that in the selections by Bill Cosby and Ralph Helfer, is largely situational.

Situational humor arises from setting. Something unpredictable or unusual happens, or something perfectly normal—like a football game—occurs in an unexpected place. Maybe the idea of going swimming in a tuxedo makes you laugh, or perhaps those people who get married jumping out of airplanes seem amusing. Whatever it is, recognize situational humor as the cause. Combine this recognition with your active reading skills, with which you pay close attention to what's going on *as you read*, and you'll find yourself getting closer to understanding what's funny and why.

DIRECTIONS: Use this graphic organizer to help you recognize situational humor. As you read, note situations you find humorous. In the first column, briefly describe the action or situation. In the second column, note the setting. In the third column, record who is acting and how. Finally, in the fourth column, tell why this situation is humorous.

Action or Situation	Setting or Location	Who Is Acting, and How?	What's Funny in Situation?
1.			
2.			
3.			
4.			

"Go Deep to the Sewer" by Bill Cosby
"Fly Away" by Ralph Helfer

Literary Analysis: Humorous Remembrance

Laughter ripples through all of our lives, but some people have a gift for looking on the funny side. Is a day partly sunny or partly cloudy? For Bill Cosby, who grew up in housing projects in Philadelphia, the world could have been dismal, but he took his memories and made bright laughter.

In a humorous remembrance such as Cosby's, the focus may be on the humor, but there is an air of truth about "Go Deep to the Sewer," however lightly told. Similarly, Ralph Helfer describes fly training for laughs, but we still believe he did it as he described it. One element of humor is that it rings true, even when exaggerated or skewed to make us chuckle. A humorous remembrance such as Cosby's often carries its laughter on a framework of truth.

DIRECTIONS: Answer each of the following questions.

1. How much of Cosby's account of childhood games is actually true, in your opinion?

   _____

   _____

2. Playing football or baseball in traffic would truly be dangerous. What serious issue does this setting bring up?

   _____

   _____

3. Are Junior, Albert, Shorty, and Jody actual people, in your opinion? What is exaggerated about them, and what might be real?

   _____

   _____

4. Cosby seems to recall fondly a childhood without many advantages. Why do you think this is so?

   _____

   _____

5. Is there any point in Ralph Helfer's "Fly Away" at which you think he's exaggerating or changing the truth?

   _____

   _____

6. Helfer's success or failure depends on a single incident. What is it? When do you know whether he succeeds or fails?

   _____

   _____

7. In your opinion, what is remarkable about Helfer's account that makes it memorable?

   _____

   _____

"An Entomological Study of Apartment 4A" by Patricia Volk

Build Vocabulary

Spelling Strategy A prefix attached to a word never affects the spelling of the original word. For example, the prefix *im–* added to the base *mortal* forms the word *immortal*.

Using the Prefix *micro-*

In "An Entomological Study of Apartment 4A," Patricia Volk writes that bugs are "microcosms." Because the prefix *micro-* means "small," and the base *-cosms* means "worlds" or "universes," the word *microcosms* literally means "little worlds." Volk is referring to bugs as tiny versions of the world.

A. DIRECTIONS: Replace the italicized phrase in each sentence with a word from the following list:

microscopic	microcomputer	microfilm	microorganisms	microwaves

1. At many libraries, newspapers and magazines are saved on *film at a reduced size*.

2. Some scientists study *animal and plant life that can be seen only with a microscope*.

3. At her office, she uses a computer attached to a large computer network, but at home she uses a *small, personal computer*.

4. That particle is *so small it cannot be seen with the naked eye*.

5. Foods cook faster with *small electromagnetic waves* than by heat in a conventional oven.

Using the Word Bank

microcosms	metaphors	poignant	malevolence	immortalized

B. DIRECTIONS: Choose the letter of the description that best fits each word below. Write the letters on the lines provided.

_____ 1. metaphors
   a. experiments
   b. organisms
   c. poems
   d. figures of speech

_____ 2. poignant
   a. depressing
   b. moving
   c. boring
   d. lengthy

_____ 3. microcosms
   a. scientists
   b. tiny insects
   c. little worlds
   d. small computers

_____ 4. immortalized
   a. given lasting fame
   b. quickly forgotten
   c. frightened
   d. given a great deal of money

_____ 5. malevolence
   a. clumsiness
   b. intelligence
   c. kindness
   d. evil

An Entomological Study of Apartment 4A **97**

"An Entomological Study of Apartment 4A" by Patricia Volk

Build Grammar Skills: Indirect Objects

An **indirect object** is a noun or pronoun that appears with a *direct object* and names the person or thing to or for whom or what something is given or done. A sentence cannot have an indirect object unless it has a direct object.

To help determine whether a word is an indirect object, first find the direct object. Then ask, *To or for whom?* or *To or for what?* after the action verb. Examples are from the selection.

> I hand *him* my hat.
> **Ask:** Hand to whom? **Answer:** him

> I show *him* an arachnid that has spun a web in its container.
> **Ask:** Show whom? **Answer:** him

Remember that a sentence cannot have an indirect object unless it has a direct object.

A. Practice: Underline the indirect objects.

1. The narrator brings him different kinds of bugs.

2. Sarkin gives her information about bugs in her home.

3. Scientists can offer us interesting facts about many subjects.

4. They teach people many useful things.

5. He told the author some obscure details about insects.

B. Writing Application: Write your own sentences using the indirect and direct objects given. Use the following action verbs to get started: *gave, taught, told, asks, bought, wrote.*

1. her teammate/the pass

_____

2. Michelle/letter

_____

3. brother/video game

_____

4. grandfather/story

_____

5. teacher/question

_____

"An Entomological Study of Apartment 4A" by Patricia Volk

Reading Strategy: Establishing a Purpose for Reading

Reading serves a variety of purposes. When you read a book or an article, sometimes you want to be entertained or inspired; other times you want to learn about specific people and places or gather facts about a particular subject. One way to get the most out of what you read is to **establish a purpose for reading** before you begin and then read to achieve your purpose. For example, if your purpose in reading "An Entomological Study of Apartment 4A" is to learn something about insects, you will focus on the facts presented by Louis Sorkin. If your purpose in reading the article is to laugh, you will pay special attention to the humor of the narrator's experience.

DIRECTIONS: Use the following table to set and achieve a purpose for reading "An Entomological Study of Apartment 4A." As you read, fill in the table with notes about the article that fulfill your purpose.

My purpose is
The kinds of items that will help me to achieve my purpose are
Details that achieve my purpose include •   •   •   •

Unit 4: The Lighter Side

"An Entomological Study of Apartment 4A" by Patricia Volk

Literary Analysis: Feature Article

Feature articles, which usually appear in newspapers or magazines, are written to entertain readers or to provide readers with interesting information. Many feature articles are human interest stories, meaning that they focus on the experiences, problems, or ideas of a person or group of individuals. A writer of a feature article tries to interest readers in a particular subject or evoke in readers an emotional response to an experience, issue, or idea.

DIRECTIONS: Explore the ways in which "An Entomological Study of Apartment 4A" fits the definition of a feature article by answering the following questions:

1. What is the main subject of the article?

   _____
   _____
   _____
   _____

2. At what moments in the article does the writer present interesting information about the main subject?

   _____
   _____
   _____
   _____

3. At what moments is the article a human interest story? What personal details about the narrator's thoughts and interests are presented?

   _____
   _____
   _____
   _____

4. What emotional response do you think the writer of "An Entomological Study of Apartment 4A" is trying to evoke in readers?

   _____
   _____
   _____
   _____

5. Why do you think "An Entomological Study of Apartment 4A" is considered a feature article, rather than a news article or a research report?

   _____
   _____
   _____
   _____

"Macavity: The Mystery Cat" by T. S. Eliot
"Problems With Hurricanes" by Victor Hernández Cruz
"Jabberwocky" by Lewis Carroll

Build Vocabulary

Spelling Strategy The *shun* sound in a suffix is usually formed by combining the letters *sion, tion,* or *ssion*. For example, the *shun* sound can be heard in the Word Bank word *levitation* and in the words *possession* and *abrasion*.

Using Portmanteau Words

Many of the words in "Jabberwocky" were actually coined, or invented, by Lewis Carroll. Some of the invented words, known as *portmanteau words,* are formed by blending two words into one. Even though many of the invented words might be unfamiliar, you can figure out their meanings because they sound like the standard English words that inspired them.

A. DIRECTIONS: Complete each of the sentences with the most appropriate nonsense word from the following list:

burbled	vorpal	chortled	frabjous

1. A _____ day is a fabulous, joyous day.

2. The word _____ is a combination of the words *chuckled* and *snort*.

3. The large, bumbling, gurgling monster _____ as it moved through the wood.

4. The boy was voracious, or eager to devour, as he moved toward the beast with his

_____ sword.

Using the Word Bank

chortled	bafflement	levitation	feline
depravity	larder	suavity	projectiles

B. DIRECTIONS: Match each word in the left column with its definition in the right column. Write the letter of the definition on the line next to the word it defines.

_____ 1. depravity   a. catlike

_____ 2. bafflement   b. the illusion of keeping a heavy body
                     in the air without visible support

_____ 3. suavity   c. made a jolly chuckling sound

_____ 4. larder   d. puzzlement; bewilderment

_____ 5. chortled   e. crookedness; corruption

_____ 6. feline   f. objects that are hurled through the air

_____ 7. projectiles   g. place where food is kept; pantry

_____ 8. levitation   h. the quality of being socially smooth

© Prentice-Hall, Inc.

Unit 4: The Lighter Side

"Macavity: The Mystery Cat" by T. S. Eliot
"Problems With Hurricanes" by Victor Hernández Cruz
"Jabberwocky" by Lewis Carroll

Build Grammar Skills: Predicate Adjectives

A **predicate adjective** is an adjective that appears with a linking verb and describes the subject of a sentence. The predicate adjectives are italicized in the following line from "Macavity: The Mystery Cat."

His coat is *dusty* from neglect, his whiskers are *uncombed*.

Note that this is a compound sentence, so there are two subjects. The predicate adjective *dusty* describes Macavity's *coat*, and the predicate adjective *uncombed* describe his *whiskers*.

Two or more adjectives appearing with a linking verb is called a **compound predicate adjective**.

Macavity's coat is *orange* and *dusty*.

A. Practice: Underline the predicate adjectives, and draw an arrow to the word each describes.

1. Macavity's color is orange.

2. According to the speaker, Macavity is respectable and crafty.

3. The cat, however, is dishonest.

4. The wind is loud and furious.

5. In Cruz's poem, mangoes are not always beautiful and sweet.

B. Writing Application: Complete the sentences with predicate adjectives. Use adjectives from the following list.

red	fast	weak	wet
light	skillful	slow	heavy
suspenseful	orange	autobiographical	lovely

1. The early sunset was

   _____

2. The writer's new novel is

   _____

3. Her tennis games are

   _____

4. The snow was very

   _____

"Macavity: The Mystery Cat" by T. S. Eliot
"Problems With Hurricanes" by Victor Hernández Cruz
"Jabberwocky" by Lewis Carroll

Reading Strategy: Contrasting the Serious and the Ridiculous

One way in which the poems "Jabberwocky," "Macavity: The Mystery Cat," and "Problems With Hurricanes" achieve humor is by combining serious details about a quest, a criminal, and a destructive hurricane, with nonsense verse and ridiculous details.

DIRECTIONS: As you read, contrast the serious and ridiculous details in each of the three poems by filling in the following table.

Serious Details "Jabberwocky"	Ridiculous Details "Jabberwocky"
Serious Details "Macavity: The Mystery Cat"	Ridiculous Details "Macavity: The Mystery Cat"
Serious Details "Problems With Hurricanes"	Ridiculous Details "Problems With Hurricanes"

"Macavity: The Mystery Cat" by T. S. Eliot
"Problems With Hurricanes" by Victor Hernández Cruz
"Jabberwocky" by Lewis Carroll

Literary Analysis: Humorous Diction

In "Jabberwocky," "Macavity: The Mystery Cat," and "Problems With Hurricanes," poets use **diction,** or word choice, to achieve humor. For example, invented, unusual words make the battle described in "Jabberwocky" humorous. A contrast between formal language and the nature of Macavity and his activities creates humor in "Macavity: The Mystery Cat," and a contrast between formal language and unexpected phrases makes "Problems With Hurricanes" a humorous poem.

DIRECTIONS: Read each of the following passages and identify which carefully chosen words and phrases contribute to the humor of each passage.

Example: The Jabberwock, with eyes of flame,/Came whiffling through the tulgey wood, And burbled as it came!

Response: Although the Jabberwock is supposed to be terrifying, the description of the beast "whiffling" through the wood and "burbling" makes the passage humorous and less frightening.

"Jabberwocky"

1. One, two! One, two! And through and through/The vorpal blade went snicker-snack!/He left it dead, and with its head/He went galumphing back.

_____

_____

"Macavity: The Mystery Cat"

2. He's outwardly respectable. (They say he cheats at cards.)/And his footprints are not found in any file of Scotland Yard's./And when the larder's looted, or the jewel case is rifled,/Or when the milk is missing, or another Peke's been stifled,/Or the greenhouse glass is broken, and the trellis past repair—/Ay, there's wonder of the thing! Macavity's not there!

_____

_____

"Problems With Hurricanes"

3. Death by drowning has honor/If the wind picked you up/and slammed you/Against a mountain boulder/This would not carry shame/But/to suffer a mango smashing/Your skull/or a plantain hitting your/Temple at 70 miles per hour/is the ultimate disgrace.

_____

_____

"Talk" by Harold Courlander and George Herzog

Build Vocabulary

Spelling Strategy In words ending in one consonant after two vowels, do not double the final consonant before adding an ending starting with a vowel. For example, examine endings added to the Word Bank word *refrain*. The ending consonant *n* remains single when *-ed* or *-ing* is added: *refrain + -ed = refrained, refrain + -ing = refraining.*

Using the Prefix re-

The prefix *re-* means "back" or "again." In "Talk," *refrain* means "to hold back."

A. DIRECTIONS: Write a definition for each italicized *re-* word. Include either *back* or *again* in your definition.

1. The men in "Talk" *recite* their stories for one another and for the chief.

   Recite means _____.

2. Do you *recall* all of the animals and objects that spoke to the farmer?

   Recall means _____.

3. Common characters and themes *reappear* in many West African folk tales.

   Reappear means _____.

4. Folk tales *reflect* the values of the culture that creates them.

   Reflect means _____.

Using the Word Bank

ford	refrain	scowling

B. DIRECTIONS: Place the appropriate words from the Word Bank in the blanks to complete the sentence.

After several minutes of _____ at the talkative farmer, the frustrated fisher-man reached a _____ in the river. He turned to the farmer and said, "Would you please _____ from talking?"

C. DIRECTIONS: Match each sentence with the appropriate definition for *refrain*. Write the letter of the definition in the blank.

_____ 1. Although few in the audience knew the rest of the words, everyone sang the *refrain*.

     a. repeated utterance

_____ 2. Please *refrain* from clapping until the end of the program.

     b. a verse repeated at intervals throughout a song

_____ 3. The music critic's *refrain* throughout the performance was "Brilliant!"

     c. hold back

"Talk" by Harold Courlander and George Herzog

Build Grammar Skills: Predicate Nominatives

A **predicate nominative** is a noun or pronoun that appears with a linking verb and re-names, identifies, or explains the subject of the sentence. If two or more nouns or pronouns appear with the linking verb, and they rename the subject, they are called a *compound predicate nominative*. The following are examples of predicate nominatives.

"The vegetable in this dish is the *yam*."

"Laura is an *editor*."

The predicate nominative *yam* identifies the subject *vegetable*. The predicate nominative *editor* identifies the subject *Laura*.

A. Practice: Underline the predicate nominatives, and draw an arrow to the word that each identifies.

1. The storyteller is a comedian.

2. The inanimate objects are big talkers.

3. The farmer may be a coward.

4. The chief was a good listener.

5. The neighborhood men were victims in this amusing folk tale.

B. Writing Application: Write the sentences using words from the list as predicate nomina-tives. Remember to add either *a* or *an* before each one.

librarian	scientist	astronaut
musician	chef	writer
athlete	actor	teacher

1. My uncle is _____.

2. Thomas wants to be _____ or _____.

3. Last year, she finally became _____.

4. Samantha's grandmother was _____.

5. I think Peter will become _____.

Name _____ Date _____

Reading Strategy: Recognizing Illogical Situations

Animals that talk? Objects that express human emotions? Logically, you know that such situations are not part of real experience. When you read about or see such events, you recognize them as illogical situations. You draw upon what you know of the world through learning and personal experience to determine that dogs don't speak and inanimate objects can't get mad at you.

Illogical situations can make fantasy humorous and entertaining. However, illogical situations may serve to highlight a more serious theme in a work of fantasy. They can call attention to a point the writer wishes to make.

DIRECTIONS: "Talk" presents a series of illogical situations that build as the story progresses. Use the following chart to keep track of the illogical situations *as you read*. Note what happens to each character in each situation, explain why it is illogical, and determine what each illogical situation adds to the story.

Character	Illogical situation(s)	Why illogical?	Adds what to story?
Farmer			
Fisherman			
Weaver			
Bather			
Chief			

"Talk" by Harold Courlander and George Herzog

Literary Analysis: Humorous Folk Tale

The folk tale "Talk" presents a series of funny encounters between people and the world they think they control. A **folk tale** is an anonymous story passed down by word of mouth from one generation to the next. A humorous folk tale uses simple characters and a far-fetched situation to make a point about human nature. Repeated words and actions often make the humorous folk tale funny and easy to retell. You can analyze the characters and situations in "Talk" to discover the story's meaning.

DIRECTIONS: Write your answers to the following questions on the lines provided.

1. What does the yam say to the farmer?

   _____

   _____

2. How does the yam feel toward the farmer?

   _____

   _____

3. What tone do the rest of the animals or objects use with the farmer?

   _____

   _____

4. How does the farmer initially respond to these words? What is his eventual reaction?

   _____

   _____

5. How do the other men first respond when they hear tales of talking animals and objects?

   _____

   _____

6. How does their reaction change when something talks back to them?

   _____

   _____

7. How does the chief respond? What happens afterward?

   _____

   _____

8. What is one truth about human nature you can discover by reading "Talk"?

   _____

   _____

"One Ordinary Day, With Peanuts" by Shirley Jackson

Build Vocabulary

Spelling Strategy   When you add an ending to a word that ends with two or more consonants, never double the final consonant. That is why *impertinent* becomes *impertinently*
and *march* becomes *marched.*

Using Related Words

You may be able to determine the meaning of an unfamiliar word if you can recognize
smaller or related words within the unfamiliar word. If you know the meaning of *omen*, for example, it can help you figure out that *ominously* means "in a dark, threatening way."

A. DIRECTIONS: Define each simple word in column one. Then use the meaning of that word to
determine the meaning of the more difficult word in column two.

repair:	irreparable:
omit:	omission:
compare:	incomparable:
judge:	judicious:

Using the Word Bank

irradiated	loitered	endeavoring	ominously
buffeted	insatiable	omen	impertinent

B. DIRECTIONS: Match each word in the left column with its definition in the right column. Write
the letter of the definition on the line next to the word it defines.

_____ 1. irradiated   a. attempting

_____ 2. loitered   b. sign foretelling the future

_____ 3. endeavoring   c. unable to be satisfied

_____ 4. ominously   d. impolite

_____ 5. buffeted   e. lingered

_____ 6. insatiable   f. in a threatening way

_____ 7. omen   g. gave forth

_____ 8. impertinent   h. knocked about

Unit 4: The Lighter Side

Name _____ Date _____

"One Ordinary Day, With Peanuts" by Shirley Jackson

Build Grammar Skills: Direct Object or Object of a Preposition?

Do not confuse a direct object with the object of a preposition. Remember that the direct object is never the noun or pronoun at the end of a prepositional phrase. A **direct object** is a noun or pronoun that usually follows the action verb in a sentence. The **object of a preposition** is a noun or pronoun that usually follows a preposition and is part of a prepositional phrase. Study these examples.

Direct Object: We ate *dinner.*

The direct object, *dinner,* follows the action verb *ate.*

Object of a Preposition: We danced after *dinner.*

The object of a preposition, *dinner,* follows the preposition *after.*
Note the direct object and the object of a preposition in the following sentence.

The pilot flew the *airplane* over the *ocean.*

Airplane is the direct object that follows the action verb *flew. Ocean* is the object of the preposition *over.*

A. Practice: Identify each underlined word as either a direct object or the object of a preposition in the following sentences, or extracts from sentences, from the story.

1. Mr. John Philip Johnson shut his front <u>door</u> behind <u>him</u>. . . .

   _____

2. He stopped in a flower <u>shop</u> and bought a <u>carnation</u> for his <u>buttonhole</u>. . . .

   _____

3. They sat on the <u>steps</u> cracking peanuts. . . .

   _____

4. He took out a <u>card</u>, and wrote a <u>name</u> on the <u>back</u>.

   _____

5. I have a <u>job</u>. . . .

   _____

B. Writing Application: Write a sentence of your own that includes a direct object, the object of a preposition, or both. Identify the item(s) you use.

   _____

   _____

   _____

"One Ordinary Day, With Peanuts" by Shirley Jackson

Reading Strategy: Questioning Characters' Actions

After you read the title and the first few paragraphs of "One Ordinary Day, With Peanuts," perhaps you relaxed. Maybe you assumed this was going to be a nice little story about a helpful, fairly cheerful man who was just a touch eccentric. As the plot unfolds, did you stay relaxed? Were your assumptions correct?

As a reader, it is up to you to think about the main character's actions, to question them, and to find answers to your questions. In the case of "One Ordinary Day, with Peanuts," you need to decide whether Mr. Johnson is an ordinary man and if it really is an ordinary day for him. Doing so will increase your understanding of both the character and the story.

DIRECTIONS: Use the following table to help you question Mr. Johnson's behavior. One example has been done for you.

Mr. Johnson's Actions	What motives did he have for the action?	What did other characters do to lead to this action?	Is this action consistent with his past behavior or remarks?
says "Good morning" with conviction	He is being friendly at the newsstand.	They happened to be at the newsstand also.	seems to be; seems generally friendly so far
1.			
2.			
3.			
4.			
5.			

Unit 4: The Lighter Side

"One Ordinary Day, With Peanuts" by Shirley Jackson

Literary Analysis: Surprise Ending

As you read "One Ordinary Day, With Peanuts" and got acquainted with Mr. Johnson, were you suspicious about what he was up to? If not, had you decided he was simply a generous man who, for some reason, didn't need to work for a living? When Mr. Johnson returned home at the end of the day, were you shocked by his conversation with his wife?

Shirley Jackson meant for you to be shocked—and entertained—by her surprise at the end of the story. Now that you know the truth about Mr. Johnson, perhaps you can recall some details in the story that might have given you hints.

DIRECTIONS: Keep the surprise ending of the story in mind as you answer these questions. Use the questions to reevaluate Mr. Johnson's actions and motives. If you had been looking for clues to the ending of the story, would you have found them?

1. What clues can you find in this sentence that Mr. Johnson is perhaps not headed for an ordinary office job?

   When he had gone several blocks uptown, Mr. Johnson cut across the avenue and went along a side street, chosen at random; he did not follow the same route every morning, but preferred to pursue his eventful way in wide detours, more like a puppy than a man intent upon business.

   _____

   _____

2. After Mr. Johnson helps the woman and little boy who are moving to Vermont, he moves on. Jackson writes that "Mr. Johnson decided to go on uptown again." What clue does this phrase contain?

   _____

   _____

3. Early in Mr. Johnson's conversation with the young woman who has bumped into him, the author makes a point of saying that Johnson's offer of money could not be "anything but the statement of a responsible and truthful and respectable man." What is the irony in this statement?

   _____

   _____

4. As Mr. Johnson leaves Mr. Adams and Miss Kent, Jackson writes this passage:

   Mr. Johnson smiled to himself and then thought that he had better hurry along; when he wanted to he could move very quickly, and before the young woman had gotten around to saying, "Well, *I* will if *you* will," Mr. Johnson was several blocks away. . . .

   What unusual piece of information in this passage might have caught your attention if you had been looking for clues? Why?

   _____

   _____

from *The Road Ahead* by Bill Gates

Build Vocabulary

Spelling Strategy   The spelling of a word is *never* changed with the addition of a prefix. For example, *pre* + *cursor* = *precursor.* This tip is useful for spelling words that often give writers trouble, such as <u>un</u>necessary and <u>mis</u>spell.

Using the Root *-simul-*

A. DIRECTIONS: Each of the following sentences includes an italicized word that contains the root *-simul-*, which means "same." Demonstrate your understanding of the italicized words by completing each sentence.

1. The actor *simulated* a fall down a hill by _____
   _____.

2. The *simultaneity* of my question about Mary's whereabouts and her entrance into the room was funny because _____
   _____.

3. During the *simulator* portion of driver's education, we _____
   _____.

Using the Word Bank

simultaneously	capacious	precursors	infrared	parlance

B. DIRECTIONS: Match each word in the left column with its definition in the right column. Write the letter of the definition on the line next to the word it defines.

____ 1. capacious   a. lying beyond one end of the visible spectrum of light

____ 2. infrared   b. existing or occurring at the same time

____ 3. parlance   c. things that prepare the way for what will follow

____ 4. precursors   d. able to hold much

____ 5. simultaneously   e. manner or mode of speech

Using Synonyms

C. DIRECTIONS: Each item consists of a word from the Word Bank, followed by four lettered words or phrases. Choose the word or phrase that is most nearly *similar* in meaning to the Word Bank word. Circle the letter of your choice.

1. simultaneously
   a. similar in tone or shade
   b. of the same duration
   c. at the same time
   d. in a similar manner

2. capacious
   a. greedy
   b. wearing a hat
   c. roomy
   d. hungry

3. parlance
   a. way of speaking
   b. banter
   c. dialogue
   d. short sword

from *The Road Ahead* by Bill Gates

Build Grammar Skills: Main and Subordinate Clauses

There are two basic kinds of clauses: a main clause (also called an *independent clause*) and a subordinate clause. Each kind of clause is a group of words that contains both a subject and a verb. A **main clause,** however, can stand by itself as a complete sentence. A **subordinate clause** cannot stand by itself as a complete sentence; it can only be part of a sentence.

Main Clause: The videocassette recorder appeared in the early 1980s.

Subordinate Clause: When the videocassette recorder appeared in the early 1980s.

Notice that although each clause contains a subject and verb, only the main clause expresses a complete thought.

A. Practice: Identify each clause as a main clause (M) or a subordinate clause (S). The items are taken from the selection.

1. _____ When I was a kid

2. _____ Conventional television allows us to decide what we watch but not when we watch it

3. _____ There won't be any intermediary VCR

4. _____ But if you were driving back from your grandparents' house

5. _____ Even after broadband residential networks have become common

6. _____ The digitized data will be retrieved from the server

7. _____ Television has been around for fewer than sixty years

8. _____ Unlike the dedicated word processors that brought the first micro-processors to many offices

B. Writing Application: Add a main clause to each subordinate clause to form a sentence expressing a complete thought.

1. because I wouldn't be home in time to watch the debate

   _____

2. which is a difficult subject for me

   _____

3. after the big thunderstorm

   _____

from *The Road Ahead* by Bill Gates

Reading Strategy: Recognizing a Writer's Motives and Bias

Like all of us, writers are individuals with many different experiences and ways of looking at the world. Their writing often reflects these personal experiences and viewpoints. Writers might have particular **motives**, or purposes, for writing something—to inform, entertain, or persuade, for example. They may write with a particular **bias**, or strong feeling for or against a subject.

As responsible readers, we need to identify the viewpoint a writer takes toward his or her subject. Then we can evaluate any possible motives or bias in the text before forming our own opinions about it.

DIRECTIONS: Read the following passages from the excerpt from *The Road Ahead*. Then answer the questions.

> One of the benefits the communications revolution will bring to all of us is more control over our schedules.

> You'll indicate what you want and presto! You'll get it.

> If somebody comes to the door, you'll be able to pause the program for as long as you like. You'll be in absolute control—

> Most viewers can appreciate the benefits of video-on-demand and will welcome the convenience it gives them.

1. Based on these passages, what are high priorities for the author?

   _____

   _____

   _____

2. How might these priorities influence, or bias, his opinions about the new technology?

   _____

   _____

   _____

3. Knowing the author's business is computers, what might his motives be in writing

   enthusiastically about video-on-demand?

   _____

   _____

   _____

from *The Road Ahead* by Bill Gates

Literary Analysis: Expository Writing

Many of the items you read—magazines, newspapers, and textbooks—contain **expository writing.** Writing that provides information or explains a process is expository. Expository writers provide information by relating details, examples, and facts. Some writers, like Bill Gates, include personal details that add interest and support the information in their writing.

As you read the excerpt from *The Road Ahead,* consider these questions: Does the selection provide enough information to satisfy you? Does the author support factual statements with explanations?

DIRECTIONS: Identify five facts and as many personal details as you can find in the excerpt from *The Road Ahead.* Record them in the following chart.

Facts	Personal Details
1.	
2.	
3.	
4.	
5.	

"The Machine That Won the War" by Isaac Asimov

Build Vocabulary

Spelling Strategy   When a word ends in *-ic*, add the *-ly* suffix by means of *-ally*. Thus, the adverbial form of the Word Bank word *erratic* is *erratically*, *realistic* becomes *realistically*, and *romantic* changes to *romantically*. An important exception to this rule is the word *public*. Its adverbial form merely adds the *-ly*, becoming *publicly*.

Using the Prefix *circum-*

The prefix *circum-* comes directly from the Latin adverb *circum*, which means "around" or "around about." Its use as a prefix almost always carries the same meaning, as we see in the words *circumnavigate* and *circumscribe*. Some words that use *circum-* as a prefix aren't common, but you can make a good guess at the meaning of the word if you know the sense of the prefix, and you have an idea of the word being prefixed.

A. DIRECTIONS: Using the information provided, come up with the meanings of the following words. Then use a dictionary to check your answers.

1. If *gyration* means "turning," what is the meaning of *circumgyration* likely to be?

   _____

2. If *ambulation* means "walking," what is the meaning of *circumambulation* likely to be?

   _____

3. If *polar* means "at the pole," what is the meaning of *circumpolar* likely to be?

   _____

4. If *fluent* means "flowing," what is the meaning of *circumfluent* likely to be?

   _____

5. If *locution* means "expression," what is the meaning of *circumlocution* likely to be?

   _____

Using the Word Bank

erratic	oracle	subsidiary	grisly
surcease	circumvent	imperturbable	

B. DIRECTIONS: Match each word in the left column with its definition in the right column. Write the letter of the definition on the line next to the word it defines.

____ 1. erratic   a. secondary

____ 2. oracle   b. calm

____ 3. subsidiary   c. end

____ 4. grisly   d. avoid

____ 5. surcease   e. inconsistent

____ 6. circumvent   f. gruesome

____ 7. imperturbable   g. prophet

"The Machine That Won the War" by Isaac Asimov

Build Grammar Skills: Adverb Clauses and Noun Clauses

An **adverb clause** is a subordinate clause that acts as an adverb. It modifies a verb, adjective, adverb or verbal by telling *where, when, in what way, to what extent, under what condition,* or *why.* It begins with a *subordinating conjunction* such as *after, as long as, because, if, since, unless,* and *while.*

> **Adverb Clause:** Amy works after school *because she wants to buy a car.*

The adverb clause *because she wants to buy a car* modifies the verb *works* and answers the question *Why?*

A **noun clause** is a subordinating conjunction that acts as a noun. It may function as a *subject, direct object, indirect object, predicate nominative,* or an *object of a preposition.*

> **Noun Clauses**: *Whichever instrument you choose* will be acceptable.
> The pianist played *whatever music Susan asked for.*

The noun clause *whichever instrument you choose* functions as the subject of the sentence. The noun clause *whatever music Susan asked for* acts as a direct object of the verb *played.*

A. Practice: Underline the clauses in the following sentences. Identify each as an adverb clause or a noun clause.

1. When he discovered the data were corrupt, Swift knew he had to do something.

   _____

2. Henderson believed that any data Multivac provided was unreliable.

   _____

3. The men thought Multivac had made the big decision until each revealed his secrets.

   _____

4. They all behaved as if the computer had made the decisions.

   _____

5. Whatever Swift's coin toss decided was inevitable now.

   _____

B. Writing Application: Combine each pair of sentences by changing one of them into an adverb clause. Use the subordinating conjunction in parentheses.

1. He typed his essay. The word processor was fixed. (when)

   _____

2. The basement floods. It rains. (whenever)

   _____

3. Jennifer plans to stay. The project is finished. (until)

   _____

"The Machine That Won the War" by Isaac Asimov

Reading Strategy: Identifying Relevant Details

As you read a story, you form impressions of the people, places, and events you encounter. You form these impressions based on information you get from explanations and details. Good writers provide information about character, setting, and action in details that are smoothly blended into the story. Some of these details may be merely "scenery," to increase the sense of realism, and some of them may be crucial to grasping the point of what is occurring. Your goal is to sort out relevant details as you read. What does the detail concern? What does it tell you? How can you add it to what you already know? As you begin to fit the pieces together, the writer's art becomes less puzzling.

DIRECTIONS: Use this graphic organizer to help you identify details as you read "The Machine That Won the War." In the first column, write details that you think might be relevant to the story. In the second column, indicate whether the detail pertains to a character (C), the setting (S)(place and time), or the action (A). In the third column, note the specific subject to which the detail pertains. Finally, in the fourth column, judge what this particular detail tells you or adds to your knowledge of the story. An example has been done for you.

Detail	Type C = Character S = Setting A = Action	Subject	Added information provided by this detail
For the first time in a decade . . .	S	the computer	Multivac has been running for ten years.

The Machine That Won the War   **119**

"The Machine That Won the War" by Isaac Asimov

Literary Analysis: Science Fiction

Science fiction is a type of literature that explores the relationship of humanity to science. Frequently set in the future, science fiction considers the effect of scientific possibilities on human beings. The events in science fiction may not be real, but the literature presumes they could happen (or could have happened) under certain circumstances, usually those involving scientific developments. Unlike fantasy, which is purely imaginative, science fiction depends upon the idea that its situations are possible in the real world even though the particular setting is fictitious. In the most effective science fiction stories, settings as well as characters hold out the possibility of being true to life.

Sometimes writers blend science fiction with fact so well that it is helpful to decide which elements of the story belong exclusively to the world of science fiction and which could appear in any work of fiction. In some cases, elements that the writer presented as science fiction when the story was written may not seem so unlikely today.

DIRECTIONS: Select two or three of the following elements of "The Machine That Won the War." Then build a science fiction story of your own around the elements you choose. On the lines provided, write a brief summary of your science fiction story.

Military command posts in remote, secure locations

The giant strategic computer named Multivac

Computers that control military equipment automatically

The opposition that has been destroyed in the story

The Executive Director of the Solar Federation

Subsidiary computers on the moon, Mars, and Titan

Coin shortage due to lack of metal

Credit systems tied to computers

Leaders who take risks based on their own intuition

_____

_____

_____

_____

_____

_____

_____

_____

_____

_____

_____

_____

_____

"All Watched Over by Machines of Loving Grace" by Richard Brautigan
"Fire and Ice" by Robert Frost
"The Horses" by Edwin Muir
"There Will Come Soft Rains" by Sara Teasdale

Build Vocabulary

Spelling Strategy   When writing words that end in one consonant preceded by two vowels, do not double the final consonant before adding a suffix starting with a vowel. For example, the suffix -ally added to the Word Bank word archaic forms the word archaically.

Using the Suffix -ous

The Word Bank word tremulous is related to the word trembling. The suffix -ous, which means "full of" or "characterized by," changes a noun into an adjective. So the word tremulous means "characterized by trembling" or "quivering."

A. DIRECTIONS: Define each noun. Then write the meaning of the related adjective, formed by the addition of the -ous suffix.

1. outrage_____

    outrageous _____

2. miracle_____

    miraculous _____

3. superstition _____

    superstitious _____

Using the Word Bank

perish	suffice	tremulous	covenant
confounds	steeds	archaic	

B. DIRECTIONS: Match each word in the left column with its definition in the right column. Write the letter of the definition on the line next to the word it defines.

____ 1. confounds   a. horses

____ 2. archaic   b. agreement

____ 3. tremulous   c. die

____ 4. steeds   d. old-fashioned

____ 5. perish   e. bewilders

____ 6. covenant   f. to be enough

____ 7. suffice   g. quivering

Grace/Fire/Horses/Rains   **121**

Unit 5: Visions of the Future

"All Watched Over by Machines of Loving Grace" by Richard Brautigan
"Fire and Ice" by Robert Frost
"The Horses" by Edwin Muir
"There Will Come Soft Rains" by Sara Teasdale

Build Grammar Skills: Adjective Clauses

An **adjective clause** is a subordinate clause that acts as an adjective. It modifies a noun or pronoun by telling *what kind* or *which one*. An adjective clause usually begins with a relative pronoun such as *that, which, who, whom,* or *whose.*

> **Adjective Clauses:** We ran in a marathon *that began before sunrise.*
> The person *who won the contest* is an amateur.

The adjective clause *that began before sunrise* modifies the noun *marathon* and tells *which one.* The adjective clause *who won the contest* modifies the noun *woman* and tells *which one.*

A. Practice: Underline the adjective clause in each sentence. Draw a line from the clause to the noun or pronoun it modifies.

1. These four poets, whose work we have just read, are from different generations.

2. Robert Frost was a prolific writer who won four Pulitzer Prizes.

3. Sara Teasdale's poems, which are often about love, reflect her own experiences.

4. The writing of Edwin Muir often includes imagery that comes from the Orkney Islands.

5. Richard Brautigan is a poet who was influenced by the beat and hippie generations.

B. Writing Application: Write sentences by adding a main clause to each adjective clause.

1. that sounded like thunder

   _____

2. whose painting is almost finished

   _____

3. who found the lost necklace

   _____

4. which was hanging in the closet

   _____

5. whom the voters elected to the Senate

   _____

"All Watched Over by Machines of Loving Grace" by Richard Brautigan
"Fire and Ice" by Robert Frost
"The Horses" by Edwin Muir
"There Will Come Soft Rains" by Sara Teasdale

Reading Strategy: Recognizing a Poet's Purpose

Understanding a poet's purpose for writing a particular poem will increase your appreciation of that poem. For example, "Fire and Ice," "All Watched Over by Machines of Loving Grace," "There Will Come Soft Rains," and "The Horses" were all written for the purpose of warning readers about possible future events. Each poet carefully chose details and phrases to convey his or her own perspective on this theme. Whenever you read a poem, try to examine why a poet has chosen certain words and what these words reflect about the poet's purpose.

DIRECTIONS: Read the lines from the poems in this grouping. Then explain the meaning of the lines and the way in which the lines can be linked to the author's purpose.

1. From what I've tasted of desire/I hold with those who favor fire.   —Robert Frost
   Meaning:_____
   _____
   Poet's Purpose:_____
   _____

2. I like to think (and/the sooner the better!)/of a cybernetic meadow/where mammals and computers/live together in mutually programming harmony . . .   —Richard Brautigan
   Meaning:_____
   _____
   Poet's Purpose:_____
   _____

3. And not one will know of the war,/Not one/Will care at last when it is done.   —Sara Teasdale
   Meaning:_____
   _____
   Poet's Purpose:_____
   _____

4. Barely a twelvemonth after/The seven days war that put the world to sleep,/Late in the evening the strange horses came.   —Edwin Muir
   Meaning:_____
   _____
   Poet's Purpose:_____
   _____

"All Watched Over by Machines of Loving Grace" by Richard Brautigan
"Fire and Ice" by Robert Frost
"The Horses" by Edwin Muir
"There Will Come Soft Rains" by Sara Teasdale

Literary Analysis: Alliteration

Alliteration, the repetition of consonant sounds at the beginning of words, can produce sounds such as a whisper or create a musical effect in a poem. Alliteration also enhances a poem's meaning by emphasizing certain words and sounds. An example of a whispering sound is the repetition of the *s* sound in the lines "There will come soft rains and the smell of/the ground,/And swallows circling with their shimmering/sound" from "There Will Come Soft Rains." This repetition emphasizes the fact that nature is at peace without human beings.

DIRECTIONS: Underline examples of alliteration in each of the following excerpts from "Fire and Ice," "All Watched Over by Machines of Loving Grace," "There Will Come Soft Rains," and "The Horses." Then, on the lines provided, explain how each instance of alliteration affects the poem's mood and overall meaning.

"Fire and Ice"

1. From what I've tasted of desire/I hold with those who favor fire.

_____

_____

"All Watched Over by Machines of Loving Grace"

2. I like to think/(right now, please!)/of a cybernetic forest/filled with pines and electronics/where deer stroll peacefully past computers.

_____

_____

"There Will Come Soft Rains"

3. Robins will wear their feathery fire/Whistling their whims on a low fence-wire:

_____

_____

4. And Spring herself, when she woke at dawn,/Would scarcely know that we were gone.

_____

_____

"The Horses"

5. We heard a distant tapping on the road,/A deepening drumming; it stopped, went on again . . .

_____

_____

"If I Forget Thee, Oh Earth . . ." by Arthur C. Clarke
from *Silent Spring* by Rachel Carson
"To the Residents of A.D. 2029" by Bryan Woolley

Build Vocabulary

Spelling Strategy When you add a suffix to a word that ends in two or more consonants, never double the final consonant. For example, *blight* + *-ed* becomes *blighted*. Other words that follow this rule are *swiftly*, *watching*, and *expectation*.

Using the Root *-ann-*

A. DIRECTIONS: The root *-ann-* comes from a Latin word that means "year." The root occurs in English in two forms: *-ann-* as in *annual* and *-enn-* as in *perennial*. Explain what each of the following words has to do with a year. If you're not sure of the meaning of a word, check a dictionary.

1. annals_____

2. anniversary_____

3. annuity_____

4. biennial _____

Using the Word Bank

purged	pyre	perennial	blight
moribund	postulated	beleaguered	schism

B. DIRECTIONS: Match each word in the left column with its definition in the right column. Write the letter of the definition on the line next to the word it defines.

_____ 1. purged   a. approaching death

_____ 2. pyre   b. cleansed

_____ 3. perennial   c. claimed as true or necessary

_____ 4. blight   d. lasting

_____ 5. moribund   e. worried, harassed

_____ 6. postulated   f. something that destroys or prevents growth

_____ 7. beleaguered   g. a split or division

_____ 8. schism   h. a burnable heap on top of which a dead body is burned

Using Expressive Language

C. DIRECTIONS: Choose the plain, overused word that could be replaced by the word from the Word Bank to make your writing more interesting. Circle the letter of your choice.

1. purged
   a. guessed
   b. cleaned
   c. burned
   d. stepped

2. beleaguered
   a. upset
   b. worked
   c. cooperated
   d. infested

3. moribund
   a. arrival
   b. correct
   c. dying
   d. steering

Forget/Spring/Residents **125**

"If I Forget Thee, Oh Earth . . ." by Arthur C. Clarke
from *Silent Spring* by Rachel Carson
"To the Residents of A.D. 2029" by Bryan Woolley

Build Grammar Skills: Compound and Complex Sentences

A **compound sentence** is a sentence that contains two or more main, or independent, clauses. The main clauses can be joined by a comma and a coordinating conjunction (*and, but, for, nor, or, so, yet*) or by a semicolon. Note how the conjunction *and* connects the two main clauses in the following sentence.

Compound Sentence: Arthur C. Clarke writes interesting science fiction, and he has written for the film industry.

A **complex sentence** has one main, or independent, clause, and one or more subordinate clauses. In the following example, the subordinate clause *who has written for the film industry* follows the main clause.

Complex Sentence: Arthur C. Clarke is a science fiction writer *who has written for the film industry.*

A. Practice: Label each sentence as a compound sentence (C) or a complex sentence (CX).

1. _____ Although there was a nuclear holocaust, the Colony survived.

2. _____ Marvin's father led him through the corridors, and they went outside.

3. _____ Rachel Carson describes a fictional town that becomes polluted.

4. _____ The animals sicken, and the plants wither.

5. _____ The author writes to a future population because he wants to leave a record.

B. Writing Application: Combine the following sentence pairs to form either a compound sentence or a complex sentence, as directed in the parentheses.

1. Rachel Carson is a writer. She writes about the environment. (complex)

_____

2. In Carson's fictional town, birds were plentiful. Fish swam in the streams. (compound)

_____

3. Marvin began his journey home. He did not look back at Earth. (complex)

_____

4. The narrator is worried about the future. He is optimistic. (compound)

_____

"**If I Forget Thee, Oh Earth . . .**" by Arthur C. Clarke
from *Silent Spring* by Rachel Carson
"**To the Residents of A.D. 2029**" by Bryan Woolley

Reading Strategy: Distinguishing Between Fact and Opinion

Writers of nonfiction, fiction, essays, and speeches combine facts and opinions in their writing. It is your job, as a reader, to distinguish between the facts and the opinions. Facts can be tested for accuracy and proved true or not. Opinions express beliefs and cannot be proved true or false. Some writers may use unsupported opinions to persuade or bias their readers. Before you draw conclusions or agree or disagree with a writer's ideas, you need to determine whether those ideas are facts, supported opinions, or unsupported opinions. To support an opinion, a writer must include facts, statistics, examples, or other evidence.

DIRECTIONS: As you read, complete the chart by writing two facts and two opinions from each selection. Then answer the questions that follow to finish your assessment of these selections.

Facts	Opinions
"If I Forget Thee, Oh Earth . . . "	
1.	1.
2.	2.
from *Silent Spring*	
1.	1.
2.	2.
"To the Residents of A.D. 2029"	
1.	1.
2.	2.

Based on the facts and opinions you noted in the selections, do you feel that each work is effectively persuasive? State your answer for each selection, and explain why.

"If I Forget Thee, Oh Earth . . ."

_____

_____

from *Silent Spring*

_____

_____

"To the Residents of A.D. 2029"

_____

_____

"If I Forget Thee, Oh Earth . . ." by Arthur C. Clarke
from *Silent Spring* by Rachel Carson
"To the Residents of A.D. 2029" by Bryan Woolley

Literary Analysis: Persuasive Appeal

The writers of these selections use **persuasive appeal,** or an urgent request or warning, to communicate with their readers. Persuasive appeal is not limited to nonfiction writing such as articles or essays. Fiction writers and even poets may make persuasive appeals to their readers. In fiction, however, the persuasive appeal is likely to be implied. That is, the writer leaves it up to the reader to figure out what the warning is. In nonfiction, writers are more likely to come right out and state their persuasive appeal. There is usually little doubt, after reading a persuasive appeal, what the writer wants you to think or feel.

DIRECTIONS: Identify the persuasive appeal in each selection. Then consider how effectively the authors have communicated their warnings.

"If I Forget Thee, Oh Earth . . . "

1. What is Arthur C. Clarke's persuasive appeal?

_____

_____

2. Is the persuasive appeal stated or implied? _____

3. Identify line(s) in the story that you think convey Clarke's persuasive appeal.

_____

_____

from *Silent Spring*

1. What is Rachel Carson's persuasive appeal?

_____

_____

2. Is the persuasive appeal stated or implied? _____

3. Identify line(s) in the selection that you think convey Carson's persuasive appeal.

_____

_____

"To the Residents of A.D. 2029"

1. What is Bryan Woolley's persuasive appeal?

_____

_____

2. Is the persuasive appeal stated or implied? _____

3. Identify line(s) in the story that you think convey Woolley's persuasive appeal.

_____

"Gifts" by Shu Ting
"Glory and Hope" by Nelson Mandela

Build Vocabulary

Spelling Strategy A number of words, such as *confer* and *refer*, end in a single consonant preceded by a single vowel and are accented on the last syllable. When you add the suffix *-ence* to these words, the final consonant is not doubled: *conference, reference*. When
adding other endings that begin with vowels, however, you should double the final consonant. For example, *confer + -ed = conferred; refer + -ing = referring*. One exception to this
rule is *occur + -ence*, in which the final consonant is doubled, for *occurrence*.

Using the Suffix *-logy*

A. DIRECTIONS: The suffix *-logy* means "the study, science, or theory of." Match these words
ending in *-logy* with their meanings.

   1. geology   a. the study of secret writing

   2. psychology   b. the science of the history of Earth

   3. cryptology   c. the study of the mind

Using the Word Bank

confer	pernicious	ideology	chasms
covenant	inalienable	pinions	hieroglyphics

B. DIRECTIONS: Replace the italicized word or words in each sentence with the appropriate word
from the Word Bank.

   1. Most of us consider maintaining our dignity as a right that is *not able to be taken away.*

   _____

   2. Mandela views black and white South Africans as separated by *deep gorges.*

   _____

   3. The *pictures or symbols* on the cave wall were a mystery at first.

   _____

   4. Nelson Mandela hopes to *give* to South Africans a sense of freedom.

   _____

   5. Mandela hopes to build a *contract or agreement* among the people of South Africa.

   _____

   6. The *system of political and social ideas* of South Africa has changed greatly.

   _____

   7. Mandela views apartheid as a *destructive* system.

   _____

   8. The *bony sections of a bird's feather* are attached to the bird's wing.

   _____

© Prentice-Hall, Inc.

"**Gifts**" by Shu Ting
"**Glory and Hope**" by Nelson Mandela

Build Grammar Skills: Parallelism: Clauses

Parallelism is the placement of equal ideas in words, phrases, or clauses of similar types. That is, it is the repetition of grammatically similar words or phrases. Writers use parallelism to create vivid images and to emphasize particular ideas. Consider these first lines from the first three stanzas of "Gifts."

My dream is the dream of a pond . . .
My joy is the joy of sunlight . . .
My grief is the grief of birds . . .

The lines are parallel clauses because the same sentence structure is repeated in each.

A. Practice: Read the following lines from Nelson Mandela's speech "Glory and Hope." Underline the instances of parallelism.

Let there be justice for all.

Let there be peace for all.

Let there be work, bread, water, and salt for all.

Let each know that for each, the body, the mind and the soul have been freed to fulfill themselves.

B. Writing Application: Use parallelism to compose four sentences containing clauses that might be the lines of a poem or speech.

_____

_____

_____

_____

_____

_____

_____

"Gifts" by Shu Ting
"Glory and Hope" by Nelson Mandela

Reading Strategy: Evaluating the Writer's Message

A **writer's message** is the idea he or she wants to communicate to readers or listeners. In a campaign speech, for example, a politician's message is likely to be that she is the best candidate. You can **evaluate** the writer's message by first identifying the message, then determining whether the message is properly supported and clearly reasoned out. You may or may not agree with the message, but you can still evaluate it.

DIRECTIONS: Use the following charts as you identify and evaluate the messages in "Glory and Hope" and "Gifts." Note that "Gifts" has a twofold message.

"Glory and Hope" by Nelson Mandela

Writer's Message	How Writer Conveys Message
	1. What facts or circumstances does Mandela cite to support his message?
	2. As a speaker, how else might Mandela have supported his message?

"Gifts" by Shu Ting

Writer's Message	How Writer Conveys Message
	1. How does Shu Ting support this message?
	2. In what lines of the poem does Shu Ting support this message?

"Gifts" by Shu Ting
"Glory and Hope" by Nelson Mandela

Literary Analysis: Tone

Think about how a literary work makes you feel. That feeling is the **tone** of the work. The tone is created by the writer's attitude toward his or her subject and audience. The tone communicated by literary works is limited only by the range of readers' responses to writing. Different people might describe the tone of the same paragraph as informal, relaxed, light, or friendly. It doesn't matter that they have used different words to describe the tone of the paragraph; they are all expressing the same *kinds* of feelings.

As you read, the key to understanding the tone is the author's word choice. Looking closely at word choice will help you determine how and why the work makes you feel the way it does. For example, in his inaugural speech, Nelson Mandela refers to the history of racism and apartheid in South Africa as an "extraordinary human disaster." These are very emotional words, and they give Mandela's speech a tragic and urgent tone. In fact, in Mandela's speech it is hard to find words that are objective, or unemotional.

DIRECTIONS: Consider the word choice in the italicized phrases in the following passages from "Glory and Hope." Think about whether the word choice is emotional or objective. Then label the tone of that passage. You might need to experiment with several different adjectives before you hit upon just the right one.

"Glory and Hope"

Passage	Tone
. . . to take possession . . . of what is, after all, *a common victory for justice, for peace, for human dignity.*	
The moment to bridge *the chasms that divide us* has come.	
. . . *a rainbow nation* at peace with itself and the world.	

Now choose passages from "Gifts" that seem to convey the tone of the poem, or that combine to convey the tone. Give reasons for your choices.

"Gifts"

Passage	Reasons

"The Gift of the Magi" by O. Henry

Build Vocabulary

Spelling Strategy In words that end in one consonant after two vowels, do not double the final consonant before adding an ending. For example, the Word Bank word *discreet* contains two vowels followed by a consonant. Therefore, the word *discreet* does not change its form when the endings -*ly* and -*ness* are added to form the words *discreetly* and *discreetness*.

Using the Prefix *de-*

Meanings of the prefix *de-* include "down," "away from," and "undo." In the word *depreciate*, the prefix *de-* means "down"; the word *depreciate* means "to go down in value."

A. DIRECTIONS: Each of the words in the left column contains the prefix *de-*. Match each word in the left column with its definition in the right column.

_____ 1. demote   a. looked down on

_____ 2. despised   b. taken down from a position of power

_____ 3. deposed   c. to undo promotion

Using the Word Bank

instigates	depreciate	cascade	chaste
meretricious	ravages	discreet	

B. DIRECTIONS: Replace each italicized word or group of words with a word from the Word Bank. Rewrite the sentence in the space provided.

1. Della's *waterfall* of brown hair shimmered in the firelight.

_____

2. Hardly *cheap or flashy*, the combs were pure tortoise shell, rimmed with jewels.

_____

3. For Della the upcoming Christmas holiday *stirs up* the desire to give Jim a special gift.

_____

4. To hide the worn leather strap, Jim took a *tactful* glance at his watch.

_____

5. Della chose the platinum fob chain because of its simple and *not ornate* design.

_____

6. So that Jim would not be startled by the *devastating damages* of her haircut, Della curled her short hair.

_____

7. The beauty of Della's hair was so great that it could *reduce in value* even the Queen's jewels.

_____

"The Gift of the Magi" by O. Henry

Build Grammar Skills: Adverb Phrases

An **adverb phrase** is a prepositional phrase that acts as an adverb. It modifies a verb, an adjective, or an adverb by pointing out *where, when, in what way,* or *to what extent.*

> **Adverb Phrases:** They were happy *in their home.*
> Jim stared *at Della's hair.*

The adverb phrase *in their home* modifies the adjective *happy* and tells *where*. The adverb phrase *at Della's hair* modifies the verb *stared* and tells *where*.

A. Practice: Underline the adverb phrases in the following sentences from "The Gift of the Magi."

1. Della finished her cry and attended to her cheeks with the powder rag.

2. Suddenly she whirled from the window and stood before the glass.

3. It reached below her knee and made itself almost a garment for her.

4. She was ransacking the stores for Jim's present.

5. Della wriggled off the table and went for him.

B. Writing Application: Use each prepositional phrase as an adverb phrase in a sentence of your own.

1. after the party

_____

2. during the film

_____

3. into the garage

_____

4. from the stereo speakers

_____

5. on the table

_____

6. around the lake

_____

7. near the desk

_____

"The Gift of the Magi" by O. Henry

Reading Strategy: Asking Questions

One way good readers monitor their comprehension of a text is by **asking questions** as they read. By stopping to question something that is unclear, you will better understand and remember what you read. Ask questions to

- clarify the meaning of a word, sentence, or idea.
- determine what caused an event to happen or why a character acted in a certain way.
- predict what will happen next.

DIRECTIONS: Read the following passages from "The Gift of the Magi." Below each one are examples of questions that readers might ask themselves as they read. Add two questions of your own.

> In the vestibule below was a letter-box into which no letter would go, and an electric button from which no mortal finger could coax a ring. Also appertaining thereunto was a card bearing the name "Mr. James Dillingham Young."

1. What does the word *vestibule* mean?

2. Why can't anyone "coax a ring" from the doorbell?

3. _____

4. _____

> Suddenly she whirled and stood before the glass. Her eyes were shining brilliantly, but her face had lost its color within twenty seconds. Rapidly she pulled down her hair and let it fall to its full length.

5. What is the meaning of *glass* in this context?

6. Why has she pulled down her hair?

7. _____

8. _____

Name _____ Date _____

Literary Analysis: Plot

The **plot** of a story leads the reader through a series of events. A well-developed plot is easy to follow and holds the reader's attention. Limited by the story's length, the writer must select events with particular care and describe them in a way that achieves a single, clear effect. The plot is traditionally divided into five parts: exposition, rising action, climax, falling action, and resolution.

The **exposition** provides background information and sets the scene for the conflict, a struggle between opposing people or forces that drives the action of the story. The introduction of the conflict marks the beginning of the **rising action,** in which the conflict intensifies until it reaches the high point, or **climax** of the story. After the climax, **falling action** takes the story to a resolution. The **resolution** shows how the situation turns out.

DIRECTIONS: As you read "The Gift of the Magi," jot down events associated with the different parts of the plot on the following diagram.

"Sonata for Harp and Bicycle" by Joan Aiken

Build Vocabulary

Spelling Strategy   If a word ends in two consonants, the two consonants remain when a suffix is added. For example, in the Word Bank word *encroaching* the *ch* of *encroach* does not change when the suffix *-ing* is added.

Using Words From Myths

When English was young, those who could write in the language were educated in classical learning, including myths. **Myths** are fictional tales that explain actions of gods or account for natural phenomena. Lightning, for example, was explained by ancient Greeks as the spear of Zeus, who was chief among the gods. The stories and names of mythological beings made their way into the English language. For example, things having to do with the military, such as *martial law* or *martial music*, came from the name for the Roman god of war, Mars.

A. DIRECTIONS: Use a dictionary or other source to explain the origin of the following words.

1. jovial _____

2. hector _____

3. Thursday _____

4. volcano _____

5. siren _____

Using the Word Bank

| encroaching | tantalizingly | furtive | menacing | reciprocate |
| ardent | gossamer | preposterous | engendered | improbably |

B. DIRECTIONS: Match each word in the left column with its definition in the right column. Write the letter of the definition on the line next to the word it defines.

____	1. encroaching	a. passionate
____	2. tantalizingly	b. produced
____	3. furtive	c. ridiculous
____	4. menacing	d. stealthy
____	5. reciprocate	e. implausibly
____	6. ardent	f. intruding
____	7. gossamer	g. wispy
____	8. preposterous	h. temptingly
____	9. engendered	i. return
____	10. improbably	j. threatening

"Sonata for Harp and Bicycle" by Joan Aiken

Build Grammar Skills: Participial Phrases

A **participle** is a form of a verb that can act as an adjective. A **participial phrase** is a participle with modifiers or complements. Like a participle, a participial phrase acts as an adjective.

Participles: *roaring*
respected

Participial Phrases: *Roaring past the house*, the tornado disappeared.
A respected judge, Mr. Jones made a fair decision.

A participial phrase should be placed close to the word it modifies, or the meaning of a sentence may be unclear.

Misplaced Modifier: *Hanging upside down on the bar*, Sam watched a monkey.
Corrected: Sam watched a monkey *hanging upside down on the bar*.

A. Practice: Underline the participles or participial phrases in the passages from "Sonata for Harp and Bicycle."

1. But, shaking her head, she stepped onto a scarlet homebound bus . . .

2. Walking as softly as an Indian, Jason passed through it . . .

3. He . . . found himself with two more endless green corridors beckoning him like a pair of dividers.

4. He led Berenice to the fire door, tucking the bottle of Médoc in his jacket pocket.

5. And she stared firmly down at the copy in front of her, . . . candyfloss hair falling over her face. . . .

6. Offices lay everywhere about him, empty and forbidding.

B. Writing Application: The following sentences contain misplaced modifiers. Rewrite them so that the meaning is clear.

1. Strapped inside the case, Peter carried the new cello.

_____

2. Jane saw an antique car walking to school.

_____

3. Dangling from a high wire, Lucy watched the trapeze artist.

_____

"Sonata for Harp and Bicycle" by Joan Aiken

Reading Strategy: Predicting

As you read you try to guess what will happen next, especially in a mystery. You may not always stop and figure it out, but part of what keeps you reading is your desire to see what happens compared to what you think might happen. We **predict** events in stories, just as we do in real life, by using information to make a judgment. We get our information from details, and we apply what we know to the situation. When we do so, we build expectations. Sometimes stories satisfy us by meeting our expectations. Sometimes they please us by surprising us. Sometimes they disappoint us by dashing our hopes.

The key to good predicting is paying close attention to details as you read. A light and lively writer like Aiken often provides many colorful details to serve as hints. Practice predicting what will happen based on details you notice.

DIRECTIONS: Use this graphic organizer to practice your predicting skills. In the left column appear details from "Sonata for Harp and Bicycle." In the center column, write a prediction of what each detail will mean to the story. After you have finished the story, write what really happens in the right column. How closely did your predictions match the actual outcomes?

Detail	Prediction	Outcome
1. Loudspeakers instruct staff to stop work, and the building empties.		
2. Miss Golden tells Mr. Ashgrove he may not know the secret until he is on the Established Staff.		
3. Jason looks down into the void from the fire escape.		
4. Miss Bell "rented a room—this room—and gave lessons in it."		
5. Jason says "We must remedy the matter."		
6. ". . . two bottles of wine, two bunches of red roses, and a large, canvas-covered bundle."		

"Sonata for Harp and Bicycle" by Joan Aiken

Literary Analysis: Rising Action

As a good story moves along, it often has a sense of **rising action** that propels readers to each new paragraph. What happens next? Where will these events lead? Eventually, the story reaches its climax, the high point of the story at which the readers' interest is at a peak.

Writers build a sense of rising action in many ways. A setting may be intriguing. We may sympathize with a character. Often, the action of a story, its plot, can be tracked. Where is your interest at its height in "Sonata for Harp and Bicycle"? What point in the story would you say is the climax? What details along the way heighten your interest? Use the following chart to plot events that build the sense of rising action for you.

DIRECTIONS: On the lines provided list events in the selection for each point on the graph. Items 1 through 4 should be events that you think build the sense of rising action. Item 5 should be the climax, and item 6 the ending of the story.

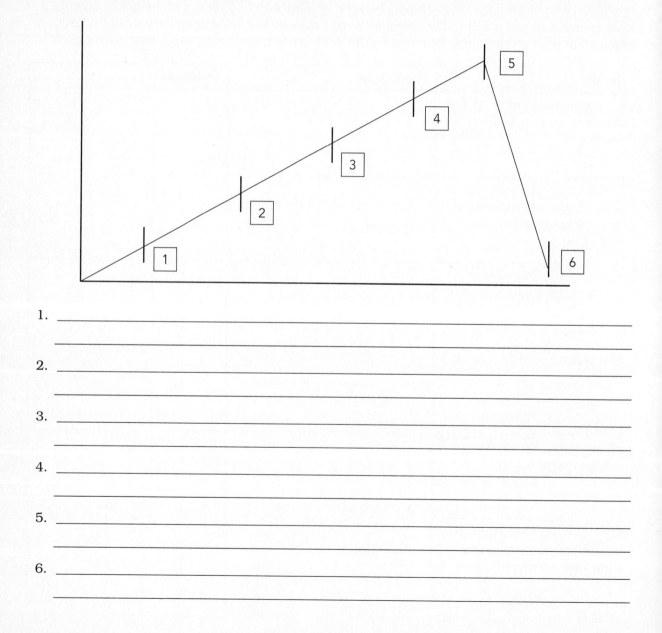

1. _____
   _____

2. _____
   _____

3. _____
   _____

4. _____
   _____

5. _____
   _____

6. _____
   _____

"The Scarlet Ibis" by James Hurst

Build Vocabulary

Spelling Strategy   When you add a suffix that begins with a vowel to a word that ends in a silent e, drop the e, and then add the suffix. For example, *evanesce + -ed = evanesced*, *shake + -ily = shakily*, and *gaze + -ing = gazing*.

Using Irregular Plurals

A. DIRECTIONS: Many nouns that end with the letter *x* have an irregular plural form based on their original Latin roots. *Vortex* is one of these words. To form the plural, change the *e* to *i*, drop the *x*, and add *-ces* for *vortices*. Some of these words also have a second plural form that follows more conventional English rules. *Vortexes* is also an acceptable plural form for *vortex*. For each dictionary entry below, fill in the correctly formed plurals. If only one blank is provided, that word requires the *-ces* plural form.

1. **codex** *n, pl* _____: a manuscript book, especially of biblical Scripture, classics, or ancient annals

2. **cortex** *n, pl* _____ also _____: the outer layer of gray matter of the cerebrum and cerebellum

3. **vertex** *n, pl* _____ also _____: the termination or intersection of lines or curves; a principal or highest point

Using the Word Bank

imminent	iridescent	precariously	vortex
infallibility	entrails	evanesced	

B. DIRECTIONS: Match each word in the left column with its definition in the right column.

____ 1. imminent   a. likely to happen soon

____ 2. iridescent   b. internal organs

____ 3. vortex   c. faded away

____ 4. infallibility d. having shifting, rainbowlike colors

____ 5. entrails   e. the center of an engulfing situation

____ 6. evanesced   f. insecurely

____ 7. precariously   g. the condition of being unable to fail

Using Synonyms

C. DIRECTIONS: Circle the letter of the best synonym for the Word Bank word.

1. imminent
   a. immediate
   b. mixed
   c. ominous
   d. looming

2. iridescent
   a. becoming redder
   b. shimmering
   c. glowing
   d. radiating heat

3. evanesced
   a. dissolved
   b. bubbled
   c. grew
   d. made even

Name _____ Date _____

Build Grammar Skills: Gerund Phrases

A **gerund** is a form of a verb that acts as a noun. For example, it may be the subject of a sentence, a direct object, an indirect object, a predicate nominative, the object of a preposition, or an appositive. Gerunds always end in *–ing*.

Gerunds: The Ryan family enjoys *biking*.
   Reading is Allison's favorite activity.

A **gerund phrase** is a gerund with modifiers or a complement, all acting together as a noun.

Gerund Phrases: Their family tried *biking over the mountain* last summer.
   Reading about nature is always enjoyable.

A. Practice: Underline the gerund phrases in these passages from "The Scarlet Ibis."

1. Renaming my brother was perhaps the kindest thing I ever did for him. . . .

2. Crawling backward made him look like a doodle-bug. . . .

3. He talked so much that we all quit listening to what he said.

4. To discourage his coming with me, I'd run with him across the ends of the cotton rows. . . .

5. When the going got rough and he had to cling to the sides of the go-cart, the hat slipped all the way down . . .

B. Writing Application: Use each of the following gerund phrases in a sentence about "The Scarlet Ibis."

1. giving Doodle swimming lessons

   _____

2. standing on his own

   _____

3. climbing the vines

   _____

4. thinking about the past

   _____

5. telling lies

   _____

Name _____ Date _____

"The Scarlet Ibis" by James Hurst

Reading Strategy: Identifying With a Character

Authors who write in the first person invite you to walk through the story in the shoes of one of the characters. As you read "The Scarlet Ibis," fill in the following chart to help you identify with the story's narrator. List key events from the story in the first column, record the narrator's reaction to each event in the second column, and note what *you* might have said, done, or thought in a similar situation in the third column. An example is provided.

	Story Event	Narrator's Reaction	How I Might Have Reacted
Example:	Doodle's birth	Disappointed	Worried Doodle might die

"The Scarlet Ibis" by James Hurst

Literary Analysis: Point of View

All stories have a **point of view.** The point of view is the vantage point from which a story is told. In a story with a third-person point of view, the narrator is *not* part of the action of the story but reveals the thoughts, words, and actions of the characters in the story. In a story with first-person point of view, such as "The Scarlet Ibis," the narrator *is* part of the action and uses the words *I* and *me* to refer to himself. This first-person narrator relates the actions of all characters, but he cannot, of course, relate their thoughts, feelings, or beliefs. He can reveal to readers only what he himself thinks, feels, or believes.

A story's point of view affects what readers are told and what they must figure out. It may affect which characters they identify or sympathize with and which characters they don't. In "The Scarlet Ibis," the first-person narrator is one of the two main characters. The narrator puts readers right in the middle of the action, and of the grief. Consider how the story would be different if the author had chosen a third-person narrator, or a first-person narrator other than Doodle's brother.

DIRECTIONS: To understand point of view, readers must examine closely its effects on the telling of the story. To do so, it is sometimes useful to consider how other points of view would affect the telling of the story. Answer the following questions to analyze the point of view in "The Scarlet Ibis."

1. Imagine that the author wrote the story in the third-person. The narrator is "omniscient," or "all knowing," meaning that he knows and can reveal the actions, thoughts, words, and beliefs of any and all characters. Review the description of the decision to teach Doodle to walk and the first few walking lessons. How would that scene be different if written from a third-person omniscient point of view?

   _____

   _____

   _____

2. Now consider the scene on the morning of Doodle's sixth birthday. Explain how it would be different if the story were written with a third-person omniscient narrator.

   _____

   _____

   _____

3. Suppose the author had chosen as his first-person narrator someone other than Doodle's brother. Choose any other character in the story and rewrite the scene about Doodle's sixth birthday from that character's point of view. Specifically, rewrite the paragraph that begins, "At breakfast on our chosen day, . . ." Remember that a first-person narrator knows only his or her own thoughts, not the thoughts or feelings of the other characters. Continue on a separate sheet of paper if you need more space.

   _____

   _____

   _____

   _____

"Blues Ain't No Mockin Bird" by Toni Cade Bambara
"Uncle Marcos" by Isabel Allende

Build Vocabulary

Spelling Strategy   Adding a prefix to a word never causes the spelling of the original word to change. This rule proves true in the Word Bank words *disconsolately*, *unrequited*, and *impassive*.

Using the Prefix *dis-*

A. DIRECTIONS: The prefix *dis-* means "opposite" or "absence of." In the Word Bank word *disconsolately*, the prefix has the sense of "absence of" or "without"—in this case, "without consolation." Apply what you know about the prefix *dis-*, and define the following words.

1. disadvantage _____

2. disarm _____

3. disable _____

Using the Word Bank

lassoed	vanquished	impassive	unrequited
formality	fetid	disconsolately	pallid

B. DIRECTIONS: Complete each of the following sentences to demonstrate your understanding of the Word Bank words.

1. Calling Myrtle by her plain first name showed a lack of formality because _____
   _____

2. It seemed as if the cameraman had his camera lassoed to him because _____
   _____

3. Uncle Marcos's affection for Cousin Antonieta was unrequited because _____
   _____

4. In addition to the fetid smoke from experiments, the animals in jars of formaldehyde probably also smelled _____

5. Severo assumed that Marcos was a vanquished hero because _____
   _____

6. The fact that Nivea wept disconsolately indicates that _____
   _____

7. As it turned out, Cousin Antonieta was impassive because she _____
   _____

8. When Clara says the plastic angels were pallid, she means that they _____
   _____

"Blues Ain't No Mockin Bird" by Toni Cade Bambara
"Uncle Marcos" by Isabel Allende

Build Grammar Skills: Infinitive Phrases

An **infinitive** is a form of a verb that generally appears with the word *to* and acts as a noun, adjective, or adverb.

Infinitive: Grandpa likes *to sing.*

An **infinitive phrase** is an infinitive with modifiers, complements, or a subject. An infinitive phrase, like an infinitive, acts as a noun, adjective, or adverb.

As a noun: *To fly in a balloon* was an exciting experience.
(*To fly in a balloon* acts as the subject.)

As an adjective: The special saw *to cut the pipe* worked well.
(*To cut the pipe* modifies the noun *saw.*)

As an adverb: He uses only two fingers *to play the piano.*
(*To play the piano* modifies the verb *uses.*)

A. Practice: Underline the infinitives and infinitive phrases in the following passages from the selections.

1. But he didn't seem to have another word to say, so he and the camera man backed on out. . . .

2. So I get into the tire to take my turn.

3. Folks like to go for him sometimes.

4. They didn't know what to do.

5. "He wants you to hand him the camera," Smilin whispers. . . .

6. He settled in as if he planned to stay forever.

7. People came from the provinces to see the sight.

8. The entire family wept . . . except for Clara, who continued to watch the sky with the patience of an astronomer.

B. Writing Application: Use each of the following infinitive phrases to write a sentence about "Blues Ain't No Mockin Bird" or "Uncle Marcos."

1. to speak with the photographers

_____

2. to ask questions

_____

3. to write a story

_____

4. to describe her uncle

_____

"Blues Ain't No Mockin Bird" by Toni Cade Bambara
"Uncle Marcos" by Isabel Allende

Reading Strategy: Making Inferences About Characters

Readers can **make inferences about characters** by evaluating and analyzing the details in a story. Writers provide small details about characters that, taken alone, might not reveal much about the character. But if readers gather those details and combine them with other pieces of information, they can draw reasonable conclusions about the character's personality, thoughts, and motives.

To learn about Granny in "Blues Ain't No Mockin Bird," readers can make inferences based on her words and actions. For example, when Granny answers the men's questions "with no smile," readers can infer that Granny doesn't feel the need to be polite. What does this say about Granny?

DIRECTIONS: Use the following charts to record information about the characters indicated. Then make inferences about the characters based on the details from the stories. An example is shown.

Cathy in "Blues Ain't No Mockin Bird"

Details About Cathy	Inferences I Can Make About Cathy
Cathy giggles twice while Granny confronts the two men.	Cathy is either shy or amused by the bold way Granny talks to the men.

Clara in "Uncle Marcos"

Details About Clara	Inferences I Can Make About Clara

"Blues Ain't No Mockin Bird" by Toni Cade Bambara
"Uncle Marcos" by Isabel Allende

Literary Analysis: Direct and Indirect Characterization

Characterization is the way a writer reveals information about a character. In **direct characterization** the writer directly states a character's personality, appearance, and actions.

> **Direct Characterization:** [Marcos] had grown a beard and let his hair grow long, and he was thinner than ever before.

In this example from "Uncle Marcos," Allende directly describes Uncle Marcos's appearance. In **indirect characterization,** the writer reveals a character's traits through the character's words and actions, and through what other characters say about him or her. Often when a writer uses indirect characterization, it is up to the reader to draw logical conclusions about the character's personality and motivations.

> **Indirect Characterization:** I didn't even ask. I could see Cathy actress was very likely to walk away and leave us in mystery about this story which I heard was about some bears.

In this example from "Blues Ain't No Mockin' Bird," readers get a glimpse of the personality of Cathy through the comments of another character—in this case, the story's first-person narrator.

DIRECTIONS: Identify each of the following passages by writing *D* if it is an example of direct characterization and *I* if it is an example of indirect characterization.

_____ 1. Each time Uncle Marcos had visited his sister Nivea's home, he had stayed for several months, to the immense joy of his nieces and nephews, particularly Clara, causing a storm in which the sharp lines of domestic order blurred.

_____ 2. Cathy say it's because he's so tall and quiet and like a king.

_____ 3. And we figure any minute, somethin in my back tells me any minute now, Granny gonna bust through that screen with somethin in her hand and murder on her mind.

_____ 4. Marcos sank into a deep depression that lasted two or three days, at the end of which he announced that he would never marry and that he was embarking on a trip around the world.

_____ 5. They abandoned their carriage-house oracle and split the profits, even though the only one who had cared about the material side of things had been Nana.

_____ 6. "That boy don't never have anything original to say," say Cathy grown-up.

_____ 7. The little girl, who was only seven at the time, had learned to read from her uncle's storybooks and been closer to him than any other member of the family because of her prophesying powers.

"The Man to Send Rain Clouds" by Leslie Marmon Silko
"The Invalid's Story" by Mark Twain

Build Vocabulary

Spelling Strategy   When adding a suffix to words ending in *y* preceded by a consonant, change the *y* to *i* unless the suffix starts with an *i*. For example, when the suffix *-ly* is added to the Word Bank word *desultory*, the adverb *desultorily* is formed. When the suffix *-ness* is added to *desultory*, the noun *desultoriness* is formed. However, when *-ing* is added to *fly*, the participle *flying* is formed.

Using the Suffix *-ous*

The suffix *-ous* means "full of" or "characterized by." When it is added to a noun it creates an adjective. For example, combining the noun *omen* with *-ous* results in the Word Bank adjective *ominous*, which means "having the character of an evil omen" or "threatening."

A. DIRECTIONS: Fill in the blanks of the paragraph with six words from the following list. Some words will make sense in more than one blank, but try to use six different words.

suspicious	outrageous	gracious
humorous	tremendous	monstrous
hideous	odorous	ambitious

Being a(n) _____ man, the narrator of "The Invalid's Story" took on the _____ task of delivering his friend's remains to the man's family in Wisconsin. The narrator boarded the train to Wisconsin without realizing that a(n) _____ mistake had been made, and instead of his friend he was delivering a box of guns and _____ cheese. The _____ smell of the cheese makes the narrator's train ride uncomfortable and leads to a(n) _____ story.

Using the Word Bank

pagans	perverse	deleterious	ominous
cloister	judicious	placidly	desultory
prodigious			

B. DIRECTIONS: Match each word in the left column with its definition in the right column. Write the letter of the definition on the line next to the word it defines.

____ 1. perverse   a. people who are not Christians, Muslims, or Jews

____ 2. placidly   b. random

____ 3. deleterious   c. threatening

____ 4. cloister   d. showing good judgment

____ 5. desultory   e. injurious; harmful to health and well-being

____ 6. ominous   f. improper; wicked

____ 7. pagans   g. calmly; quietly

____ 8. judicious   h. enormous

____ 9. prodigious   i. place devoted to religious seclusion

"The Man to Send Rain Clouds" by Leslie Marmon Silko
"The Invalid's Story" by Mark Twain

Build Grammar Skills: Infinitive or Prepositional Phrase?

Take care not to confuse a prepositional phrase beginning with *to* with an infinitive. When distinguishing between an **infinitive** and a **prepositional phrase**, remember that a prepositional phrase always ends with a noun or pronoun. An infinitive always ends with a verb.

Prepositional Phrases: The dog ran *to its owner.*
My sister went *to the concert.*

Infinitives: The dog loved *to run.*
My sister learned *to sing.*

A. Practice: Identify the underlined words in these passages from the selections as infinitives (I) or prepositional phrases (PP).

1. _____Leon and his brother-in-law, Ken, gathered the sheep . . . before they returned <u>to the cottonwood tree</u>.

2. _____We were just out <u>to the sheep camp</u>.

3. _____You really shouldn't allow him <u>to stay</u> at the sheep camp alone.

4. _____I guess he sat down <u>to rest</u> in the shade and never got up again.

5. _____They both stooped <u>to fit</u> through the low adobe entrance.

6. _____I was greatly shocked and grieved, but there was no time <u>to waste</u> in emotions. . . .

7. _____I took the card . . . and hurried off through the whistling storm <u>to the railway station</u>.

8. _____Presently I began <u>to detect</u> a most evil and searching odor stealing about on the frozen air.

9. _____All that went before was just simply poetry <u>to that smell</u>. . . .

10. _____This is my last trip; I am on my way home <u>to die</u>.

B. Writing Application: Write your own sentences using the infinitives and prepositional phrases below. Then label each one *I* or *PP*.

1. to laugh

_____

2. to the finish line

_____

3. to stumble

_____

4. to his class

_____

5. to relax

_____

Name _____ Date _____

"The Man to Send Rain Clouds" by Leslie Marmon Silko
"The Invalid's Story" by Mark Twain

Reading Strategy: Using Your Senses

Writers use images, or word pictures, to appeal to a reader's various senses. When you read "The Man to Send Rain Clouds," you can almost see the desert sunset, feel the cool night air, and taste the beans and hot bread consumed by the characters. When you read "The Invalid's Story," you can almost hear the rumbling train and smell the unusual odors that fill its express car. Silko and Twain carefully created these images to help readers experience the settings, characters, and events in their stories.

DIRECTIONS: As you read "The Man to Send Rain Clouds" and "The Invalid's Story," keep track of specific images that appeal to your senses. In the following chart, describe each image in the appropriate section. You may enter an image more than once, since some images may appeal to more than one sense.

Senses	"The Man to Send Rain Clouds"	"The Invalid's Story"
Touch	pinches of corn meal and pollen	the stove getting hotter and hotter
Taste		
Smell		
Hearing		
Sight		

Rain/Invalid's **151**

"The Man to Send Rain Clouds" by Leslie Marmon Silko
"The Invalid's Story" by Mark Twain

Literary Analysis: Setting

A story's **setting** is the time, place, and culture in which the story unfolds. Setting is often an important element of a story, influencing the ideas and actions of characters and shaping events. In "The Man to Send Rain Clouds" and in "The Invalid's Story," setting plays a particularly important role. Think about how the specific details of setting are directly related to the events that occur in each story.

DIRECTIONS: As you read the stories, concentrate on the specific details about setting that each author provides. List some of these details, and then describe why they are important to the story.

"The Man to Send Rain Clouds"

Details of characters' physical surroundings: _____

_____

_____

Details that reflect the era in which the story takes place: _____

_____

_____

Details that reflect the culture of the characters: _____

_____

_____

Importance of setting: _____

_____

_____

"The Invalid's Story"

Details of characters' physical surroundings: _____

_____

_____

Details that reflect the era in which the story takes place: _____

_____

_____

Details that reflect the culture of the characters: _____

_____

_____

Importance of setting: _____

_____

_____

"The Necklace" by Guy de Maupassant
"The Harvest" by Tomás Rivera

Build Vocabulary

Spelling Strategy   For words that end in silent *e*, keep the *e* before adding an ending that begins with a consonant. For example, -*ful* added to the word *rue* forms the Word Bank word *rueful.*

Using the Root *-ject-*

When Madame Loisel discovers that she's lost the diamond necklace, she and her husband look at each other "in utter dejection." The word *dejection* is formed from the root *-ject-*, which means "to throw." The prefix *de-* means "down", and the suffix *-tion* means "the state of being"; so *dejection* refers, literally, to a throwing down of the spirits, or a lowness of spirits. Other words that are formed from the root *-ject-* include *project*, meaning "to throw forward," and *reject*, meaning "to throw something out as useless."

A. DIRECTIONS: Define the italicized words in each sentence, using your understanding of the root *-ject-*. Knowing these prefixes will help you: *re-* = "back"; *sub-* = "under"; *inter-* = "between."

1. Madame Loisel wanted to be part of the world of the wealthy, but felt only *rejection.*

   _____

2. After buying the necklace, M. and Mme. Loisel were *subjected* to a life of debt and hard work.

   _____

3. Madame Forestier *interjected*, "But Mathilde, my necklace was false!"

   _____

Using the Word Bank

déclassé	rueful	resplendent	astutely
profoundly	harrowed	disheveled	

B. DIRECTIONS: Match each word in the left column with its definition in the right column. Write the letter of the definition on the line next to the word it defines.

____ 1. harrowed   a. shining brightly

____ 2. disheveled   b. feeling sorrow or regret

____ 3. resplendent   c. cleverly or cunningly

____ 4. profoundly   d. broken up and leveled by a frame with spikes or disks drawn
                           by a tractor

____ 5. déclassé   e. lowered in social status

____ 6. rueful   f. deeply and intensely

____ 7. astutely   g. disarranged and untidy

"The Necklace" by Guy de Maupassant
"The Harvest" by Tomás Rivera

Build Grammar Skills: Appositive Phrases

An **appositive** is a noun or pronoun placed near another noun or pronoun to rename or give additional information about the first usage. An appositive that can be dropped from a sentence without changing the meaning of the sentence must be set off with commas or dashes. If the appositive is essential to the sentence, it is not set off by commas. When an appositive has its own modifiers, it is an **appositive phrase**.

Appositive:
Today, we read Guy de Maupassant's story *"The Necklace."*

Appositive Phrase:
The poverty of her rooms—*the shabby walls, the worn furniture, the ugly upholstery*—caused her pain.

A. Practice: Underline the appositive phrase in each sentence.

1. Guy de Maupassant, a famous short-story writer, wrote "The Necklace."

2. Madame Forstier lends Mathilde a necklace, a strand of worthless diamonds, to wear to the reception.

3. Mathilde does not realize Madame Forstier, a very wealthy woman, has lent her fake diamonds.

4. She agonizes over the loss of the necklace, a seemingly colossal debt.

5. After firing the maid, Mathilde cleaned the mess, a mountain of dirty dishes.

B. Writing Application: Combine each pair of sentences into one sentence with an appositive phrase.

1. Autumn is the best time of year. It marks the end of the harvest.

   _____

2. Don Trine is a migrant worker. He confuses the townspeople with his strange behavior.

   _____

3. All alone, Don Trine takes walks. His walks are long strolls in the afternoon.

   _____

4. Rumors began to circulate throughout the town. There were speculations that Don Trine had a lot of money.

   _____

   _____

5. The boys came upon a mystery. They found odd holes in the ground that they could not explain.

   _____

   _____

"The Necklace" by Guy de Maupassant
"The Harvest" by Tomás Rivera

Reading Strategy: Drawing Conclusions

By piecing together what you know about characters in these stories, you can draw conclusions about the reasons for their actions. You can then use your understanding of their behavior to draw broader conclusions about human nature.

DIRECTIONS: As you read "The Necklace" and "The Harvest," fill in the following chart. For each story, choose one character. Then, in the first column, note the character's actions; in the second column, note the related character traits; in the third column, use these details to draw conclusions about why the character acts as he or she does. Finally, in the fourth column, draw conclusions about how the characters' actions might relate to the theme of the story.

	Characters' Actions	Related Character Traits	Reasons for the Actions	What This Suggests About Theme
"The Necklace"				
"The Harvest"				

"The Necklace" by Guy de Maupassant
"The Harvest" by Tomás Rivera

Literary Analysis: Theme

The **theme** of a literary work is the general insight about life that it shares with readers. Literary works often communicate theme through the experiences of characters, details describing the events and setting of the work, and literary devices such as symbolism and irony. In "The Necklace" and "The Harvest," themes are conveyed indirectly through the comments and actions of the characters. What insights about life can you find in the experiences of Madame Loisel and the descriptions of the society in which she lives? What insights are shared through the actions of Don Trine and the other people in his town?

DIRECTIONS: After you've read the stories, think about which of each story's details and events lead you to the story's theme, or general insight about life. Then read the following passages from each story and describe how each passage relates to theme.

"The Necklace"

1. She was one of those pretty, charming young women who was born, as if by an error of Fate, into a petty official's family. She had no dowry, no hopes, not the slightest chance of being appreciated, understood, loved, and married by a rich and distinguished man.

   What does this passage say about the society in which Madame Loisel lives? _____

   _____

   _____

   _____

   How does the passage relate to a theme of the story? _____

   _____

   _____

   _____

"The Harvest"

2. And that's how all the rumors about Don Trine's walks got started. The folks couldn't figure out why or what he got out of taking off by himself every afternoon. . . . The fact of the matter is that everybody began to say he was hiding the money he had earned that year or that he had found some buried treasure and every day, little by little, he was bringing it back to his coop.

   What does this passage reveal about the townspeople? _____

   _____

   _____

   _____

   How does the passage relate to a theme of the story? _____

   _____

   _____

   _____

"**Single Room, Earth View**" by Sally Ride

Build Vocabulary

Spelling Strategy   For words that end in silent *e*, drop the *e* before a suffix beginning with a vowel. For example, when adding the suffix *-ing* to *extrapolate*, drop the silent *e*: *extrapolate* + *-ing* = *extrapolating*.

Using the Root *-nov-*

A. DIRECTIONS: The root *-nov-* means "new." Complete each sentence with a *-nov-* word from the following list.

> novice   novelty   renovated

1. In the 1950s, television was still a _____ that fascinated audiences.

2. After the architect _____ the run-down Victorian house, the building looked like new.

3. "Janey plays remarkably well for a _____," commented the coach at tryouts.

Using the Word Bank

articulate	surreal	ominous	novice	muted
subtle	eddies	eerie	diffused	extrapolating

B. DIRECTIONS: Match each word in the left column with its definition in the right column. Write the letter of the definition on the line next to the word it defines.

____ 1. articulate   a. weaker; less intense

____ 2. extrapolating   b. strange; fantastic

____ 3. subtle   c. not obvious

____ 4. ominous   d. threatening

____ 5. surreal   e. circular currents

____ 6. eerie   f. spread out

____ 7. muted   g. arriving at a conclusion by making inferences based on known facts

____ 8. novice   h. beginner

____ 9. eddies   i. expressing oneself clearly and easily

____ 10. diffused   j. mysterious; creepy

Understanding Verbal Analogies

C. DIRECTIONS: Each of the following questions consists of a related pair of words in CAPITAL LETTERS followed by four lettered pairs of words. Choose the pair that best expresses a relationship *similar* to that expressed in the pair in capital letters.

1. SUBTLE : OBVIOUS ::
   a. agitated : worried
   b. hazily : clear
   c. apparent : known
   d. unremarkable : noteworthy

2. EDDIES : CIRCLES ::
   a. highways : straight
   b. tornadoes : funnels
   c. boxes : containers
   d. oranges : rounded

"Single Room, Earth View" by Sally Ride

Build Grammar Skills: Subject -Verb Agreement

For a subject and verb to agree in number, both must be singular or both must be plural. When making a verb agree with its subject, identify the subject and determine whether it is singular or plural. Notice the **subject-verb agreement** in the following sentences.

Singular Subject and Verb: The *astronaut writes* about her experiences in space.
Plural Subject and Verb: *Astronauts get* a unique view of the earth.
A *jet* and a *space shuttle are* very different.

In the examples, the singular verb *writes* agrees in number with the singular subject *astronaut*. The plural verb *get* agrees with the plural subject *astronauts*. The compound subject *jet* and *space shuttle* agrees with the plural verb *are*.

When you check your subject-verb agreement, be sure to determine the subject correctly. Sometimes a word or phrase between the subject and verb can be confusing, as in the following sentence.

The *pollution* in some cities *was* apparent from space.

The singular verb *was* agrees with the singular subject *pollution*.

A. Practice: Underline the subject of each sentence. Then, circle the verb form that agrees in number with the subject.

1. The space shuttle, which is home for several astronauts, (orbit/orbits) the earth in just ninety minutes.

2. Some human activities (harm/harms) the environment.

3. A lightning storm observed from above the clouds (is/are) an unusual sight.

4. Moonlight on the Mississippi River (create/creates) an eerie scene.

5. The wake of a ship and the contrails of an airplane (is/are) in view from the space shuttle.

6. Sally Ride's description of her observations (inspire/inspires) me to be an astronaut.

B. Writing Application: Complete the sentences, using one of the verb forms given. Make sure that the verb you choose agrees in number with the subject.

1. Sally Ride's description of her space flights (is/are) _____

_____

2. As they look at the earth, astronauts (see/sees) _____

_____

3. Pollution in the rain forests (appear/appears) _____

_____

4. From space, city lights and stars (is/are) _____

_____

"Single Room, Earth View" by Sally Ride

Reading Strategy: Varying Your Reading Rate

When you read, you speed up or slow down depending on the type of material and your purpose for reading it. This is called **varying your reading rate**. Read quickly if you are reviewing familiar material or scanning for specific information. Slow down when the material is unfamiliar or complex, or if you must understand and remember all of it fully.

DIRECTIONS: Read the following passages from "Single Room, Earth View" and answer the questions that follow. Then, explain whether you read slowly or quickly to determine the answer, and why.

> One day, as I scanned the sandy expanse of Northern Africa, I couldn't find any of the familiar landmarks—colorful outcroppings of rock in Chad, irrigated patches of the Sahara. Then I realized they were obscured by a huge dust storm, a cloud of sand that enveloped the continent from Morocco to the Sudan.

1. Above what continent was Ride flying?

   _____

   _____

2. Why couldn't Ride see familiar landmarks that day?

   _____

   _____

> Scientists' understanding of the energy balance in the oceans has increased significantly as a result of the discoveries of circular and spiral eddies tens of kilometers in diameter, of standing waves hundreds of kilometers long, and of spiral eddies that sometimes trail into one another for thousands of kilometers. If a scientist wants to study features on this scale, it's much easier from an orbiting vehicle than from the vantage point of a boat.

3. What discoveries about the ocean have helped scientists understand its energy balance?

   _____

   _____

4. What is the main idea of this passage?

   _____

   _____

"Single Room, Earth View" by Sally Ride

Literary Analysis: Observation

Scientists use their powers of observation to note facts and events in the hope of proving specific theories. Careful observation is vital to our understanding of the world around us.

DIRECTIONS: Choose one of the following quotations; then in a few paragraphs, discuss how Sally Ride's observations support or refute the quotation.

"Observation is a passive science, experimentation is an active science."

—Claude Bernard (1865)

"For every man the world is as fresh as it was at the first day, and as full of untold novelties for him who has the eyes to see them."

—Thomas Huxley (1868)

" . . . we have to remember that what we observe is not nature in itself but nature exposed to our method of questioning."

—Werner Karl Heisenberg (1958)

_____

_____

_____

_____

_____

_____

_____

_____

_____

_____

_____

_____

_____

_____

_____

_____

_____

_____

_____

_____

"The Washwoman" by Isaac Bashevis Singer
"On Summer" by Lorraine Hansberry
"A Celebration of Grandfathers" by Rudolfo A. Anaya

Build Vocabulary

Spelling Strategy Form the plurals of words ending in z, x, sh, ch, s, or y by adding -es or -ies to the base word. For example, the word *perplex* becomes the Word Bank word *perplexes*.

Using the Prefix *fore-*

" . . .this washwoman, small and thin as she was, possessed a strength that came from generations of peasant forebears." The word *forebears* uses the common prefix *fore-*, which means "before" or "occurring earlier." *Forebears* means, literally, "relatives who came before us," or "ancestors."

A. Directions: Rewrite each of the following sentences, replacing the italicized word or phrase in each sentence with an appropriate word from the following list of *fore-* words.

foretold	forecast	foresight	forestall

1. Singer's mother claimed a premonition *told her beforehand* that something would happen to the washwoman.

_____

2. The courageous women in Lorraine Hansberry's story wished to *interrupt the onset of* death.

_____

3. Rudolfo Anaya and his grandfather wished they could *predict* rain for their crops.

_____

4. Having *a clear and sensible view of the future,* Grandfather encouraged Anaya to speak both English and Spanish.

_____

Using the Word Bank

forebears	rancor	obstinacy	pious
aloofness	perplexes	permeate	epiphany

B. DIRECTIONS: Circle the letter of the description that best fits each word below.

1. rancor
   a. bitter hate
   b. intense love
   c. carelessness
   d. terror

2. aloofness
   a. kindness
   b. brilliance
   c. distance
   d. cleanliness

3. forebears
   a. studies
   b. plans
   c. family
   d. ancestors

4. perplexes
   a. attaches
   b. orders
   c. confuses
   d. discusses

5. obstinacy
   a. violence
   b. stubbornness
   c. hopelessness
   d. distance

6. permeate
   a. flow throughout
   b. lasting
   c. dream
   d. organize

7. pious
   a. devoted
   b. depressed
   c. hungry
   d. humorous

8. epiphany
   a. episode
   b. letter
   c. revelation
   d. impossibility

"**The Washwoman**" by Isaac Bashevis Singer
"**On Summer**" by Lorraine Hansberry
"**A Celebration of Grandfathers**" by Rudolfo A. Anaya

Build Grammar Skills: Consistency of Verb Tenses

When we speak and write, we use **verb tenses** to indicate when something occurs. A tense is a form of a verb that shows the time of an action or condition. Examples of the six verb tenses in their basic forms are given below.

Present: he talks   **Present Perfect:** he has talked
Past: he talked   **Past Perfect:** he had talked
Future: he will talk   **Future Perfect:** he will have talked

It is important to use verb tenses with **consistency**. For example, if you are describing something that happened in the past, you should use verbs in the past tense throughout your description.

Incorrect: When he arrives at home, she was no longer there.
Correct: When he arrived at home, she was no longer there.

A. Practice: In these passages from the selections, underline each verb and identify its tense.

1. _____ My story is about one of these.

2. _____ When she started washing for us, she was already past seventy.

3. _____ "With the help of God you will live to be a hundred and twenty. . . ."

4. _____ And I have retained my respect for the noblest of seasons.

5. _____ "Me, I will live my last days in my valley."

6. _____ After he had covered my welts with the cool mud from the irrigation ditch . . .

B. Writing Application: Rewrite the sentences using the correct tense of the verb in parentheses.

1. When the washwoman didn't return, the family thought that she (had died/has died).

_____

2. After she delivered the laundry, the washwoman never (will come/came) back.

_____

3. The author (remembers/ remembered) some significant summers in her life, so she decided to write about them.

_____

4. While she was in Maine, Hansberry (met/will meet) a woman who bravely battled cancer.

_____

5. As a child, the author (learns/learned) to greet his grandfather respectfully.

_____

6. I wonder whether the author (has lived/will live) in New Mexico when he is an old man.

_____

"The Washwoman" by Isaac Bashevis Singer
"On Summer" by Lorraine Hansberry
"A Celebration of Grandfathers" by Rudolfo A. Anaya

Reading Strategy: Identifying the Author's Attitude

An **author's attitude** is his or her feeling toward a particular subject. You can identify a writer's attitude toward a subject by noticing the details he or she chooses, and the words and phrases he or she uses to describe these details. For example, Isaac Bashevis Singer shows his respect for the washwoman when he writes " . . . this washwoman, small and thin as she was, possessed a strength that came from generations of peasant forebears." From this line you can tell that he notices her strength and feels that it is extraordinary.

DIRECTIONS: Read the following passages from the selections. Identify each author's attitude toward his or her subject, and then list the specific words and phrases that express this attitude.

"The Washwoman"

1. "Her soul passed into those spheres where all holy souls met, regardless of the roles they played on this earth, in whatever tongue, of whatever creed. I cannot imagine paradise without this Gentile washwoman. I cannot even conceive of a world where there is no recompense for such effort."

Attitude toward the washwoman's death: _____

_____

Words and phrases that express this attitude: _____

_____

"On Summer"

2. " . . . more than the coming autumn with its pretentious melancholy; more than an austere and silent winter which must shut dying people in for precious months; more even than the frivolous spring, too full of too many false promises, would be the gift of another summer with its stark and intimate assertion of neither birth nor death but life at the apex."

Attitude toward summer: _____

_____

Words and phrases that express this attitude: _____

_____

"A Celebration of Grandfathers"

3. "Vision blurs, health wanes; even the act of walking carries with it the painful reminder of the autumn of life. But this process is something to be faced, not something to be hidden away by false images. Yes, the old can be young at heart, but in their own way, with their own dignity. They do not have to copy the always young image of the Hollywood star."

Attitude toward his grandfather's views on aging, and the importance of these views in the modern world: _____

_____

Words and phrases that express this attitude: _____

_____

"The Washwoman" by Isaac Bashevis Singer
"On Summer" by Lorraine Hansberry
"A Celebration of Grandfathers" by Rudolfo A. Anaya

Literary Analysis: Essay

An **essay** is a short piece of nonfiction in which a writer expresses a personal view of a topic. The selections you have read illustrate three distinct types of essays. "The Washwoman" expresses ideas by telling a story, so it is a narrative essay. "On Summer" tries to persuade readers to accept a position or take a course of action, so it is a persuasive essay. "A Celebration of Grandfathers" is a reflective essay because it focuses on the writer's personal reflections about a topic important to him.

DIRECTIONS: As you read, focus on the distinct styles of each essay. Then answer the following questions.

1. What are some memorable details about Isaac Bashevis Singer's washwoman?

_____

_____

2. Why does Singer tell the story of the washwoman? What points is he trying to make?

_____

_____

_____

3. What opinion does Lorraine Hansberry present in "On Summer"?

_____

_____

_____

4. What are some of the specific ideas Hansberry presents to persuade readers to accept her opinion?

_____

_____

_____

5. On what does Rudolfo Anaya reflect in "A Celebration of Grandfathers"?

_____

_____

_____

6. What do Anaya's reflections reveal about his personal view of his topic?

_____

_____

_____

from *A White House Diary* by Lady Bird Johnson
"Arthur Ashe Remembered" by John McPhee
"Georgia O'Keeffe" by Joan Didion

Build Vocabulary

Spelling Strategy   A prefix attached to a word never affects the spelling of the original word. For example, *im-* + *mutable* = immutable.

Using the Root *-sent-/-sens-*

A. DIRECTIONS: Knowing that the word root *-sent-* (sometimes spelled *-sens-*) means "feeling or perceiving," write definitions for the following words.

1. sensation _____

2. sensible _____

3. sentimentality _____

Using the Word Bank

tumultuous	implications	poignant	legacy	enigma
condescending	sentimental	genesis	rancor	immutable

B. DIRECTIONS: Match each word in the left column with its definition in the right column.

____ 1. tumultuous   a. anything handed down from an ancestor

____ 2. implications   b. characterized by looking down on someone

____ 3. poignant   c. excessively or foolishly emotional

____ 4. legacy   d. birth; origin; beginning

____ 5. enigma   e. greatly disturbed

____ 6. condescending   f. never changing

____ 7. sentimental   g. hatred; spite

____ 8. genesis   h. suggestions or indirect indications

____ 9. rancor   i. a puzzling or baffling matter; a riddle

____ 10. immutable   j. drawing forth pity, compassion; moving

Understanding Sentence Completions

C. DIRECTIONS: Circle the letter of the word that best completes each sentence.

1. Although the biographer claimed to admire his subject, his writing had a _____ tone.
   a. tumultuous   c. condescending
   b. sentimental   d. poignant

2. A younger generation of strong-minded female painters is evidence of O'Keeffe's _____.
   a. implications   c. enigma
   b. legacy   d. genesis

from *A White House Diary* by Lady Bird Johnson
"Arthur Ashe Remembered" by John McPhee
"Georgia O'Keeffe" by Joan Didion

Build Grammar Skills: Subject -Verb Agreement: Confusing Subjects

Subjects and verbs must agree in number, regardless of the order in which the words appear in a sentence. One type of **confusing subject** is the hard-to-find subject that comes after the verb. A sentence in which the subject comes after the verb is said to be inverted. Subject and verb order is usually inverted in questions. In the following examples, the subjects and verbs are inverted.

In the motorcade *were* many *cars.*
Is Arthur Ashe the U.S. Open champion?

The verb *were* agrees with the subject *cars.* The verb *is* agrees with the subject *Arthur Ashe.*

To check inverted sentences for subject-verb agreement, reword them so that the subject comes at the beginning.

Inverted: There *were* many *pictures* in the museum.
Reworded: Many <u>pictures</u> *were* in the museum.

Note that the words *there* and *here* at the beginning of a sentence often signal an inverted sentence. The words *there* and *here* never function as subjects of sentences.

A. Practice: The following sentences are inverted. Write *C* if the subject-verb agreement is correct. Write *I* if the subject-verb agreement is incorrect. Then, on the line following each sentence, write the correct form of the verb.

1. _____ As they rounded the curve, there were a loud noise. _____

2. _____ Was Lyndon Johnson the next President? _____

3. _____ There is several versions of the event. _____

4. _____ On the wall was many of Georgia O'Keeffe's paintings. _____

5. _____ Are they well known in the world? _____

B. Writing Application: Rewrite the paragraph, correcting all errors in subject-verb agreement.

In this article about Arthur Ashe, there is several stories about the tennis player's inner strength. Here is some examples: Ashe did not let the other players know what he was feeling. There were always a sense of control about him. Among his strengths were unpredictability. He often tried high-risk shots. Do the author admire Ashe? There is no doubt about it!

_____

_____

_____

_____

_____

from *A White House Diary* by Lady Bird Johnson
"Arthur Ashe Remembered" by John McPhee
"Georgia O'Keeffe" by Joan Didion

Reading Strategy: Finding Writer's Main Points and Support

The writer of an autobiographical or biographical work wants you to understand certain points about his or her subject. At times, the writer will state a main point directly, either at the beginning or end of a paragraph. Details within the paragraph support the main point. In other instances, the writer will hint at the main point rather than state it directly. You must look carefully at the details the writer provides and draw conclusions about the main point based on those supporting details.

DIRECTIONS: For each main point, list two details that the writer provides as support. Supporting details can include direct quotations, anecdotes, and descriptions.

1. Main Point: President Kennedy's death deeply affected all who knew him.
   a. Supporting Detail:

   _____
   _____
   _____

   b. Supporting Detail:

   _____
   _____
   _____

2. Main Point: Arthur Ashe never betrayed "an inward sense of defeat."
   a. Supporting Detail:

   _____
   _____
   _____

   b. Supporting Detail:

   _____
   _____
   _____

3. Main Point: Georgia O'Keeffe always had a strong sense of who she was.
   a. Supporting Detail:

   _____
   _____
   _____

   b. Supporting Detail:

   _____
   _____
   _____

© Prentice-Hall, Inc.

Unit 7: Nonfiction

from *A White House Diary* by Lady Bird Johnson
"Arthur Ashe Remembered" by John McPhee
"Georgia O'Keeffe" by Joan Didion

Literary Analysis: Biographical and Autobiographical Writing

Biographical and autobiographical writing gives us a glimpse of the life of a person. In biographical writing, a writer tells the story of another person's life. In autobiographical writing, a person tells about his or her own life. Writers of both types of nonfiction use direct quotations, anecdotes, and vivid details to bring their subjects to life.

The main difference between the two types of writing is point of view. Biographical writing gives you the writer's view of a subject's life; however, you don't have direct access to the subject's thoughts and feelings. For example, in "Arthur Ashe Remembered" and "Georgia O'Keeffe," the writers share their impressions of their subjects. On the other hand, autobiographical writing lets you share the subject's point of view. In *A White House Diary*, Lady Bird Johnson reveals her thoughts and feelings about well-known people and events.

DIRECTIONS: Write your answers to the following questions.

1. What are two ways in which John McPhee supports his belief that "When things got tough . . ., [Ashe] had control"?

   _____

   _____

2. Lady Bird Johnson realized "the enormity of what had happened" when she saw a flag at half mast. What does this detail add to her personal account?

   _____

   _____

3. What would Didion, the author of "Georgia O'Keeffe," say was Georgia O'Keeffe's main motivation?

   _____

   _____

4. What personal characteristics does Lady Bird Johnson reveal about herself?

   _____

   _____

5. What writing techniques does McPhee use to give readers a detailed portrait of Arthur Ashe?

   _____

   _____

"**Understanding Comics**" by Scott McCloud

Build Vocabulary

Spelling Strategy   When adding a suffix that starts with either a vowel or a consonant to a word ending in two consonants, the word retains both consonants. Examples: *obsessed*, *lurking, harshly, contentment.*

Using the Root -*stat*-

A. DIRECTIONS: Each of the following words contains the root -*stat*-, meaning "to stand." For each word, write a sentence in which the meaning of the word is apparent from the context. If you don't know the meaning of a word, check a dictionary.

1. station _____

   _____

2. stature _____

   _____

3. thermostat _____

   _____

Using the Word Bank

obsessed	aesthetic	arbitrary

B. DIRECTIONS: Demonstrate your understanding of the Word Bank words by completing each sentence in the space provided.

1. Because Scott McCloud really was obsessed with comics, he probably _____

   _____

   _____

   _____

2. McCloud's argument is that there is aesthetic value in comics, meaning that _____

   _____

   _____

   _____

3. The first draft of the definition seems arbitrary because the words were _____

   _____

   _____

   _____

"Understanding Comics" by Scott McCloud

Build Grammar Skills: Varieties of English: Standard, Nonstandard

English can be **standard** (formal) or **nonstandard** (informal). Writers use nonstandard English when they want an informal, more conversational tone or want to add to a realistic portrayal of characters and events. Writers use standard English to address subjects in a more formal, sometimes more serious, way. Look at these examples from *Understanding Comics*.

> **Nonstandard:** Hi, I'm Scott McCloud. When I was a little kid, I knew exactly what comics were.

> **Standard:** Notice that this definition is strictly neutral on matters of style, quality, or subject matter.

Standard English does not contain contractions or slang; it conforms to standard grammar. Nonstandard English often contains contractions, slang, or popular expressions.

A. Practice: Identify each of the sentences as standard (S) or nonstandard (N) English.

1. _____ Soon, I was hooked!

2. _____ Don't gimme that comic book talk, Barney!

3. _____ The world of comics is a huge and varied one.

4. _____ Hey, what about animation?

5. _____ Master comic artist Will Eisner uses the term *sequential art* when describing comics.

6. _____ Anyway, this should make it a bit more specific.

B. Writing Application: Rewrite the sentences in standard English.

1. Hey, toss me that pencil.

_____

2. So what's up with you?

_____

3. She thought the concert was so cool.

_____

4. These directions are making me crazy.

_____

5. I called him and told him to get over here fast.

_____

Name _____ Date _____

Reading Strategy: Using Visuals as a Key to Meaning

One can hardly ignore the old saying "A picture is worth a thousand words," but what does it really mean? In light of Scott McCloud's visual essay, perhaps we can say that pictures fill out or complete the meaning of words. Do you think McCloud would agree with that?

Whether pictures complete the meaning of words or replace words altogether, we can learn from them, acquire information from them, and be moved by them. If we, as readers, are going to learn from pictures, we need to think about *how* they work with the text that accompanies them. Pictures may fill different roles when accompanied by different kinds of writing. An illustration in a technical manual that identifies twenty-seven different knobs and dials on a so-phisticated stereo system is vital to *clarifying* the accompanying text. A visual essay like McCloud's, however, serves other purposes.

In McCloud's essay, some pictures add humor, particularly when accompanied by straight-forward comments or statements. In other frames, McCloud's pictures add ideas or details that take much less room to *depict* than to *write*. Finally, other pictures indicate flashbacks in time or represent a fantasy.

DIRECTIONS: Think about how McCloud's pictures support or extend his written ideas. In the following chart, identify two frames that fit into each category. Explain why the frames you have chosen fit into the category.

Pictures That Add Humor	
Description of Frame	**Why It Fits This Category**

Pictures That Add Details	

Pictures That Signal Flashbacks or Fantasies	

"Understanding Comics" by Scott McCloud

Literary Analysis: Visual Essay

Reading Scott McCloud's visual essay may not have felt at all like reading a standard, written essay. The visual aspect changed your reading experience significantly. However, McCloud's work has all the characteristics of a persuasive essay. Did you recognize them as you read?

DIRECTIONS: Explain how Scott McCloud's visual essay demonstrates each characteristic of a persuasive essay.

Characteristics of a Persuasive Essay	How Accomplished in Visual Essay
Contains logical and/or emotional appeals	
Opinions supported by reasons and evidence	
Facts, statistics, examples, anecdotes	
Expert opinions	
Identifies opposing positions	

"Earhart Redux" by Alex Chadwick
In These Girls, Hope Is a Muscle by Madeleine Blais,
a book review by Steve Gietschier
In These Girls, Hope Is a Muscle by Madeleine Blais, book jacket

Build Vocabulary

Spelling Strategy   When an adjective of more than one syllable ends in -*le*, change it to its adverbial form by replacing *e* with *y*. Do not double the final *l*. Thus the Word Bank word *improbable* becomes *improbably*, *noble* becomes *nobly*, and *able* becomes *ably*. In one-syllable words ending in -*le*, the final consonant may double, as in *whole* and *wholly*.

Using the Root -*dyna*-

A. DIRECTIONS: Explain how the root -*dyna*-, meaning of "strength" or "power" contributes to the definition of each of the following words.

1. dynamic _____

2. dynamite _____

Using the Word Bank

| aerodynamics | hydraulic | pursue | improbable | derides |
| legacy | riveting | ruminative | adept | compelling |

B. DIRECTIONS: Demonstrate your understanding of the Word Bank words by completing each sentence in the space provided.

1. *Aerodynamics* affect flight performance, so airplanes today compared to those in the 1930s

_____

2. Because modern aircraft, unlike Earhart's and Finch's, use *hydraulic* systems, their controls _____

3. To *pursue* financial success might be enough for some, but Finch has also chosen _____

_____

4. It is *improbable* that we will ever know for certain what happened to Amelia Earhart because _____

5. When author Blais *derides* the town of Amherst, she _____

6. The *legacy* of success of the girls' team in Amherst had _____

7. The book blurb says *In These Girls, Hope Is a Muscle* is *riveting* because _____

8. Another way to say that the girls' team was *ruminative* would be to say _____

9. *Adept* at capturing the life of an American town, writer Madeleine Blais _____

_____

10. One would consider this account of a championship season *compelling* because _____

_____

"**Earhart Redux**" by Alex Chadwick
In These Girls, Hope Is a Muscle by Madeleine Blais,
a book review by Steve Gietschier
In These Girls, Hope Is a Muscle by Madeleine Blais, book jacket

Build Grammar Skills: Usage: There, They're, and Their

Because they sound alike, the words *there*, *they're*, and *there* are often misused. *There* is used to indicate place. *They're is* a contraction of the words *they* and *are*. *Their* is a possessive adjective showing ownership. Review the following examples.

There is Sam's new car.
They're going to give us a ride in it.
Their new car has a sunroof.

When you proofread your writing, check that you have used these words correctly.

A. Practice: Circle the word in parentheses that correctly completes each sentence.

1. The airplane is over (there, they're, their) inside the hanger.

2. Many pilots tried to fly (there, they're, their) planes solo across the Atlantic Ocean.

3. The Pratt and Whitney engines had an extraordinary weight-power ratio for (there, they're, their) day.

4. The basketball team had a very successful year; (there, they're, their) state champions.

5. (There/They're/Their) admired by many athletes for (there, they're, their) skill.

6. (There/They're/Their) are plans to try again next year.

B. Writing Application: Read the following sentences. If *there, they're,* or *their* is used incorrectly, write the corrected sentence on the line. If the usage is correct, write *correct*.

1. Astronomers think their will be an eclipse of the moon next week.

   _____

2. Many people are planning to observe it from their back yards.

   _____

3. There hoping to see a full eclipse.

   _____

4. The children are studying astronomy in they're classes.

   _____

"Earhart Redux" by Alex Chadwick

In These Girls, Hope Is a Muscle by Madeleine Blais,
a book review by Steve Gietschier

In These Girls, Hope Is a Muscle by Madeleine Blais, book jacket

Reading Strategy: Determining Author's Purpose

You can usually recognize quickly the general purpose of most writing. Chadwick conducts an interview with Linda Finch. Gietschier is reviewing a book, and the book-jacket writer introduces us to what's inside. This much is simple enough, but why are they doing it?

One of the easiest ways to figure out why the author is writing is to pay attention to details. How are they presented? Why are they there? What difference does it make to Chadwick's interview, for example, that Linda Finch is a "46-year-old grandmother"? After you note some details and think about the impressions they create, you can determine the author's purpose.

DIRECTIONS: Use the following chart to help you collect evidence to determine the author's purpose. Choose one of the selections, and write a sentence expressing the general purpose in the space provided. Then, in the column labeled "Detail," note some detail or phrase that captures your attention. In the column labeled "Impression," record the feeling, concept, or idea that the detail gives you about what you're reading. Finally, in the space labeled "Particular Purpose," express what you believe to be the author's particular purpose, based on your impressions of details.

Selection:	
General Purpose:	
Detail	**Impression**
Particular Purpose:	

"Earhart Redux" by Alex Chadwick
In These Girls, Hope Is a Muscle by Madeleine Blais,
a book review by Steve Gietschier
In These Girls, Hope Is a Muscle by Madeleine Blais, book jacket

Literary Analysis: Career Writing

These selections were written as part of the authors' jobs, so they are examples of workplace writing. **Career writing** is writing that is done in the course of one's employment.

It has always been important in business to have effective writing skills and to be able to put together a good résumé or a crisp memorandum. Now, as the global economy shifts more and more from manufacturing and production jobs to service and information careers, communication skills are critical to success. With the reliance of business on telecommunication, the ability to compose clear faxes, well-organized documents, and effective E-mail is a career skill you cannot do without.

Career writing has some strict requirements. Clarity is the most important asset. If your readers don't understand your point, you've wasted your time and theirs. Brevity is another virtue of workplace writing. You have about three seconds with the reader of E-mail before he or she decides to read or delete your message. You also need to speak in the vocabulary of the business you're in, and that means knowing your audience.

DIRECTIONS: Consider the nature of career writing as you answer the following questions.

1. List two or three occupations in which workplace writing would be a key to a successful career. After each, explain how writing well would help.

   _____
   _____
   _____

2. Which of the following is *not* an example of career writing? Explain why not.
   • an explanation of your job history in a letter accompanying your résumé
   • a letter to an old friend in a similar company recalling your high school days
   • an E-mail about the upcoming company picnic
   • a World Wide Web page describing your company's services

   _____
   _____

3. Rank in importance the writing skills that you think would be most helpful for career writing. Put a *1* beside the most important, and an *6* beside the least important.

   _____ An understanding of what your audience knows

   _____ A large and impressive vocabulary

   _____ The capability of writing long documents

   _____ Knowledge of business terminology

   _____ The ability to get to the point quickly

   _____ An aptitude for clear and concise language

The Dancers by Horton Foote

Build Vocabulary

Spelling Strategy   When adding a suffix to a word that ends in *y* preceded by a consonant, change the *y* to *i* and then add the suffix. For example, the word *mortify* ends in *y* preceded by the consonant *f*. When the suffix *-ed* is added, the *y* is changed to *i* to form the Word Bank word *mortified*.

Using Homographs

A **homograph** is a word that has two or more meanings but is always spelled the same. The Word Bank word *console* is a homograph. As a verb pronounced "kun **sohl**," *console* means "to comfort." As a noun pronounced "**kon** sohl," *console* means "the control unit of a computer or other mechanical or electrical system."

A. DIRECTIONS: Read each sentence. Then, using the context of each sentence, define the italicized homograph.

1. The sharp nail pierced the *sole* of her foot.

   Sole means _____ .

2. He is the *sole* remaining member of what was once a large family.

   Sole means _____ .

3. The *bow* of the boat pointed our direction out to sea.

   Bow means _____ .

4. After a successful performance, the dancers *bow* to the audience and acknowledge their applause.

   Bow means _____ .

Using the Word Bank

genteel	mortified	defiance	console

B. DIRECTIONS: Replace each italicized word or group of words with a word from the Word Bank.

1. Elizabeth Crews is *humiliated* by her daughter's refusal to go to the dance with Horace.

   _____

2. Herman Stanley voices his *resistance* to his wife's plan for Horace's visit.

   _____

3. Emily makes an effort to *comfort* her mother when she is crying.

   _____

4. Neither Elizabeth Crews nor Inez Stanley is as *polite* as she pretends to be.

   _____

Unit 8: Drama

The Dancers by Horton Foote

Build Grammar Skills: Pronoun Case

Pronoun case refers to the different forms that a pronoun takes to indicate its function in a sentence. The three cases of pronouns are the **nominative**, the **objective**, and the **possessive**. The *nominative case* is used when the pronoun is the subject or a predicate nominative. The *objective case* is used when the pronoun is a direct object, indirect object, object of a preposition, or object of a verbal. The *possessive case* is used when the pronoun shows ownership.

> **Nominative:** *He* arrived on the bus.
> **Objective:** Horace gave *her* the corsage.
> **Possessive:** Horace was visiting *his* sister.

The nominative-case pronouns include *I, you, he, she, it, we,* and *they.* Objective-case pronouns are *me, you, him, her, it, us,* and *them.* The possessive-case pronouns are *my, mine, your, yours, his, her, hers, its, our, ours, their,* and *theirs.*

A. Practice: Write the case of each underlined pronoun in the following sentences.

1. <u>I</u> know he's going to be thrilled when I tell <u>him</u>.

   _____

2. And <u>she</u> thinks <u>you</u> would make a very nice couple.

   _____

3. Mother wrote <u>me</u> <u>you</u> were learning.

   _____

4. <u>He</u> is very light on <u>his</u> feet.

   _____

5. The river doesn't overflow anymore since <u>they</u> took the raft out of <u>it</u>.

   _____

B. Writing Application: Rewrite each sentence, replacing the underlined words with a pronoun in the correct case.

1. Horace looked thin to <u>Inez</u>.

   _____

2. <u>Inez and Elizabeth</u> are very close friends.

   _____

3. <u>Inez</u> has planned a busy schedule for <u>Horace</u>.

   _____

4. <u>The dance</u> will be a new experience for <u>Mary Catherine and Horace</u>.

   _____

5. Mary Catherine enjoys <u>Horace's</u> company.

   _____

The Dancers by Horton Foote

Reading Strategy: Picturing the Action

When you **picture the action** of a play, you form an image in your mind as you read dialogue and stage directions. One way to picture the action is to imagine the expressions on a character's face, a character's gestures, or a character's physical response to another character. Another way to picture the action is to imagine how a particular scene would look in real life. For example, think of Horace sitting at the counter of the drug store. What kind of stool is he sitting on? What shape is the counter? Are there gleaming banks of stainless steel milkshake machines behind the counter? Envisioning the action of a play can enrich your experience.

DIRECTIONS: Read each of the following stage directions and lines from the play. Then write your answer to each question on the lines provided.

ELIZABETH CREWS *and her daughter* EMILY *come into the drugstore.* EMILY *is about seventeen and very pretty. This afternoon, however, it is evident that she is unhappy.*

1. What facial expressions, physical appearance, or actions do you picture Emily using to express her unhappiness?

_____

INEZ. Well, just try guessing....

HORACE. Well...uh...*[He is a little embarrassed. He stands trying to think. No names come to him.]* I don't know.

2. What facial expressions and gestures do you picture Horace using to show his embarrassment?

_____

HERMAN. What's the matter with you? You look down in the dumps.

INEZ. No, I'm just disgusted.

HERMAN. What are you disgusted about?

INEZ. Horace. I had everything planned so beautifully for him and then that silly Emily has to go and hurt his feelings.

HERMAN. Well, honey, that was pretty raw, the trick she pulled.

INEZ. I know. But he's a fool to let that get him down. He should have just gone to the dance by himself and proved her wrong. . . . Why like I told him. Show her up. Rush a different girl every night. Be charming. Make yourself popular. But it's like trying to talk to a stone wall. He refused to go out any more. He says he's going home tomorrow.

3. What do you picture Herman doing as he listens to Inez?

_____

4. What do you picture Inez doing as she tells Herman what happened to Horace?

_____

5. How do Inez's actions and expressions show her disgust?

_____

The Dancers by Horton Foote

Literary Analysis: Staging

Staging is the way a play is presented or brought to life. The elements of staging include the sets, lighting, sound effects, costumes, and the way actors move and deliver their lines. When you see a play performed on stage, costumed actors move on and off the stage, props and sets create a sense of place, and lighting and sound create dramatic effects and enhance the play's action. When you read a play, you use the stage direcitons and your imagination to present the play in your mind.

A playwright expresses how to present a play through his or her stage directions. Appearing throughout the play, the italicized and bracketed stage directions describe sets, props, lighting, sound effects, and the appearance, personalities, and movements of the characters. Some play-wrights write very detailed stage directions. Other playwrights, such as Horton Foote, write short, simple stage directions that allow the people who work on the play a great deal of free-dom in interpreting the play's staging.

DIRECTIONS: Read the following stage directions, which appear at the beginning of Horton Foote's play *The Dancers*. Then write an answer to each question on the lines provided.

[Scene: The stage is divided into four acting areas: downstage left is the living room of INEZ and HERMAN STANLEY. Downstage right is part of a small-town drugstore. Upstage right is the living room of ELIZABETH CREWS. Upstage left, the yard and living room of MARY CATHERINE DAVIS. Since the action should flow continuously from one area to the other, only the barest amount of furnishings should be used to suggest what each area represents. The lights are brought up on the drugstore, downstage right. WAITRESS is there. INEZ STANLEY comes into the drugstore. She stands for a moment thinking. The WAITRESS goes over to her.]

1. What "barest amount of furnishings" would suggest each of the four areas of the stage?

   _____

   _____

2. How might the living rooms of Inez and Herman Stanley and Elizabeth Crews differ?

   _____

   _____

3. What reason is suggested in the stage directions for dividing the stage into four areas?

   _____

   _____

4. With a divided stage, what specific function does the lighting perform?

   _____

   _____

5. What costumes might the waitress and Inez wear to place the action of the play in the mid-1950s?

   _____

   _____

The Tragedy of Romeo and Juliet, **Act I,** by William Shakespeare

Build Vocabulary

Spelling Strategy   When adding a suffix to a word that ends in two consonants, do not double the final consonant. Example: *augment + ing = augmenting.*

Using the Prefix *trans-*

A. DIRECTIONS: Use what you know about the prefix *trans-*, meaning "through" or "across," to complete the following sentences.

1. A transient visitor is one who _____

2. A transatlantic traveler is one who _____

3. A transfusion is the process of _____

4. A transfer ticket allows you to _____

5. The transcontinental railroad takes people _____

Using the Word Bank

pernicious	augmenting	grievance	transgression	heretics

B. DIRECTIONS: Match each word in the left column with its definition in the right column. Write the letter of the definition on the line next to the word it defines.

____ 1. pernicious

____ 2. transgression

____ 3. heretics

____ 4. augmenting

____ 5. grievance

a. wrongdoing, sin

b. increasing, enlarging

c. injustice, complaint

d. those who hold a belief opposed to the established teachings of a church

e. causing great injury or ruin

Recognizing Antonyms

C. DIRECTIONS: For each Word Bank word, choose the word or phrase that is most nearly *opposite* in meaning. Circle the letter of your choice.

1. pernicious
   a. deadly
   b. beneficial
   c. pleasant
   d. polite

2. augmenting
   a. boring a hole
   b. expanding
   c. reducing
   d. bearing ill will

3. grievance
   a. gratitude
   b. sadness
   c. complaint
   d. generosity

4. transgression
   a. a good deed
   b. the crossing of a valley
   c. a passage through something
   d. contraction

5. heretics
   a. officials
   b. the faithful
   c. the poor
   d. enemies

The Tragedy of Romeo and Juliet, Act I   **181**

The Tragedy of Romeo and Juliet, **Act I,** by William Shakespeare

Build Grammar Skills: Pronoun Case in Elliptical Clauses

In an **elliptical clause,** some words are omitted because they are understood. In selecting the case of the pronoun in an elliptical clause, you must know what the unstated words are. In the following examples, the unstated words are in brackets.

> Mary ordered the same sandwich as *he* [did].
> Jack likes mustard better than *I* [like mustard].
> The waiter brought Sally the same dessert as [he brought] *her.*

Notice that elliptical clauses are often used to draw comparisons. In elliptical clauses beginning with *than* or *as,* use the form of the pronoun that you would use if the clause were fully stated.

To help choose the correct pronoun case, first say the unstated clause to yourself. Doing so will allow you "hear" the agreement more clearly. If the words left out come *after* the pronoun, use a nominative pronoun. If the words left out come *before* the pronoun, use an objective pronoun because the pronoun will be an object.

A. Practice: Circle the pronoun that correctly completes the elliptical clause.

1. The Montagues have been as stubborn as (they, them).

2. Although Romeo has been in love with Rosaline, he discovers that he loves Juliet more than (she, her).

3. Juliet is as interested in a relationship as (he, him).

4. When talking to other Capulets, Tybalt seems more upset about Romeo's presence than (they, them).

5. Even though Paris wants to marry her, Juliet is more drawn to Romeo than (he, him).

6. I don't think anyone likes Mercutio's Queen Mab speech as much as (I, me).

7. There is another literature class that has read more Shakespeare than (we, us).

B. Writing Application: Write a pronoun that correctly completes the elliptical clause.

1. My friend Dan enjoys drama more than _____.

2. Of all his friends, he tries out for more plays than _____.

3. When Alice saw her lines, she found that the director had given Dan the same lines to practice as _____.

4. Alice was not as happy as _____ about the long hours of rehearsal.

5. I think Dan is more dedicated to drama than _____.

The Tragedy of Romeo and Juliet, **Act I,** by William Shakespeare

Reading Strategy: Using Text Aids

Most versions of Shakespeare's works include **text aids**—explanations, usually written in the margins, of words, phrases, or customs that may be unfamiliar to modern-day readers. Even with the help of text aids, the language of sixteenth-century England seems awkward to us. The key to success is to read slowly and carefully, remembering to pause where punctuation indicates, not necessarily at the end of each line.

When you come upon a numbered or footnoted text aid, read the explanation carefully and then return to the text. Reread the sentence, applying the meaning or explanation you obtained from the text aid. It might take two tries to make sense of it before you go on.

DIRECTIONS: Use the text aids to answer the following questions about what you read in Act I.

1. In your own words, tell what is happening in Verona, based on lines 1–4 of the Prologue.

   _____

   _____

   _____

2. In Scene i, as the two Montague servingmen approach the two Capulet servingmen, Sampson says, "Let us take the law of our sides; let them begin." What does he mean?

   _____

   _____

   _____

3. Later in Scene i, Benvolio and Montague talk about how unhappy Romeo has been. Then they see Romeo; Benvolio tells Montague to leave so that he can talk to Romeo alone. Montague says, "I would thou wert so happy by thy stay/To hear true shrift." Put this wish in your own words.

   _____

   _____

   _____

4. In Scene iii, Juliet's mother tells her to "Read o'er the volume of young Paris' face." Refer to that passage and, with the help of footnotes 9 and 10, restate the advice Lady Capulet gives to her daughter.

   _____

   _____

   _____

   _____

5. Romeo's last words in Scene iv prove prophetic. Why does he have misgivings? Restate the passage.

   _____

   _____

   _____

   _____

The Tragedy of Romeo and Juliet, **Act I,** by William Shakespeare

Literary Analysis: Character

Every story or play has **characters**—people or animals who take part in the action. Some characters are fully developed; the author reveals their many different traits—faults as well as virtues—to the readers. Such characters are **round characters.** Other characters are not developed. These characters, **flat characters,** may display only a single trait or quality. In Shakespeare's works, flat characters often provide comic relief.

Characters in plays may have contrasting characteristics or personalities. When they interact, the characters' contrasting traits are emphasized. Contrasting characters are called **dramatic foils.** One example in Act I is Mercutio, whose carefree attitude about love—and about being unhappy about love—contrasts with Romeo's sad, moody talk about love. Mercutio is a dramatic foil for Romeo.

DIRECTIONS: Use the chart on this page to organize what you know about the characters in Act I. List each character in the appropriate column. Then indicate whether the character is round or flat. For each round character, list two or three characteristics revealed in the play about him or her. Following are the characters you should consider, listed in order of appearance in Act I.

Sampson	Tybalt	Romeo
Gregory	Capulet	Paris
Abram	Lady Capulet	Nurse
Balthasar	Montague	Juliet
Benvolio	Lady Montague	Mercutio

Capulet (family and friends)	Round or Flat	Montague (family and friends)	Round or Flat

The Tragedy of Romeo and Juliet, Act II, by William Shakespeare

Build Vocabulary

Spelling Strategy   When adding a suffix beginning with a vowel to a word that ends in a single consonant preceded by a single vowel, do not double the final consonant. So *waver + -er* becomes *waverer* and *peril + -ous* is *perilous.* Exceptions include words of one syllable (*rob + -er = robber*) and words having their stress on the last syllable (*control + -ing = controlling*).

Using the Prefix *inter-*

A. DIRECTIONS: The prefix *inter-* is a common one. It can lend the meaning of "among," "in the midst," "located or carried on between," "shared by two or more," or "within" to the word to which it is attached. Use what you know about the prefix *inter-* to define the following words.

1. interact _____

2. intercrop _____

3. interglacial _____

4. intermission _____

5. intersect _____

Using the Word Bank

cunning	procure	vile	sallow	unwieldy
waverer	predominant	intercession	lamentable	

B. DIRECTIONS: Match each word in the left column with its definition in the right column. Write the letter of the definition on the line next to the word it defines.

____ 1. predominant   a. distressing, sad

____ 2. cunning   b. of a sickly, pale-yellowish complexion

____ 3. intercession   c. having dominating influence over others

____ 4. procure   d. one who changes or is unsteady

____ 5. vile   e. worthless, cheap, low

____ 6. sallow   f. get, obtain

____ 7. lamentable   g. cleverness, slyness

____ 8. waverer   h. awkward, clumsy

____ 9. unwieldy   i. the act of pleading in behalf of another

Unit 8: Drama

The Tragedy of Romeo and Juliet, **Act II,** by William Shakespeare

Build Grammar Skills: Using the Possessive Case of Personal Pronouns

The **possessive case** of personal pronouns shows possession before nouns and gerunds, and it can also be used alone.

Before a noun: *Their* families distrust each other.
Before a gerund: *His* marrying them is risky.
By itself: The choice was *hers.*

Be careful not to spell possessive pronouns with apostrophes or to confuse them with contractions.

Incorrect: Happiness was *their's.*
Correct: Happiness was *theirs.*
Possessive Pronoun: *Its* ending is sad.
Contraction: *It's* a sad ending.

A. Practice: Circle the possessive pronouns in the following lines, and partial lines, from *Romeo and Juliet,* Act II.

1. I have a night's cloak to hide me from their eyes . . .

2. Blind is his love and best befits the dark.

3. Thou knowest the mask of night is on my face . . .

4. I must upfill this osier cage of ours . . .

5. As mine on hers, so hers is set on mine.

6. For this alliance may so happy prove to turn your households' rancor to pure love.

7. What says he of our marriage?

B. Writing Application: Rewrite the sentences. Supply a possessive pronoun from the list to complete each sentence.

my	his	our	their
mine	her	ours	theirs
your	hers	yours	its

1. Ann and Jody are working together on _____ script for the play.

   _____

2. I was surprised when I saw the size of _____ part.

   _____

3. I asked Jeff about _____ helping me with my lines.

   _____

4. Miriam was disappointed because she had thought that part was _____.

   _____

5. We decided to work together on _____ lines.

   _____

The Tragedy of Romeo and Juliet, **Act II,** by William Shakespeare

Reading Strategy: Reading Blank Verse

As modern-day readers, we tend to view the **blank verse** of Shakespeare's plays as literature because books are more readily available to us than acting companies that can perform the plays. Gaining full meaning from reading the text, however, is more difficult than hearing it performed. The rhythm, the line endings, and the rhymes can all combine to make the *meaning* of the text a little difficult to comprehend, especially for someone who is new to Shakespeare.

DIRECTIONS: Study this passage from Act II, Scene ii, in which Juliet continues her conversation with Romeo from her bedroom window. Reread the passage a number of times. Answer the questions that follow the passage to help you unravel the meaning of some of the more difficult lines.

JULIET. What man art thou, thus bescreened in night,
So stumblest on my counsel?

ROMEO. By a name
I know not how to tell thee who I am.
My name, dear saint, is hateful to myself
Because it is an enemy to thee.
Had I it written, I would tear the word.

JULIET. My ears have yet not drunk a hundred words
Of thy tongue's uttering, yet I know the sound.
Art thou not Romeo, and a Montague?

ROMEO. Neither, fair maid, if either thee dislike.

JULIET. How camest thou hither, tell me, and wherefore?
The orchard walls are high and hard to climb,
And the place death, considering who thou art,
If any of my kinsmen find thee here.

ROMEO. With love's light wings did I o'erperch these walls;
For stony limits cannot hold love out,
And what love can do, that dares love attempt.
Therefore thy kinsmen are no stop to me.

1. Look at Juliet's first question. What would be an easier way to say "What man art thou, . . . So stumblest on my counsel?" (The footnote indicates *counsel* means "secret thoughts.")

   _____

2. Examine the lines: "The orchard walls are high and hard to climb,/And the place death, considering who thou art,/If any of my kinsmen find thee here." The first line is easily understood. Rephrase the rest of the sentence here to make sure you know what Juliet says.

   _____

3. The line "And what love can do, that dares love attempt" is missing several words that we would add in modern-day speech. Rephrase this line.

   _____

Unit 8: Drama

The Tragedy of Romeo and Juliet, Act II, by William Shakespeare

Literary Analysis: Blank Verse

Shakespeare wrote his plays largely in blank verse. **Blank verse** is a term used to label poetry written in unrhymed iambic pentameter. An **iamb** is a two-syllable unit called a foot, in which the first syllable is unstressed and the second syllable is stressed. The word *above* is an iamb, for example. "Pentameter" means that there are five such units in each line of poetry. We use ˘ to mark unstressed syllables and ´ to mark stressed syllables.

> Căn Í gŏ fórwařd whén mў héart iš hére?

Shakespeare occasionally alters the iambic rhythm. He also intersperses rhymed couplets amidst the blank verse. A **rhymed couplet** consists of two consecutive lines of poetry whose final syllables rhyme. These couplets are also in iambic pentameter. Here are two rhymed couplets from Act II, Scene ii.

> Sleep dwell upon thine eyes, peace in thy breast!
> Would I were sleep and peace, so sweet to rest!
> Hence will I to my ghostly friar's close cell,
> His help to crave and my dear hap to tell.

The end rhyme emphasizes the words of the speaker and creates a feeling of completeness. For that reason, Shakespeare often used rhymed couplets to end scenes, important speeches, and especially important or emotional dialogue.

DIRECTIONS: Mark the stressed and unstressed syllables in these lines from Act II, Scene v. Put a check mark next to the line that has one extra syllable and the line *not* written in iambic pentameter. The first line has been marked for you.

> **JULIET.** Thĕ clóck strŭck níne whĕn Í dĭd sénd thĕ núrse;
>
> In half an hour she promised to return.
>
> Perchance she cannot meet him. That's not so.
>
> O, she is lame! Love's heralds should be thoughts,
>
> Which ten times faster glide than the sun's beams
>
> Driving back shadows over low'ring hills.
>
> Therefore do nimble-pinioned doves draw Love,
>
> And therefore hath the wind-swift Cupid wings.
>
> Now is the sun upon the highmost hill
>
> Of this day's journey, and from nine till twelve
>
> Is three long hours; yet she is not come.
>
> Had she affections and warm youthful blood,
>
> She would be as swift in motion as a ball;
>
> My words would bandy her to my sweet love,
>
> And his to me.
>
> But old folks, many feign as they were dead—
>
> Unwieldy, slow, heavy and pale as lead.

The Tragedy of Romeo and Juliet, Act III, by William Shakespeare

Build Vocabulary

Spelling Strategy   Subjects and verbs must agree in person. That is why we say "I run" and "He runs." To make a verb in the present tense agree with a third-person subject, we add an -s. We generally add -es to verbs ending in ss, sh, and ch (passes, washes, touches).

Using Words From Myths

A. DIRECTIONS: Ancient Greek and Roman myths are the source of a number of important English words. For example, from the name of the Roman god of war, Mars, we get the adjective *martial*, which means "warlike." Look up the following words to discover their mythical origins. Connect the origin of each word to its modern English meaning.

1. arachnid _____

_____

2. panic _____

_____

3. museum _____

_____

4. jovial _____

_____

5. saturnine _____

_____

6. calliope _____

_____

Using the Word Bank

gallant	fray	martial
exile	eloquence	fickle

B. DIRECTIONS: Match each word in the left column with its definition in the right column. Write the letter of the definition on the line next to the word it defines.

____ 1. gallant   a. noisy fight

____ 2. fray   b. changeable

____ 3. martial   c. brave and noble

____ 4. exile   d. speech that is vivid, forceful, graceful, and persuasive

____ 5. eloquence   e. military

____ 6. fickle   f. banish

Unit 8: Drama

The Tragedy of Romeo and Juliet, **Act III,** by William Shakespeare

Build Grammar Skills: *Who* and *Whom*

You would probably ask a friend, "Who did you call last night?" Even though "Whom did you call?" would be more correct, the use of *who* in informal speech is often acceptable. However, in formal speech and writing, it is important to use *who* and *whom* correctly.

The pronoun **who** functions as the subject of a verb.

> **Subject:** *Who* will take charge?
> The discussion is about *who* will take charge.

[In both examples, *who* is the subject of the verb *will take*.]

The pronoun **whom** serves as the object of a verb or as an object of a preposition.

> **Object of preposition:** The discussion is about *whom?*

> **Object of verb:** The discussion is about Gina, *whom* we told to take charge.

[In the first example, *whom* is the object of the preposition *about*. In the second example, *whom* is a direct object of the verb *told:* we told *whom*.]

To test whether you need *who* or *whom* in a sentence, turn the sentence around and try to replace the word in question with the word *him* or *her* or *he* or *she*. If *he* or *she* fits, use *who*. For example: In "*Who* will take charge?" *She* will take charge. On the other hand, "The discussion is about *whom?*" "about *him*" (not *he*), so *whom* is the choice for that sentence.

A. Practice: Circle the pronoun that correctly completes each sentence. Then label the pronoun S if it is a subject, OV if it is the object of a verb, or OP if it is the object of a preposition.

1. Tybalt thrusts at Mercutio's chest, (who/whom) then turns his sword on Tybalt.

2. Tybalt returns to the scene, where Romeo, (who/whom) has just begun to think of revenge, still stands.

3. Juliet again waits for Nurse, from (who/whom) she expects news of Romeo.

4. Instead, Nurse has news of Tybalt, (who/whom) is Juliet's cousin.

5. Romeo, for (who/whom) banishment is foul punishment, says he would have preferred an actual death sentence.

6. Lady Capulet scolds Juliet, (who/whom) she had told with eagerness of her marriage to Paris.

B. Writing Application: Follow the instructions given to write sentences in which you use *who* and *whom* correctly.

1. Use the pronoun *who* as the subject of a sentence about Capulet.

_____

2. Use *whom* as the object of a verb in a sentence about Juliet.

_____

3. Use *whom* as the object of a preposition in a sentence about Nurse.

_____

The Tragedy of Romeo and Juliet, **Act III,** by William Shakespeare

Reading Strategy: Paraphrasing

According to the ancient Greeks, from whom the word **paraphrase** comes, to paraphrase is "to point out alongside of." In other words, a paraphrase is a restatement of a text or passage, giving the meaning ("pointing it out") in another, more understandable form. An ancient Greek scholar would have done this in the margin of his manuscript, thus the "alongside of" part.

Paraphrasing can be a useful study tool. If you stop to paraphrase a paragraph from your social studies textbook, you might be more likely to remember the causes of the Boston Tea Party than if you don't. Don't confuse summarizing with paraphrasing, though. A summary is a highly condensed restatement of only the key ideas in a passage. A paraphrase is a restatement *in your own words* that allows for more detail than a summary.

Paraphrasing Shakespeare's material can serve two purposes. It can help you sort through the sometimes long and involved sentences. And it can help you identify and remember important ideas. Here's an example.

> **Shakespeare:** Come, come, thou art as hot a Jack in thy mood as any in Italy; and as soon to be moody, and as soon moody to be moved.
>
> **Paraphrase:** You are as hot in your anger as any other man in Italy. And you are as quick to be stirred to anger as you are eager to be stirred to anger.

DIRECTIONS: Paraphrase the following passages from Act III. Remember that a paraphrase is a restatement in your own words for clarity, not a summary.

1. Romeo, the love I bear thee can afford
   No better term than this: thou art a villain.

   _____

   _____

2. My blood for your rude brawls doth lie a-bleeding;
   But I'll amerce you with so strong a fine
   That you shall all repent the loss of mine.

   _____

   _____

   _____

3. . . . So tedious is this day
   As is the night before some festival
   To an impatient child that hath new robes
   And may not wear them.

   _____

   _____

   _____

   _____

© Prentice-Hall, Inc.

Name _____ Date _____

The Tragedy of Romeo and Juliet, **Act III,** by William Shakespeare

Literary Analysis: Soliloquy, Aside, and Monologue

An actor, with his back to the other actors on stage, speaks to the audience in a conspiratorial whisper. This is a sure sign that the script calls for an **aside,** a short remark delivered only for the audience's benefit. Asides often are sarcastic, and usually reveal a character's true feelings, unbeknown to other characters.

In the next scene, an actress is alone on stage. She delivers a long **soliloquy** to the audience. What's the difference? First, the actress is alone. Second, the speech is long, not like a short aside. In soliloquies, just as in asides, characters are likely to reveal their true feelings or opinions.

Finally, an actor delivers a **monologue** at the end of the scene. This long speech is addressed to the other characters who are on stage with him. Shakespeare's plays contain many famous monologues. Perhaps you have heard one that goes "Friends, Romans, countrymen, lend me your ears;" [*Julius Caesar,* Act III, Scene ii, line 79].

Asides, soliloquies, and monologues have different effects on the audience because of both their content and their manner of delivery. Audience members are likely to connect and sympathize with a character who utters numerous asides, feeling that the character is letting them into his or her confidence. A character who delivers monologues, on the other hand, may be viewed as authoritative or important, but the audience will probably not feel as close to such a character. When Shakespeare's characters are delivering soliloquies, they may be pouring out their hearts or plotting schemes, so the audience's response to soliloquies is varied.

DIRECTIONS: Answer the questions that follow about an aside, a soliloquy, and a monologue.

1. In Scene v, Juliet's mother refers to Romeo as a villain. Juliet's aside is "Villain and he be many miles asunder." What is the effect of the aside? Why do you think Shakespeare wrote just the one remark as an aside?

   _____

   _____

2. At the close of Scene v, Juliet delivers a soliloquy. What makes her last eight lines a soliloquy?

   _____

   _____

3. Review Juliet's final eight lines. What important thoughts does Juliet reveal? Why was it important for her to be alone when she spoke these lines?

   _____

   _____

4. Earlier in Scene v, Capulet delivers a monologue when he discovers that Juliet has rejected the match with Paris. What makes this a monologue?

   _____

   _____

5. Why was it important for Juliet and the others to hear these lines?

   _____

   _____

The Tragedy of Romeo and Juliet, **Act IV**, by William Shakespeare

Build Vocabulary

Spelling Strategy   When spelling a word that ends in an "ij" sound, you will usually spell it with -age. Examples include *foliage, luggage, tonnage, marriage, usage, damage, wreckage, voyage, advantage, postage,* and *storage.*

Using the Suffix -*ward*

The suffix -*ward* means "in the direction of," or "having a specified direction."

A. DIRECTIONS: Rewrite each of the following sentences, replacing the phrase in italics with a word having the suffix -*ward.*

1. Romeo travels *in the direction of east* to the rising sun.

   _____

2. *Bound in the direction of home* after the party, Mercutio wonders where Romeo is.

   _____

Using the Word Bank

pensive	vial	enjoined	wayward
dismal	loathsome	pilgrimage	

B. DIRECTIONS: Circle the letter of the word most nearly *similar* in meaning to each of the following Word Bank words.

1. pensive
   a. hopeful
   b. thoughtful
   c. literary
   d. vast

2. vial
   a. bottle
   b. evil
   c. instrument
   d. competitive

3. enjoined
   a. tied
   b. married
   c. allied
   d. ordered

4. wayward
   a. unruly
   b. certain
   c. departed
   d. homebound

5. dismal
   a. dismissed
   b. fateful
   c. depressing
   d. slight

6. loathsome
   a. solitary
   b. fearful
   c. disgusting
   d. ironic

7. pilgrimage
   a. icon
   b. journey
   c. duty
   d. apparel

Unit 8: Drama

The Tragedy of Romeo and Juliet, **Act IV,** by William Shakespeare

Build Grammar Skills: Degrees of Comparison

Most adjectives and adverbs have different forms to show degrees of comparison. The three **degrees of comparison** are *positive,* *comparative,* and *superlative.* The more common method of forming the comparative and superlative degree of most one- and two- syllable modifiers is to add *-er* or *-est* to the end. However, if adding *-er* or *-est* makes a word sound awkward (eagerer, for example), then *more* and *most* are used (more eager). *More* and *most* are used for all modifiers with three or more syllables, and for adverbs that end in *-ly.* Note that the comparative compares two things, while the superlative compares three or more things.

Positive: This building is *tall.*

My book is *interesting.*

Comparative: This building is *taller* than that one.

My book is *more interesting* than yours.

Superlative: This building is the *tallest* one of all.

This book is the *most interesting* one I've ever read.

Adverbs ending in *-ly*: slowly, more slowly, most slowly

Remember, however, that some modifiers have irregular comparative and superlative forms.

Irregular modifiers: bad, worse, worst   good, better, best   much, more, most

A. Practice: Underline the comparative terms in the quotations below, and identify each as positive, comparative, or superlative.

1. "Thou wrong'st it more than tears with that report."

_____

2. ". . . Environèd with all these hideous fears, And madly play..."

_____

3. "Most lamentable day, most woeful day..."

_____

4. "And all the better is it for the maid."

_____

B. Writing Application: Rewrite these sentences using the form of the modifier specified in the correct degree of comparison.

1. Juliet knows she will be _____ with Romeo than with Paris. (happy)

_____

2. Of everyone around Juliet, the nurse is the _____. (understanding)

_____

3. Paris is _____ than Juliet for their wedding day to arrive. (eager)

_____

4. Juliet contemplates that _____ things await her in the tomb. (horrible)

_____

Name _____ Date _____

The Tragedy of Romeo and Juliet, **Act IV**, by William Shakespeare

Reading Strategy: Predicting

As the tension builds in Act IV, the future of the lovers seems threatened. We begin to speculate more and more. Is there no way out? Each event in the play now crackles with expectation as the plot winds tighter. What will happen next?

Part of the pleasure of literature is **predicting** what will come to pass as a result of each event. Use the graphic organizer as you read to predict what will occur. Check your predictions later.

DIRECTIONS: In the left column are some of the major events of Act IV. As you read, consider what you think may be the outcome or consequence of each event. Write your prediction in the center column. In the right column, record the actual outcome.

Event	Prediction	Outcome
1. On her way to Friar Lawrence, Juliet meets Paris, who says the wedding "must be, love, on Thursday next."		
2. Juliet threatens suicide if the wedding goes on, and Lawrence, seeing her desperation, offers her a risky plan.		
3. Juliet returns home and calms her parents. Capulet, thrilled, makes haste with wedding preparations.		
4. Juliet worries. What if the potion fails? What if Lawrence is poisoning her to hide his role in her marriage to Romeo?		
5. She takes the potion. The Capulets and Paris find Juliet, apparently dead on her wedding day.		

Unit 8: Drama

The Tragedy of Romeo and Juliet, **Act IV**, by William Shakespeare

Literary Analysis: Dramatic Irony

In Act IV, the strain from the urgency of events begins to show. Juliet is under real pressure now as the marriage to Paris looms. Romeo is out of reach, and events seem beyond control.

As members of the audience, we know things characters don't. The difference between what we know and what they don't know often leads to **dramatic irony,** a contradiction between a character's understanding and the actual situation. When Paris says Juliet weeps "immoderately" over Tybalt's death, we know that she is not weeping for Tybalt, but for her banished Romeo. Part of the genius of Shakespeare is that he keeps these double meanings in play, line after line, often wittily. Look for them.

Sometimes dramatic irony occurs in small exchanges, as in the previous example. Sometimes it foreshadows the entire turn of events. At the end of Scene ii, Capulet is joyful that Juliet has apparently agreed to the marriage. He concludes the scene, saying that "all things shall be well, I warrant thee," even as plans and events to the contrary are developing.

DIRECTIONS: Respond to each of the following quotations by explaining the dramatic irony it creates.

1. Scene i (Lawrence asks Paris to leave.):

   FRIAR. My lord, we must entreat the time alone.
   PARIS. God shield I should disturb devotion!
   Juliet, on Thursday early will I rouse ye.

   _____

   _____

   _____

2. Scene ii (Juliet has told her father she will go through with the wedding; he begins to provision for the celebration.):

   CAPULET. My heart is wondrous light,
   Since this same wayward girl is so reclaimed.

   _____

   _____

   _____

3. Scene iii (Juliet prepares for bed.):

   LADY CAPULET. What are you busy, ho? Need you my help?
   JULIET. No, madam; we have culled such necessaries
   As are behoveful for our state tomorrow.
   . . . .
   LADY CAPULET. Good night.
   Get thee to bed, and rest: for thou hast need.

   _____

   _____

   _____

The Tragedy of Romeo and Juliet, **Act V**, by William Shakespeare

Build Vocabulary

Spelling Strategy   To form the plural of a noun ending in a *y* preceded by a consonant, change the *y* to *i* and add *es*. For example, the plural form of *ambiguity* is *ambiguities.*

Using the Prefix *ambi-*

A. DIRECTIONS: The prefix *ambi-* means "both" or "around." Using each of the following words, write a sentence in which the sense of *ambi-* is clear from the context.

1. ambidextrous (able to use both hands with equal ease) _____

_____

2. ambivalent (having conflicting feelings) _____

_____

Using the Word Bank

remnants	penury	haughty
sepulcher	ambiguities	scourge

B. DIRECTIONS: Match each word in the left column with its definition in the right column. Write the letter of the definition on the line next to the word it defines.

____ 1. remnants

____ 2. penury

____ 3. haughty

____ 4. scourge

____ 5. sepulcher

____ 6. ambiguities

a. extreme poverty

b. statements or events whose meanings are unclear

c. whip or other instrument for inflicting punishment

d. remaining persons or things

e. tomb

f. arrogant

Making Verbal Analogies

C. DIRECTIONS: The following consists of a related pair of words in CAPITAL LETTERS followed by four lettered pairs of words. Choose the pair that best expresses a relationship *similar* to that expressed in the pair in capital letters. Circle the letter of your choice.

1. WEALTH : PENURY ::
   a. displeasure : delight
   b. house : door
   c. work : fatigue
   d. pain : sensation

2. REMNANTS : LEFTOVERS ::
   a. overflow : shortage
   b. net : tennis
   c. necessities : essentials
   d. needle : sewing

3. HAUGHTY : FRIENDLY ::
   a. demonstrative : modest
   b. stroll : hike
   c. scribble : color
   d. puddle : rain

The Tragedy of Romeo and Juliet, **Act V,** by William Shakespeare

Build Grammar Skills: Agreement With Indefinite Pronouns

Indefinite pronouns are pronouns such as *everyone, anybody, each, either, neither, no one, both, many, several, any, most,* and *some.* Some indefinite pronouns are always singular, and some are always plural. Some may be either singular or plural. Look at the use of indefinite pronouns in the following examples.

Singular: *Each* of the families *hates* the other.
Plural: *Both* families *are* vengeful.

Singular: *All* of his hope *was* gone.
Plural: *All* of his friends *were* sorry.

When you write a sentence that has an indefinite pronoun as its subject, you must make sure that the *verb* agrees. Use a *singular verb* to refer to a *singular indefinite pronoun* and a *plural verb* to refer to a *plural indefinite pronoun.*

Singular: <u>Each</u> of the men <u>wants</u> Juliet to be his wife.
Plural: <u>Both</u> of the families <u>were</u> grief stricken about their children's deaths.

A. Practice: Circle the verb that agrees with the indefinite pronoun in each sentence.

1. Everyone in the Capulet and Montague families (was, were) upset.

2. Neither Romeo nor Juliet (was, were) alive at the end of the play.

3. All of the onlookers (was, were) listening to Friar Lawrence's story.

4. Most of Friar Lawrence's story (is, are) confirmed in Romeo's letters.

5. Each of the families (offer, offers) to build a statue honoring the young lovers.

B. Writing Application: Read each sentence. If it is correct, write *correct.* If there is an agreement problem, rewrite the sentence correctly.

1. Each of the actors have learned the lines perfectly.

_____

2. Both of them are expecting to get standing ovations.

_____

3. Either the stage manager or the director help us with the lighting.

_____

4. No one in the play has seen it performed before.

_____

5. Most of the girls have started reading her lines for tomorrow's rehearsal.

_____

Name _____ Date _____

The Tragedy of Romeo and Juliet, **Act V,** by William Shakespeare

Reading Strategy: Identifying Causes and Effects

Looking at a story or play in terms of its causes and effects helps us understand why events occur, why characters behave as they do, and why things turn out the way they do. Since everything has a cause and an effect, events in a story are linked. This connection is referred to as a chain of events. Consider this chain of events from Acts III and IV of *Romeo and Juliet.*

There are, of course, more events weaving their way in and out of those listed here, many of which have more than one cause and more than one effect.

| Tybalt kills Mercutio. | → | Romeo kills Tybalt. | → | Romeo is banished. | → | Juliet plots with Friar Lawrence to escape marriage to Paris. |

| Juliet drinks potion. | → | Juliet falls into deathlike sleep. | → | Juliet's family arranges her funeral. |

DIRECTIONS: As you read Act V, fill in the boxes in this chain-of-events graphic organizer. The first event of each scene is filled in for you. Note that Scene iii has two chains of events. When your chain of events is complete, notice how the events in one scene have produced effects in later scenes.

Scene i

| Balthasar arrives in Mantua. | → | | → | |

Scene ii

| Friar Lawrence's message has not been delivered. | → | |

| Paris arrives at churchyard. | → | | → | | → | | → | |

| | → | |

Scene iii (first half)

| Friar Lawrence arrives at churchyard. | → | | → | | → | | → | |

Name _____ Date _____

The Tragedy of Romeo and Juliet, **Act V,** by William Shakespeare

Literary Analysis: Tragedy

The genre of **tragedy** has existed for more than 2,000 years. It is discussed and analyzed in historical documents that date to the fourth century B.C. The tragedies that we read today take their form and structure from those of ancient Greek tragedies. Aristotle (384–322 B.C.) took a particular interest in tragedy and perhaps influenced it the most profoundly.

Aristotle held that a perfect tragedy should imitate real-life actions that excite "pity and fear." He went on to characterize the "perfect" tragic hero. He must be neither villain nor completely virtuous, but somewhere in between. His misfortune is brought about not by baseness but by some error or frailty. This human weakness or frailty is referred to as a tragic flaw, and it is supposed to be the thing that causes the hero's downfall. Examples of tragic flaws include excessive pride, ambition, greed, and so on. Ancient and modern tragedians also use fate, chance, or luck as the cause, or at least partial cause, of a hero's downfall. Blaming too much misfortune on fate was viewed by some as "less tragic," since it did not allow for a lesson to be learned. If a hero dies as a result of his ambition, we can learn that too much ambition is not a good thing. If a hero dies simply because he was under the wrong tree during a thunderstorm, then we learn nothing about life.

Aristotle identified another element that is common to most tragedies: the hero's recognition of the whole tragic situation.

Two thousand years later, William Shakespeare sits down to write a play. He has a copy of a story about two "star-crossed" lovers and has decided to adapt the story for his acting company. He doesn't follow Aristotle's "rules" exactly, but his play does contain the elements of tragedy.

DIRECTIONS: Consider the element of tragedy as they relate to *The Tragedy of Romeo and Juliet.* Answer the following questions.

1. In what ways does Romeo fit the description of the tragic hero? How does he *not* fit the description? Include a consideration of the tragic flaw. Explain your answer.

   _____

   _____

   _____

   _____

   _____

2. Shakespeare also deviates from Aristotle's idea about the hero's recognition of the whole tragic situation. In *Romeo and Juliet,* it is not the hero Romeo who experiences recognition, but other characters in the play. Who are they and when does the recognition occur?

   _____

   _____

   _____

   _____

   _____

   _____

"I Wandered Lonely as a Cloud" by William Wordsworth

Build Vocabulary

Spelling Strategy   When adding a suffix that begins with a consonant to a word that ends in silent *e*, do not drop the *e*. For example, if you add the suffix *-ly* to the Word Bank word *pensive*, you form the adverb *pensively*. When you add the suffix *-ness* to *pensive*, you form the noun *pensiveness*.

Using Poetic Contractions

William Wordsworth writes, "I wandered lonely as a cloud/That floats on high o'er vales and hills . . ." The word *o'er* (over) is an example of a **poetic contraction.** A poet will use a poetic contraction—a word in which a letter is replaced by an apostrophe—to maintain a poem's rhythm and rhyme. For instance, the full word *over* would have interrupted the iambic rhythm (soft/STRESSED) of the poem, while the contraction *o'er* fits into the poem's rhythm.

A. DIRECTIONS: Fill in the blanks of the poem with appropriate poetic contractions from the following list. In the parentheses next to each blank, write the original word(s) from which each contraction is formed.

ne'er   whene'er   'twill

_____ (_____) I hear the whistle blow,

My thoughts of freedom burn—

_____ (_____) not be long before I go,

And _____ (_____) will I return.

Using the Word Bank

host	glee	pensive	bliss

B. DIRECTIONS: The following items consist of a related pair of words in CAPITAL LETTERS followed by four lettered pairs of words. Choose the pair that best expresses a relationship *similar* to that expressed in the pair in capital letters. Circle the letter of your choice.

____   1. THOUGHTFUL : PENSIVE ::
    a. careless : careful
    b. polite : courteous
    c. warm : hot
    d. kindness : happiness

____   2. GLEE : LAUGHING ::
    a. joke : smiling
    b. tears : crying
    c. angry : shout
    d. grief : weeping

____   3. BLISS : DESPAIR ::
    a. small : tiny
    b. happy : sad
    c. excitement : boredom
    d. fun : merriment

____   4. CROWD : HOST ::
    a. flock : swarm
    b. many : mass
    c. multitude : single
    d. tree : forest

"I Wandered Lonely as a Cloud" by William Wordsworth

Build Grammar Skills: Semicolons and Colons

The **semicolon (;)** is a punctuation mark that signals the reader to pause longer than for a comma but without the finality of a period. It is used to join independent clauses that are closely related to each other but that are not already joined by a coordinating conjunction.

William Wordsworth loved the out-of-doors; his poems are often about nature.

The **colon (:)** acts mainly as an introductory device. It points ahead to additional information, directing the reader to look further. Lists, summaries, and explanations are commonly introduced by colons, as are quotations that have no "he said/she said" expressions.

The Romantic Movement in literature emphasized three human traits: the emotions, the imagination, and an appreciation of nature.

The teacher suggested a helpful strategy for approaching poetry: Read it aloud.

A. Practice: Decide where a semicolon or a colon is needed in each sentence. Write the punctuation mark and the words on either side of it on the lines given.

    Example: I read the poem yesterday it has stayed on my mind.
             yesterday; it

1. The speaker feels lonely at first he is walking alone.

    _____

2. The speaker uses the word "crowd" to describe the number of daffodils that word makes the flowers seem like people.

    _____

3. The daffodils are doing several things dancing, fluttering, and tossing their heads.

    _____

4. The flowers are a bright spot beside a lake however, they make their own waves.

    _____

5. Because I love rhythm, it's easy to guess what I like to read poetry and songs.

    _____

B. Writing Application: Write a brief paragraph describing a walk you have taken recently: to school, around your neighborhood, down a movie aisle. Include specific things you noticed, such as what you saw, heard, felt, and smelled. Use at least one semicolon and one colon in your paragraph.

_____

_____

_____

_____

_____

Name _____ Date _____

Reading Strategy: Using Your Senses

Writers use words to recreate thoughts or experiences in the minds of their readers. Poets, in particular, rely on descriptions and rich imagery to express ideas. They do this by choosing words that appeal to the **senses** of hearing, sight, touch, taste, and smell.

When you read a poem, in addition to simply trying to determine the overall meaning, imagine the sensory elements the language tries to evoke, and enjoy the experiences the poet relates. Expect to read a poem more than once in order to experience all of its sensory effects. For example, in the first lines of "I Wandered Lonely as a Cloud," the words *cloud* and *float* appeal to our sense of hearing, but also tell us about a feeling of lightness, of buoyancy.

> When all at once I saw a crowd,
> A host, of golden daffodils;

Notice how Wordsworth's use of the words *crowd* and *host* helps readers "see" a large number of flowers. The word *crowd* also suggests movement and some sound, as in a crowd of people. In addition, the word *golden* gives us a lovely, bright, rich visual image.

DIRECTIONS: Read the lines from the poem and answer the questions.

> Beside the lake, beneath the trees,
> Fluttering and dancing in the breeze.

1. What words help you picture the larger surroundings?

   _____

2. What words help you imagine how the daffodils are moving?

   _____

3. What word allows you to "feel" the weather?

   _____

> The waves beside them danced; but they
> Outdid the sparkling waves in glee;

4. What words help you picture the bright movement of the waves?

   _____

5. What word could help you "hear" a joyful sound?

   _____

"I Wandered Lonely as a Cloud" by William Wordsworth

Literary Analysis: Rhyme Scheme

A **rhyme scheme** is a regular pattern of rhyming words at the end of each line in a poem. As you read, you can indicate a poem's rhyme scheme by using a sequence of letters, assigning a new letter to each new rhyme in a poem. For example, the first stanza of "I Wandered Lonely as a Cloud" reads,

> I wandered lonely as a cloud
> That floats on high o'er vales and hills,
> When all at once I saw a crowd,
> A host, of golden daffodils;
> Beside the lake, beneath the trees,
> Fluttering and dancing in the breeze.

In this stanza, line 1 rhymes with line 3, line 2 with line 4, and line 5 with line 6; so the rhyme scheme is *ababcc*. In the poem's second stanza, Wordsworth uses the same pattern of rhyme with new rhymes, so the rhyme scheme is *dedeff*.

DIRECTIONS: Read "My Heart Leaps Up," another poem by William Wordsworth. In this poem, Wordsworth writes about his childhood fascination with the beauty of nature. He wishes to preserve this fascination and sense of wonder throughout his adult life. As you read, identify the rhyme scheme of the poem and think about how it emphasizes the poem's meaning. Then compare its rhyme scheme to the rhyme scheme of "I Wandered Lonely as a Cloud."

> **My Heart Leaps Up**
> My heart leaps up when I behold
>   A rainbow in the sky:
> So was it when my life began;
> So is it now I am a man;
> 5   So be it when I shall grow old,
>   Or let me die!
> The Child is father of the Man;
> And I could wish my days to be
> Bound each to each by natural piety.[1]
>
> 1. devotion to ordinary things in the natural world

1. What is the rhyme scheme of this poem?

_____

2. How does the rhyme scheme help to set off the last two lines of the poem?

_____

3. How does setting off the last two lines of the poem reinforce the poem's meaning?

_____

4. What other words or lines in the poem are reinforced by the poem's rhyme scheme?

_____

5. How is this poem's rhyme scheme both similar to and different from the rhyme scheme of "I Wandered Lonely as a Cloud"?

_____

"The Eagle" by Alfred, Lord Tennyson
"'Hope' is the thing with feathers—" by Emily Dickinson
"Dream Deferred" and **"Dreams"** by Langston Hughes

Build Vocabulary

Spelling Strategy   If a word of more than one syllable ends in a single consonant following a single vowel, and the accent falls on the last syllable of the base word, the final consonant is usually doubled before a suffix starting with a vowel. For example, double the final *r* in *defer* before adding the suffix *-ed: defer + -ed = deferred.*

Using Color Words

Poets use specific color words to create precise meanings and images. Tennyson's use of *azure* rather than simply *blue* creates a vivid image of a bright blue sky in just one word.

A. DIRECTIONS: Use a dictionary to find the meanings of the following color words. Rewrite each sentence, substituting the more precise color word for each underlined word.

    crimson   amber   indigo

1. The beach was bathed in the *yellow* light of sunset.

_____

2. *Blue* waves broke on the rocky shore.

_____

3. The blazing *red* sun sank slowly beneath the horizon.

_____

Using the Word Bank

azure	deferred	fester
barren	sore	abash

B. DIRECTIONS: Match each word in the numbered columns with its definition in the lettered columns. Write the letter of the definition on the line next to the word it defines.

____ 1. azure   a. embarrass   ____ 4. sore   d. fierce; cruel

____ 2. deferred   b. form pus   ____ 5. abash   e. put off

____ 3. barren   c. blue   ____ 6. fester   f. empty

Understanding Verbal Analogies

C. DIRECTIONS: The following items consist of a related pair of words in CAPITAL LETTERS followed by four lettered pairs of words. Choose the pair that best expresses a relationship *similar* to that expressed in the pair in capital letters. Circle the letter of your choice.

1. DEFERRED : POSTPONEMENT ::
   a. questioned : answer
   b. appreciated : gratitude
   c. waited : delayed
   d. returned : departure

2. INFECTION : FESTER ::
   a. doctor : hospital
   b. thunder : lightning
   c. confusing : apparent
   d. rain : flooding

Eagle/Hope/Dream   **205**

Unit 9: Poetry

"The Eagle" by Alfred, Lord Tennyson
"'Hope' is the thing with feathers—" by Emily Dickinson
"Dream Deferred" and **"Dreams"** by Langston Hughes

Build Grammar Skills: Dashes

The **dash**, a long, horizontal mark made above the writing line (—), is used to set off material in text. It signals an abrupt change of thought, dramatically sets off an interrupting idea, or sets off a summary statement.

> This poem—I just discovered it last year—is one I recommend to everyone.
> To express strong feelings—this is the goal of most poets.

A dash is also used to set off a nonessential appositive or modifier.

> Poetry about birds—for example, "The Eagle"—always interests me.
> Emily Dickinson—who never published anything in her lifetime—is considered one of America's most important poets.

A. Practice: Copy the following sentences, using one or two dashes in each.

1. I saw an eagle once in the wild what an amazing sight!

   _____

   _____

2. Megan gave a report on Emily Dickinson she has read all of the poet's work and we learned a lot.

   _____

   _____

3. Langston Hughes drew on many life experiences teacher, farmer, cook, and sailor to write his poetry.

   _____

   _____

B. Writing Application: Read these lines from the selections. Consider the effect the poet's use of a dash has on the reader. Briefly explain why the poet might have chosen to use a dash at that point in the line.

1. Does it stink like rotten meat?
   Or crust and sugar over—
   Like a syrupy sweet?

   _____

   _____

2. And sings the tune without the words—
   And never stops—at all—

   _____

   _____

"The Eagle" by Alfred, Lord Tennyson
"'Hope' is the thing with feathers—" by Emily Dickinson
"Dream Deferred" and **"Dreams"** by Langston Hughes

Reading Strategy: Paraphrasing

When you **paraphrase,** you use your own words to express what someone else has written. Often, when you paraphrase, you examine more complex language and write it in simpler language. Paraphrasing can help you understand a writer's ideas and meaning.

DIRECTIONS: Paraphrase the following quotations about dreams and hope.

1. True hope is swift, and flies with swallow's wings;
   Kings it makes gods, and meaner creatures kings.
   —William Shakespeare

   _____

   _____

2. Dreams are necessary to life.
   —Anaïs Nin

   _____

3. But I, being poor, have only my dreams;
   I have spread my dreams under your feet;
   Tread softly because you tread on my dreams.
   —William Butler Yeats

   _____

   _____

   _____

4. I know how men in exile feed on dreams of hope.
   —Aeschylus

   _____

5. Hope deferred maketh the heart sick.
   —Proverbs 13:12 (King James Version)

   _____

6. Why should there not be a patient confidence in the ultimate justice of the people? Is there any better or equal hope in the world?
   —Abraham Lincoln

   _____

   _____

Name _____ Date _____

"The Eagle" by Alfred, Lord Tennyson
"'Hope' is the thing with feathers—" by Emily Dickinson
"Dream Deferred" and **"Dreams"** by Langston Hughes

Literary Analysis: Figurative Language

Figurative language uses figures of speech—such as simile, metaphor, and personification—to state something in a fresh, unexpected way. A **simile** compares one thing to another and uses the word *like* or *as*. A **metaphor** compares one thing to another without using *like* or *as*. **Personification** gives human characteristics to an animal, object, or idea.

A. DIRECTIONS: Each of the following lines is an example of either simile, metaphor, or personification. Write *S* (simile), *M* (metaphor), or *P* (personification) in the blank.

_____ 1. Does it dry up like a raisin in the sun?

_____ 2. [The eagle] clasps the crag with crooked hands.

_____ 3. Life is a broken-winged bird.

_____ 4. "Hope" is the thing with feathers.

_____ 5. And like a thunderbolt he falls.

_____ 6. Maybe it just sags/like a heavy load.

_____ 7. [Hope] asked a crumb—of Me.

_____ 8. Life is a barren field.

B. DIRECTIONS: Write your own similes and metaphors by completing the following phrases.

1. A cat darted by like _____.

2. The wind sounded like _____.

3. Gym class is _____.

4. These flowers are as delicate as _____.

5. A snow day is _____.

C. DIRECTIONS: Create personifications by completing each sentence with a word or phrase from the box. Use each word or phrase only once.

nervousness	ancient oak	mosquito

1. Groaning about his age, the _____ slowly stretched his stiff arms.

2. The _____ had drawn up his battle plans, and I was his next target.

3. The night before my audition, _____ paid me an unwelcome visit.

"Blackberry Eating" by Galway Kinnell
"Memory" by Margaret Walker
"Woman's Work" by Julia Alvarez
"Meciendo" by Gabriela Mistral
"Eulogy for a Hermit Crab" by Pattiann Rogers

Build Vocabulary

Spelling Strategy   When adding a suffix that begins with a vowel to a word that ends in a silent *e*, drop the *e* before adding the suffix. The Word Bank illustrates the rule: *prime + ed = primed*. The rule also applies to *ripest, making,* and *squeezed.*

Using the Root *-prim-*

A. DIRECTIONS: The root *-prim-* lends to words the sense of "being first in importance or time" or "making ready." Write a sentence using each of the following words. Consult a dictionary if you are uncertain of a meaning.

1. (primer) _____

2. (prima donna)_____

Using the Word Bank

unbidden	sinister	primed	meticulously	divine

B. DIRECTIONS: Replace the italicized word or phrase in each sentence with the appropriate word from the Word Bank. Rewrite the sentence on the lines provided.

1. The candidate was *made ready* for the campaign. _____

_____

2. Dark streets on a rainy night may appear to be *ominous.* _____

_____

3. To nature lovers, the ocean's shore might be a *sacred* place._____

_____

4. We were glad that the children had returned *without being asked.* _____

_____

5. The server *very carefully* brushed the crumbs from her apron._____

_____

Unit 9: Poetry

"Blackberry Eating" by Galway Kinnell
"Memory" by Margaret Walker
"Woman's Work" by Julia Alvarez
"Meciendo" by Gabriela Mistral
"Eulogy for a Hermit Crab" by Pattiann Rogers

Build Grammar Skills: Ellipses

An **ellipsis mark (. . .)** is used to show that something has been omitted. It may signal

- words left out of a quotation
- a series that continues beyond the items named
- a hesitation in the action that suggests the passage of time
- unspoken or implied comments

Ellipses may be used in running text or at the beginning, middle, or end of a quotation. If you use an ellipsis at the end of a sentence, be sure to add the correct end punctuation as well. Review the following examples, two of which are taken from the selections.

Quotation Excerpt: The poet refers to "The wind wandering by night. . . ."

Continuing Series: Waiting for the others to hide, Juan counted one, two, three . . . until he reached one hundred.

Hesitation: I struck out . . . but became my mother's child:
a woman working at home on her art,
housekeeping paper as if it were her heart.

A. Practice: Read the following sentences. If the ellipsis is used correctly, write *C.* If the ellipsis is used incorrectly, write *I.*

_____ 1. For a week, Aaron painted with every color on his palette: red, orange, yellow, green, blue . . . at last he was done.

_____ 2. The two science projects Laura submitted, one on electricity and one on . . . magnetism, won prizes at the science fair.

_____ 3. Sarah had only one line in the play . . .

_____ 4. The teacher told Amy to read the paragraph that began, "In the early years of his life. . . ."

_____ 5. The newspaper quoted Mrs. Chandra as having said, "The whole school participated, including . . . the kindergartners through the eighth graders."

B. Writing Application: Write your own sentences, using the items that follow. Include an ellipsis in each sentence.

1. ten, nine, eight, seven _____

_____

2. he thought and thought _____

_____

3. apples, oranges, lemons _____

_____

"Blackberry Eating" by Galway Kinnell
"Memory" by Margaret Walker
"Woman's Work" by Julia Alvarez
"Meciendo" by Gabriela Mistral
"Eulogy for a Hermit Crab" by Pattiann Rogers

Reading Strategy: Picturing the Imagery

If you were to see a poster in the grocery store with the words "Eat Apples" on it, you wouldn't pay much attention. But what if the poster said "Red. Shiny. Crisp. Juicy. Sweet. Buy one today"? This second poster might have captured your attention because it uses **imagery;** it appeals to your senses. The adjectives *red* and *shiny* appeal to your sense of sight; you can *see* a red, shiny apple. *Crisp* appeals to your sense of touch; crispness is something you can feel. *Juicy* may appeal to your sense of taste or touch. And *sweet,* of course, appeals to your sense of taste. Even though the poster has no picture on it, you can certainly **picture** the apple.

Like the writer of the hypothetical poster, poets use words that appeal to our senses; they create imagery. As a reader, you owe it to yourself to *use* your senses to explore fully the images the poets create.

DIRECTIONS: Listed in the following table are examples of imagery from each of the five poems in this section. Identify the sense or senses to which each image appeals—sight, hearing, touch, smell, or taste.

Image	Sense(s) to Which Image Appeals
"Blackberry Eating"	
1. . . . the ripest berries/fall almost unbidden to my tongue,	
2. one-syllabled lumps,/which I squeeze, squinch open, . . .	
"Memory"	
3. their muttering protests, their whispered oaths,	
4. smelling a deep and sinister unrest	
"Woman's Work"	
5. She'd shine the tines of forks, . . .	
"Meciendo"	
6. The sea rocks her thousand waves.	
"Eulogy for a Hermit Crab"	
7. . . . in and out of their salty/Slough holes . . .	
8. . . . single spotlight/Of the sun . . .	

"Blackberry Eating" by Galway Kinnell
"Memory" by Margaret Walker
"Woman's Work" by Julia Alvarez
"Meciendo" by Gabriela Mistral
"Eulogy for a Hermit Crab" by Pattiann Rogers

Literary Analysis: Imagery

Have you ever said, "It's raining cats and dogs" or "I'm so hungry I could eat a horse"? These expressions create pictures in people's minds. When we talk or write in this way, we are using **imagery**—words that cause our listeners or readers to form mental pictures. To create a mental picture in a reader's mind, the image has to appeal to at least one of the reader's senses: sight, touch, hearing, taste, smell. Here's an example from "Eulogy for a Hermit Crab":

   the gritty orange curve of your claws

The word *gritty* appeals to our sense of touch. *Orange curve* and *claws* appeal to our sense of sight; we can see the orangeness and the curving claws.

DIRECTIONS: Use all of your senses as you read the following lines of poetry. Describe in full detail the complete image that each passage creates in your mind and the senses to which the passage appeals.

1. the fat, overripe, icy, black blackberries ("Blackberry Eating")

   _____

   _____

   _____

2. heads under shabby felts and parasols
   and shoulders hunched against a sharp concern ("Memory")

   _____

   _____

   _____

3. . . . when the summer sun would bar/the floor I swept till she was satisfied. ("Woman's Work")

   _____

   _____

   _____

4. The wind wandering by night rocks the wheat. ("Meciendo")

   _____

   _____

   _____

5. In a tangle of blinding spume and spray/And pistol-shot collisions. . . . ("Eulogy for a Hermit Crab")

   _____

   _____

   _____

"**Uphill**" by Christina Rossetti
"**Summer**" by Walter Dean Myers
Ecclesiastes 3:1–8, The King James Bible
"**The Bells**" by Edgar Allan Poe

Build Vocabulary

Spelling Strategy   A prefix attached to a word never affects the spelling of the original word. For example, when the prefix *mono-* is added to the word *tone*, the spelling of *tone* remains the same: *mono-* + *tone* = *monotone*.

Using the Prefix *mono-*

A. DIRECTIONS: Knowing that the prefix *mono-* means "one," write a definition for each italicized word in the following sentences.

1. In most cultures, *monogamy* is the standard for marriage._____

2. The artist creates *monochrome* works in either red or blue. _____

3. Alone on stage, the actor delivered her *monologue.* _____

4. The sullen boy gave *monosyllabic* answers of yes or no._____

Using the Word Bank

wayfarers	voluminously	palpitating	monotone	paean

B. DIRECTIONS: On the blank next to each sentence, write true or false.

_____ 1. You might encounter *wayfarers* on a vacation.

_____ 2. *Voluminously* draped curtains would leave a window almost bare.

_____ 3. A *palpitating* heart might signal a health problem.

_____ 4. Most engaging public speakers have *monotone* voices.

_____ 5. A *paean* is often played at funerals.

Understanding Antonyms

C. DIRECTIONS: The following items consist of a word in CAPITAL LETTERS followed by four lettered words or phrases. Choose the word or phrase that is most nearly *opposite* in meaning to the word in capital letters. Circle the letter of your choice.

1. PAEAN:
   a. carol
   b. dirge
   c. ditty
   d. ballad

2. PALPITATING:
   a. beating smoothly
   b. touching
   c. thumping
   d. resting

"Uphill" by Christina Rossetti
"Summer" by Walter Dean Myers
Ecclesiastes 3:1–8, The King James Bible
"The Bells" by Edgar Allan Poe

Build Grammar Skills: End Punctuation

At first glance, **end punctuation marks**—periods, question marks, and exclamation marks—seem simply to indicate the end of a sentence. However, they often signal meaning or feeling, particularly in poetry, where a few words can convey great meaning. Look at the following lines from "Uphill":

But is there for the night a resting place?
A roof for when the slow dark hours begin.

The question mark at the end of the first line indicates the speaker's anxiety. The next line, a reply to the speaker's question, ends with a period and conveys reassurance and comfort.

A. Practice: Write a word or phrase to describe the feeling or meaning that the end punctuation indicates.

1. There are no vacant rooms at the inn? _____

2. There are no vacant rooms at the inn. _____

3. Summer is here! _____

4. Summer is here? _____

5. The time to take action has come! _____

6. The time to take action has come. _____

B. Writing Application: Write responses to the following questions or statements, using end punctuation to create the feeling or meaning indicated in parentheses.

1. Are you going to the concert tonight? (excited response)

_____

_____

2. I only have a ticket for myself. (anxious response)

_____

_____

3. I told you weeks ago that you should get your own ticket. (angry response)

_____

_____

4. Don't worry; you can buy a ticket at the door. (relieved response)

_____

_____

"Uphill" by Christina Rossetti
"Summer" by Walter Dean Myers
Ecclesiastes 3:1–8, The King James Bible
"The Bells" by Edgar Allan Poe

Reading Strategy: Listening

You can best appreciate the musical quality of lyric poems if you read them aloud and listen to your speech. Listen specifically for sound devices such as rhythm, rhyme, alliteration, and onomatopoeia.

DIRECTIONS: Read the following lines from "Summer" and "The Bells," and write your answers to the questions that follow each excerpt.

> I like hot days, hot days
> Sweat is what you got days
> Bugs buzzin from cousin to cousin
> Juices dripping
> Running and ripping
> Catch the one you love days

1. What kind of rhythm do you hear and feel in these lines from "Summer"?

_____

_____

2. At what speed do you read the lines?

_____

_____

3. How does the rhythm reinforce the poem's meaning?

_____

_____

> Oh, the bells, bells, bells!
> What a tale their terror tells
>   of Despair!
> How they clang and clash and roar!
>   What a horror they outpour
> On the bosom of the palpitating air!

4. What musical quality do the sound devices in these lines from "The Bells" re-create?

_____

_____

5. How do rhyme and rhythm enhance the poem's effect?

_____

_____

_____

"Uphill" by Christina Rossetti
"Summer" by Walter Dean Myers
Ecclesiastes 3:1–8 The King James Bible
"The Bells" by Edgar Allan Poe

Literary Analysis: Lyric Poetry and Sound Devices

Lyric poetry is highly musical verse that expresses the observations and feelings of a single speaker. Poets achieve a musical quality through the use of **sound devices** such as **rhythm** (the pattern of beats or stresses in language), **alliteration** (the repetition of initial consonant sounds), **rhyme** (repetition of sounds at the ends of words), and **onomatopoeia** (use of words that imitate the sounds). For example, read the first few lines from "Summer":

I like hot days, hot days
Sweat is what you got days
Bugs buzzin from cousin to cousin

The pattern of beats and the rhymes within and at the end of lines create a musical quality. Additionally, the word *buzzin* imitates the sound made by the bugs.

In Poe's "The Bells," alliteration plays an important role. In the line "What a <u>t</u>ale of <u>t</u>error now their <u>t</u>urbulency <u>t</u>ells!" the repetition of the initial *t* sound echoes the sound of bells and creates a frantic tone.

DIRECTIONS: Analyze each poem. On the chart, note how the poems incorporate each sound device. If a poem does not use a particular sound device, write *None*.

Poem	Rhythm	Alliteration	Rhyme	Onomatopoeia
"Uphill"				
"Summer"				
Ecclesiastes 3:1–8				
"The Bells"				

"The Raven" by Edgar Allan Poe
"The Seven Ages of Man" by William Shakespeare

Build Vocabulary

Spelling Strategy   When a word ends in silent *e*, drop the e when adding a suffix that
begins with a vowel. For example, beguile + *-ing* = beguiling.

Using the Word Root *-sol-*

The word root *-sol-* comes from the Latin word *solus*, which means "alone". The Word Bank
word *desolate*, which means "deserted" or "abandoned," contains the root *-sol-*. When someone
feels desolate, he or she feels completely alone, deserted, or abandoned.

A. DIRECTIONS: Use what you know about the root *-sol-*, meaning "alone," and the context of
each sentence to define each italicized word.

1. In his *soliloquy*, the character revealed his thoughts about love and death.

   _____

2. Free to journey where she wished, the *solitary* cyclist pedaled along the winding coast.

   _____

3. Before performing, the piano *soloist* limbered his fingers by playing sets of scales.

   _____

Using the Word Bank

quaint	beguiling	respite	desolate
pallid	woeful	treble	

Using Antonyms

B. DIRECTIONS: Choose the word or phrase that is most nearly *opposite* in meaning to the Word
Bank word. Write the letter of your choice on the line provided.

____ 1. pallid
   a. flushed
   b. pale
   c. golden
   d. ashy

____ 2. woeful
   a. excited
   b. angry
   c. joyous
   d. dejected

____ 3. quaint
   a. uneven
   b. curious
   c. old-fashioned
   d. ordinary

____ 4. beguiling
   a. bewitching
   b. repelling
   c. charming
   d. deceiving

____ 5. desolate
   a. deserted
   b. dry
   c. popular
   d. abandoned

____ 6. respite
   a. pressure
   b. jealousy
   c. pleasure
   d. relief

____ 7. treble
   a. triple
   b. difficult
   c. alto
   d. high

Unit 9: Poetry

"The Raven" by Edgar Allan Poe
"The Seven Ages of Man" by William Shakespeare

Build Grammar Skills: Punctuation With Quotation Marks

Writers use **quotation marks** when they are representing a person's exact speech, writing, or thoughts. Quotation marks are also used when writing some titles, as for a short story or a poem. When you use quotation marks in your writing, make sure to place the other punctuation marks correctly. Always place a comma or a period *inside* the final quotation marks.

> "Quoth the raven, "Nevermore."

Always place a semicolon or a colon *outside* the final quotation marks.

> Her favorite poem was "The Raven"; that is, until she read "The Bells."

Place a question mark or exclamation mark inside the final quotation marks if the end mark is part of the quotation.

> "Be that word our sign of parting, bird or fiend!" I shrieked. . . .

Place a question mark or exclamation mark outside the final quotation marks if the end mark is not part of the quotation.

> Do you prefer the poem "The Bells" or "The Raven"?

A. Practice: Read the following sentences. If the quotation is punctuated correctly, write *C*. If it is punctuated incorrectly, write *I*.

_____ 1. When the speaker hears a tapping sound, he says to himself, "Someone must be knocking at the door".

_____ 2. For suspense and terror, be sure to read "The Tell-Tale Heart."

_____ 3. The speaker shouts, "Get away from my door!"

_____ 4. The teacher asked Molly, "Have you read any of Shakespeare's other poems"?

B. Writing Application: Rewrite the paragraph, correcting any punctuation errors.

Last night, I heard a strange noise, and I said to myself, "It's probably the wind;" however, when it got louder, I asked in a trembling voice, "Who's there"? When my cat wandered into my room, I sighed, "Oh, it was only Goldie".

_____

_____

_____

_____

_____

Name _____ Date _____

Reading Strategy: Drawing Inferences About the Speaker

From what a speaker says, and how he or she says it, you can draw all sorts of inferences about a speaker's personality, attitudes and outlooks, and so on. When you **draw an inference,** you draw a conclusion about the speaker. For example, in Poe's narrative poem "The Raven," the speaker says, "And the silken, sad, uncertain rustling of each purple curtain/Thrilled me—filled me with fantastic terrors never felt before." From his words, we can infer that the speaker is terribly frightened. What else can you infer about the speakers in the poems "The Raven" and "The Seven Ages of Man"?

DIRECTIONS: Read each of the lines from "The Raven" and "The Seven Ages of Man" included in the following charts. Then, answer each question concerning what inference can be made about the speaker, his situation, attitudes, or personality traits based on those lines.

"The Raven"	Inferences About Speaker
Once upon a midnight dreary, while I pondered, weak and weary, . . .	1. What inference can be made about the speaker's state of mind? What words in the text lead you to this inference? _____ _____ _____
Eagerly I wished the morrow—vainly I had tried to borrow/ From my books surcease of sorrow—sorrow for the lost Lenore—	2. What inference can be made about the speaker's situation? _____ _____ _____

"The Seven Ages of Man"	Inferences About Speaker
All the world's a stage,/And all the men and women merely players	1. What inference can be made about the speaker's general attitude? _____ _____ _____
And then the lover,/Sighing like furnace, with a woeful ballad/Made to his mistress' eyebrow.	2. What is the speaker's attitude toward lovers? _____ _____ _____

Name _____ Date _____

"The Raven" by Edgar Allan Poe
"The Seven Ages of Man" by William Shakespeare

Literary Analysis: Narrative and Dramatic Poetry

A **narrative poem** is similar to a short story in that it tells a story and has a plot, characters, and a setting. Poe's poem "The Raven" is an example of narrative poetry.

The poem "The Seven Ages of Man," which is from Shakespeare's comedy *As You Like It,* is an example of dramatic poetry. In a **dramatic poem,** lines are spoken by one or more characters. When the dramatic poem has a single speaker who expresses his or her thoughts within a developing situation as this poem does, the poem is a **dramatic monologue.**

DIRECTIONS: As you read "The Raven" and "The Seven Ages of Man," answer the following questions.

"The Raven"

1. Who is the speaker in this narrative poem? What kind of person is the speaker?

   _____

2. What other characters figure in the poem?

   _____

3. Describe the poem's setting.

   _____

4. What story does this poem tell?

   _____

5. What conflict is central to the poem?

   _____

"The Seven Ages of Man"

1. What kind of person is the speaker of this dramatic monologue?

   _____

2. Do you think the speaker is old or young? Why?

   _____

3. What is the speaker's topic and how does he feel toward it?

   _____

4. Why do you think the speaker feels the way he does toward "the lover"?

   _____

5. What difference do you think it makes to read this poem separately and not as part of the play? What information do you not know?

   _____

   _____

"On the Grasshopper and the Cricket" by John Keats
Sonnet 30 by William Shakespeare
Three Haiku by Bashō and Chiyojo
"Hokku Poems" by Richard Wright

Build Vocabulary

Spelling Strategy   When adding a suffix to a word ending in *y* preceded by a consonant, change the *y* to *i* and then add the suffix: *drowsy* + *-ness* = *drowsiness*.

Using the Suffix *-ness*

A. DIRECTIONS: The suffix *-ness* turns an adjective into a noun indicating "the state or condition of." The situations in the left column below might cause the conditions in the right column. Match each situation to an appropriate condition. Write the letter of the condition on the line.

____ 1. staying up late   a. anxiousness

____ 2. receiving a special award b. drowsiness

____ 3. looking for a missing pet c. happiness

____ 4. getting a surge of adrenaline   d. boldness

Using the Word Bank

woe	ceasing	wrought	drowsiness

B. DIRECTIONS: Answer each question with a sentence containing a word from the Word Bank. Use each Word Bank word once.

1. After reading the haiku, what did the sculptor create?

_____

2. What did the poet feel having lost touch with his friend?

_____

3. What state might be created by listening to a cricket's chirping?

_____

4. What signals a "perfect evening" for the speaker in Bashō's poem?

_____

Understanding Verbal Analogies

C. DIRECTIONS: The following items consist of a related pair of words in CAPITAL LETTERS followed by four lettered pairs of words. Choose the pair that best expresses a relationship *similar* to that expressed in the pair in capital letters. Circle the letter of your choice.

1. WOE : MOURNER ::
   a. happy : elated
   b. greed : miser
   c. childish : pout
   d. consider : pondering

2. DROWSINESS : SLEEP ::
   a. music : piano
   b. hug : fondness
   c. inventiveness : creativity
   d. boastful : pride

"On the Grasshopper and the Cricket" by John Keats
Sonnet 30 by William Shakespeare
Three Haiku by Bashō and Chiyojo
"Hokku Poems" by Richard Wright

Build Grammar Skills: Hyphens

Hyphens are used to connect words. They are used at the ends of lines if a word must be divided. They are used to connect two-word numbers and fractions used as adjectives. Hyphens are used to connect words with the prefixes *all-*, *ex-* and *self-*, and the suffix *-elect*. Look at the following examples of how hyphens are used.

Line Break: Although writing haiku seems easy, expressing important thoughts in so few words is harder than it appears.

Two-word Number: She cooked hot dogs for twenty-five people.

Certain Prefixes: Include a self-addressed envelope with your entry.

Some compound words are connected with hyphens; use a dictionary to help identify which ones. Hyphens are used to connect a compound modifier that comes before a noun.

Compound Word: My brothers rode the merry-go-round all afternoon.
Compound Modifier: The gray-brown bird was camouflaged in the leaves.

A. Practice: Add hyphens as they are needed in words in the following sentences. Write the hyphenations. If no hyphens are needed, write *correct*.

1. Both the grasshopper and the cricket have greenish brown coloring.

   _____

2. The never ceasing round of seasons is a common topic in poetry.

   _____

3. John Keats was only twenty five when he died.

   _____

4. The poet Chiyojo studied with a well known teacher.

   _____

5. Richard is president elect of our school's poetry club.

   _____

B. Writing Application: Write a two-line summary of one of the poems. Use at least one hyphenation.

   _____

   _____

   _____

"On the Grasshopper and the Cricket" by John Keats

Sonnet 30 by William Shakespeare

Three Haiku by Bashō and Chiyojo

"Hokku Poems" by Richard Wright

Reading Strategy: Reading in Sentences

Because of a poem's requirements for line length and rhyme, lines of poems do not always form complete sentences. To understand a poem better, **read in sentences,** or pause only at punctuation marks rather than at the end of each line. For instance, look at the first four lines of Shakespeare's Sonnet 30:

> When to the sessions of sweet silent thought
> I summon up remembrance of things past,
> I sigh the lack of many a thing I sought,
> And with old woes' new wail my dear times waste:

If you read in sentences, you pause first at the end of line 2 and come to a full stop at the end of line 4. Reading these lines as a single sentence helps you understand the poem's meaning.

DIRECTIONS: Read these lines from "On the Grasshopper and the Cricket," and write your answers to the questions that follow.

> The poetry of earth is never dead:
> When all the birds are faint with the hot sun,
> And hide in cooling trees, a voice will run
> From hedge to hedge about the new-mown mead;
> 5 That is the Grasshopper's—he takes the lead
> In summer luxury,—he has never done
> With his delights; for when tired out with fun
> He rests at ease beneath some pleasant weed.

1. How does pausing only at the punctuation marks help you understand the idea expressed in lines 2–5?

   _____

   _____

   _____

2. At which points in these lines do you find the longest pauses or stops? How do you know?

   _____

   _____

   _____

3. Rewrite lines 5–8 as three complete sentences.

   _____

   _____

   _____

   _____

   _____

Unit 9: Poetry

"On the Grasshopper and the Cricket" by John Keats
Sonnet 30 by William Shakespeare
Three Haiku by Bashō and Chiyojo
"Hokku Poems" by Richard Wright

Literary Analysis: Sonnets and Haiku

A **sonnet** is a lyric poem of fourteen lines usually written in rhymed iambic pentameter (five-syllable lines in which every second syllable is accented). In a Shakespearean sonnet, the rhyme scheme is *abab cdcd efef gg.* The first four lines, or quatrain, present an idea, the next two quatrains explore the idea, and the final two lines, or couplet, reach a conclusion about the idea. A Petrarchan sonnet consists of an octave (eight lines) and a sestet (six lines). The octave has a rhyme scheme of *abbaabba,* while the sestet rhyme scheme can vary.

A **haiku** is a three-line poem in which the first and third lines have five syllables and the second line has seven syllables. Usually, a haiku presents two contrasting images whose associations create a dominant impression.

DIRECTIONS: Write your answers to the following questions.

> The poetry of earth is ceasing never:
> On a lone winter evening, when the frost
> Has wrought a silence, from the stove there shrills
> The cricket's song, in warmth increasing ever,
> And seems to one in drowsiness half lost,
> The Grasshopper's among some grassy hills.

1. What is the rhyme scheme of the lines? (Begin with *c.*) _____

2. How do you know that these are the final six lines of a Petrarchan sonnet, not a Shakespearean sonnet?

_____

_____

_____

> Temple bells die out.
> The fragrant blossoms remain.
> A perfect evening!

3. What are the two dominant images in the above haiku?

_____

_____

_____

4. What impression do the contrasting images create?

_____

_____

_____

Name _____ Date _____

Build Vocabulary

Spelling Strategy If a word of more than one syllable ends in a single consonant following a single vowel, and the accent *is not* on the last syllable, do not double the final consonant before a suffix beginning with a vowel: *plunder + -ed = plundered.*

Using Words From Myths

A. DIRECTIONS: The following words and phrases come from mythology. Use one word or phrase to complete each sentence.

calypso	helium	titanic	Trojan horse

1. Hundreds of _____ balloons floated high above the auditorium.

2. The new employee was actually a _____, sent to steal secrets from the rival company.

3. Originating in the West Indies, _____ music features lively rhythms.

4. The _____ vessel weighs over eighty tons.

Using the Word Bank

plundered	squall	dispatched	mammoth	titanic
assuage	bereft	ardor	insidious	

B. DIRECTIONS: Match each word in the left column with its definition in the right column. Write the letter of the definition on the line next to the word it defines.

____ 1. plundered   a. passion; enthusiasm

____ 2. squall   b. enormous

____ 3. dispatched   c. deprived

____ 4. mammoth   d. finished quickly

____ 5. titanic   e. took goods by force; looted

____ 6. assuage   f. brief, violent storm

____ 7. bereft   g. characterized by treachery

____ 8. ardor   h. of great size or strength

____ 9. insidious   i. calm; pacify

C. DIRECTIONS: Circle the letter of the word that best completes the meaning of each of the following sentences.

1. With their _____ voices, the sirens lured sailors to their death.
   a. mammoth   c. bereft
   b. titanic   d. insidious

2. Tiresias warned Odysseus that a horrible fate would come to him and his men if anyone _____ the cattle of the sun god.
   a. plundered   c. assuage
   b. dispatched   d. bereft

Unit 10: The Epic

The *Odyssey*, **Part 1** by Homer

Build Grammar Skills: Usage: *Like* and *As If*

The words **like** and **as if** are not interchangeable. *Like* is a preposition meaning "similar to" or "such as."

Odysseus looks and acts *like* a hero.

The term *as if* is a subordinating conjunction. Subordinating conjunctions connect two complete ideas by making one of the ideas subordinate to, or dependent upon, the other.

The Lotus-Eaters ate the flowers *as if* they were harmless.

The word *as* is also a subordinating conjunction that should not be confused with the preposition *like*.

Odysseus acts *as* he speaks—forcefully.

A. Practice: Rewrite each sentence, correctly using *like*, *as*, or *as if*.

1. _____ he traveled home, Odysseus learned a lot about himself.

_____

2. The Cyclopes were _____ uncivilized beasts.

_____

3. Cyclops crushed the men _____ they were puppies.

_____

4. Odysseus plunged the burning spike _____ a dagger into Cyclops' eye.

_____

5. _____ the Sirens sang, Odysseus and his crew passed by unharmed.

_____

6. Odysseus and his men would experience great anguish, _____ Tiresias warned.

_____

7. Odysseus and his men encountered Scylla and Charybdis _____ the island of the sirens faded into the distance.

_____

B. Writing Application: Write three sentences describing your reaction to the *Odyssey* so far. Use *like*, *as*, and *as if* at least once.

_____

_____

_____

_____

_____

_____

The *Odyssey*, Part 1 by Homer

Reading Strategy: Reading in Sentences

Like most epic poetry, the *Odyssey* is written in verse. If you **read in sentences** rather than in lines, you will better understand Homer's epic tale. Ignore line breaks and read the words as you would a novel or newspaper article, stopping only at natural breaks such as commas, dashes, semicolons, or periods.

DIRECTIONS: Read the lines from the *Odyssey* and respond to the items that follow.

> Dear friends,
>
> more than one man, or two should know those
>
> things
>
> Circe foresaw for us and shared with me,
>
> so let me tell her forecast: then we die
>
> with our eyes open, if we are going to die,
>
> 690 or know what death we baffle if we can.
>
> Sirens weaving a haunting song over the sea
>
> we are to shun, she said, and their green shore
>
> all sweet with clover; yet she urged that I
>
> alone should listen to their song. Therefore
>
> 695 you are to tie me up, tight as a splint,
>
> erect along the mast, lashed to the mast,
>
> and if I shout and beg to be untied,
>
> take more turns of the rope to muffle me. [ll. 686–698]

1. Copy Circe's warning, beginning with line 691 and ending at the word *clover* in line 693, as a single sentence.

   _____

   _____

   _____

2. Rephrase lines 686–690 in your own words.

   _____

   _____

   _____

3. Write Odysseus' words in lines 695–698 as a numbered set of directions.

   _____

   _____

   _____

   _____

Unit 10: The Epic

Name _____ Date _____

The *Odyssey*, Part 1 by Homer

Literary Analysis: The Epic Hero

In the *Odyssey*, **the epic hero** Odysseus embodies the Greek ideals of a "strong mind in a strong body." He is someone who nobly represents a balance of physical and intellectual possibilities, what a man can and should be. Homer's work influenced later generations in Greece, including the great philosophers Plato, Socrates, and Aristotle.

DIRECTIONS: Consider the adventures in the left column of the following chart. Then determine what evidence is contained in each adventure to support the position that Odysseus had superior physical and intellectual prowess. Write your answers in the chart.

Adventure	Evidence of Physical Ability	Evidence of Intellectual Prowess
1. The Lotus-Eaters		
2. The Cyclops		
3. The Sirens		
4. Scylla and Charybdis		

The *Odyssey*, Part 2 by Homer

Build Vocabulary

Spelling Strategy   When adding a suffix beginning with a vowel to words that end in silent *e*, drop the *e* and add the suffix: *bemuse + ing = bemusing.*

Using the Root *-equi-*

A. DIRECTIONS: Use what you know about the root *-equi-*, meaning "equal," to determine the meanings of the italicized words in the following sentences.

1. A traveler wants to find a town *equidistant* from his home and his destination in which to spend the night. That town will be _____.

2. If you were a careful fruit vendor who sells fruit by the pound, you would likely *equilibrate*, or _____ your scales regularly.

3. Because you are a very nervous person, your friends recommend that you strive for some *equanimity*, or _____, in your life.

4. As an architect studying weight-bearing structures, you are particularly interested in constructions that include *equilateral*, or _____, triangles.

Using the Word Bank

dissemble	lithe	incredulity	bemusing
glowering	equity	maudlin	contempt

B. DIRECTIONS: Match each word in the left column with its definition in the right column. Write the letter of the definition on the line next to the word it defines.

____ 1. dissemble   a. stupefying or muddling

____ 2. lithe   b. conceal with false appearances

____ 3. incredulity   c. supple, limber

____ 4. bemusing   d. tearfully sentimental

____ 5. glowering   e. condition of being despised

____ 6. equity   f. inability to believe

____ 7. maudlin   g. staring with anger

____ 8. contempt   h. fairness, justice

Recognizing Antonyms

C. DIRECTIONS: Each Word Bank word is followed by four words or phrases. Choose the word or phrase that is most nearly *opposite* in meaning to the word from the Word Bank.

1. lithe
   a. rough
   b. enormous
   c. stiff

2. maudlin
   a. amazed
   b. cheerful
   c. angry

3. contempt
   a. bored
   b. dissatisfied
   c. regard

Build Grammar Skills: Usage: *Among* and *Between*

The prepositions **among** and **between** are often confused because they are similar in meaning. Use *among* when referring to three or more items. Use *between* when you are referring to two items. Look at Homer's use of *among* and *between* in these lines from the *Odyssey*.

> Eumaeus crossed the court and went straight forward
> Into the megaron *among* the suitors:
>
> . . . he draws *between* his thumb and forefinger
> a sweet new string upon a peg . . .

A. Practice: Circle the word in parentheses that correctly completes the sentence.

1. Odysseus tells Telemachus that (between/among) Zeus and Athena, they need no more help.

2. Odysseus plans to find (between/among) the people in the palace those who have remained loyal to him.

3. Disguised as a beggar, Odysseus tells Penelope that her husband will return some time (between/among) this night and the next.

4. Penelope asks Odysseus that there be no anger (between/among) them.

5. Athena commands that there be peace (between/among) Odysseus and the relatives of the slain suitors.

6. What do you think will happen to the relationship (between/among) Odysseus and his wife now that they have been reunited?

B. Writing Application: Complete the following sentences about the *Odyssey*, using either *among* or *between*.

1. In ancient Greece, stories were passed around _____

_____

2. In the *Odyssey*, there is a big fight _____

_____

3. There is a strong relationship _____

_____

4. Penelope has grown very weary of living _____

_____

The *Odyssey*, Part 2 by Homer

Reading Strategy: Summarizing

A summary is a condensed, or shortened, restatement of main ideas. When you **summarize** material, use your own words. In general, a summary is one fourth to one third the length of the original material. You can use this as a guide as to whether you are including too many details in your own summary.

DIRECTIONS: After you read each section of Part 2 of the *Odyssey*, summarize the main events. Indicate *why* each event occurs. For this worksheet, use notes rather than complete sentences to record the main ideas.

Odysseus' Return to Ithaca
Argus
The Suitors
Penelope
The Challenge
Odysseus' Revenge
Penelope's Test

Name _____ Date _____

The **Odyssey, Part 2** by Homer

Literary Analysis: Epic Simile

A simile is a figure of speech used to make a comparison between two basically unlike ideas or objects. Epics often contain elaborate similes, known as **epic similes,** that can continue for several lines. Think about who or what is being compared in each of the following similes and what such a comparison suggests.

DIRECTIONS: Read Homer's epic similes that follow. Then circle the letter of the answer that best completes the sentence.

A. But the man skilled in all ways of contending,
satisfied by the great bow's look and heft,
like a musician, like a harper, when
with quiet hand upon his instrument
he draws between his thumb and forefinger
a sweet new string upon a peg; so effortlessly
Odysseus in one motion strung the bow.

1. The analogy of Homer's that most closely matches *archer : bow* is
   a. musician : instrument.
   b. peg : string.
   c. musician : harp.
   d. hand : forefinger.

2. The comparison suggests that, like the musician, Odysseus
   a. is nervous before he begins.
   b. works with a stringed instrument.
   c. is proficient in music.
   d. knows his instrument and where to get good strings.

B. Think of a catch that fishermen haul in to a half-moon bay
in a fine-meshed net from the whitecaps of the sea:
how all are poured out on the sand, in throes for the salt sea,
twitching their cold lives away in Helios' fiery air:
so lay the suitors heaped on one another.

1. The analogy of Homer's that most closely matches *Odysseus : suitors* is
   a. big fish : little fish.
   b. hunter : catch.
   c. Odysseus : enemies.
   d. fisherman : fish.

2. The comparison suggests that
   a. Odysseus was also a good fisherman.
   b. the suitors had as much chance against Odysseus as hungry fish.
   c. something fishy was going on and it remained for someone like Odysseus to expose it.
   d. the setting of much of the book is the Greek isles.

232 Selection Support

"An Ancient Gesture" by Edna St. Vincent Millay

"Siren Song" by Margaret Atwood

"Prologue" and **"Epilogue"** from *The Odyssey* by Derek Walcott

"Ithaca" by Constantine Cavafy

Build Vocabulary

Spelling Strategy When writing words ending in one consonant preceded by two vowels, do not double the final consonant before adding a suffix starting with a vowel. For example, *-ed* added to the word *defraud* forms the Word Bank word *defrauded*. Similarly, *-ing* added to the word rain forms the word *raining*, and *-able* added to the word bear forms the word *bearable*.

Using the Suffix *-esque*

The suffix *-esque* means "like" or "having the quality of." The speaker in "Siren Song" says that she does not enjoy "squatting on this island/looking picturesque and mythical." Knowing the meanings of the word *picture* and the suffix *-esque*, you can figure out that *picturesque* means "like a picture," or "pleasing to the eye."

A. DIRECTIONS: Write the definitions of the following words, using a dictionary or, if possible, your knowledge of the root words and the suffix *-esque*. Then use each word in a sentence.

1. grotesque

   definition: _____

   sentence: _____

2. statuesque

   definition: _____

   sentence: _____

3. Romanesque

   definition: _____

   sentence: _____

Using the Word Bank

beached	picturesque	tempests
amber	ebony	defrauded

B. DIRECTIONS: Match each word in the left column with its definition in the right column. Write the letter of the definition on the line next to the word it defines.

____ 1. beached   a. like a picture; pleasantly strange

____ 2. picturesque   b. hard, dark wood

____ 3. tempests   c. cheated

____ 4. amber   d. washed up and lying on a beach

____ 5. ebony   e. violent storms with strong winds

____ 6. defrauded   f. yellowish resin used in jewelry

"An Ancient Gesture" by Edna St. Vincent Millay
"Siren Song" by Margaret Atwood
"Prologue" and **"Epilogue" from** *The Odyssey* by Derek Walcott
"Ithaca" by Constantine Cavafy

Build Grammar Skills: Varying Sentence Lengths

Good writing not only provides information that readers need, but it also has a rhythm that keeps readers engaged. One way to create a rhythm in your writing is to **vary the lengths of your sentences**. Use a combination of shorter and longer sentences to eliminate choppiness and build an interesting rhythm.

If your writing contains many short sentences, try combining them with a coordinating conjunction such as *and*, *or*, or *but*. Or, use a subordinating conjunction such as *since* or *although* to create a sentence with an independent and a dependent clause.

Short Sentences: I read the poem slowly. I got a feeling for its rhythm.
Combined: I read the poem quickly, so I got a feeling for its rhythm.
Combined: Because I read the poem slowly, I got a feeling for its rhythm.

If your writing contains long, rambling sentences, try breaking them up and omitting unnecessary words.

Long Sentence: We read a whole article about the background of Derek Wolcott, and we
learned that he grew up on an island, and his poetry has lots of images from
his childhood.
Improved: We read an article about Derek Wolcott. He grew up on an island, and his poetry
contains many images from his childhood.

Practice: Improve the following passages by varying the lengths of the sentences. You might combine short sentences, break up long sentences, or both.

1. The Sirens sing a song. It must be irresistible. It always forces me to leap overboard.

   _____

   _____

   _____

2. Odysseus traveled from Troy. He hoped to arrive safely, but he had many adventures on his travels that caused him and his crew a lot of pain and bad times, but many of them survived long enough to make it home.

   _____

   _____

   _____

3. The difficult journey of Odysseus and his men to Ithaca was worthwhile because it presented challenging and valuable experiences such as fighting Cyclops and Poseidon and seeing lots of seaports and visiting Egyptian cities.

   _____

   _____

   _____

"**An Ancient Gesture**" by Edna St. Vincent Millay

"**Siren Song**" by Margaret Atwood

"**Prologue**" and "**Epilogue**" from *The Odyssey* by Derek Walcott

"**Ithaca**" by Constantine Cavafy

Reading Strategy: Comparing and Contrasting

All of these poems are based on Homer's classic epic the *Odyssey*. As you read each poem, you will notice that many important details, characters, and events in the four updated works are similar to those in the original work, and many are quite different. Noticing these similarities and differences—or **comparing and contrasting**—can help you to understand and appreciate both the modern adaptations and Homer's original epic.

DIRECTIONS: Choose one of the four selections. Use the following Venn diagram to identify similarities and differences between it and Homer's *Odyssey*. Write the differences in the outer sections of the circles and the similarities where the circles overlap.

(Selection Title)

_____

Unique Qualities

Homer's *Odyssey*

Unique Qualities

Shared Qualities

"An Ancient Gesture" by Edna St. Vincent Millay
"Siren Song" by Margaret Atwood
"Prologue" and **"Epilogue" from *The Odyssey*** by Derek Walcott
"Ithaca" by Constantine Cavafy

Literary Analysis: Contemporary Interpretations

In her poem "Siren Song," Margaret Atwood takes material from the *Odyssey* and reinterprets it, placing emphasis on feminine psychology and the nature of women. She alters Homer's description of the Sirens as grasping, evil temptresses by painting them as more complex than people think. In "Ithaca," Constantine Cavafy takes the basic patterns and elements of Homer's epic and interprets them in a way that speaks to him and to many modern readers. The poem raises questions about life and the goals that people set for themselves.

DIRECTIONS: Circle the letter of the answer that best completes the sentence.

1. In "Siren Song," the poet's interpretation of the sirens suggests that
   a. women are much more complex than they may have been given credit for.
   b. the poet herself is not very clever.
   c. men are more clever than they think they are.
   d. women enjoy the roles they play.

2. In "Siren Song," the phrase ". . . will you get me out of this bird suit?" implies that
   a. being referred to as a bird is not very flattering.
   b. women may be tired of certain costumes and appearances and of putting on an act.
   c. women are very fond of changes in fashion.
   d. women want the freedom to wear whatever they choose.

3. In "Siren Song," the use of the siren as the speaker in the poem indicates that
   a. women have their own ideas about Homer.
   b. some women can serve as leaders of groups.
   c. women do not want more control of their fate.
   d. women are more than pretty faces or pretty voices.

4. In "Ithaca" the poet sees the wanderings of Odysseus as representing
   a. a grand vacation to exotic places.
   b. the journey through life itself.
   c. a voyage of discovery made possible by such modern things as a credit card.
   d. a trip without a real purpose.

5. In "Ithaca," the lines "Always keep Ithaca fixed in your mind,/. . ./But do not hurry the voyage at all" suggest that
   a. the journey is more important than the destination.
   b. we need to know where we are going in life.
   c. everyone should have a home.
   d. some places always remain the same, no matter how other places may change.

ANSWERS
Unit 1: Spine Tinglers

"The Cask of Amontillado"
by Edgar Allan Poe

Build Vocabulary (p. 1)

A. Suggested responses:

1. The directions said to <u>precondition</u> the fabric to avoid permanent stains.

2. A select group of patrons was allowed to <u>preview</u> the exhibit.

3. The crew gave the airplane a thorough <u>preflight</u> inspection.

4. Manufacturers now <u>prefabricate</u> whole sections of buildings and then deliver them to a building site.

5. Avoid waiting in line by <u>preregistering</u>.

B. 1. c 2. d 3. e 4. g 5. h 6. b 7. a 8. f

Build Grammar Skills: Common and Proper Nouns (p. 2)

A. 1. short story; "The Cask of Amontillado"; Montresor

2. catacombs; Fortunato's

3. Fortunato; family; motto; Latin

4. main; characters; narrator

5. Allan; Poe; actors; poet; critic

B. Sample Answers:

My family celebrates Veterans' Day each year by going to the parade in downtown Chicago. My Uncle Rick served in Vietnam.

My little sister, Kelly, likes the movie *To Kill A Mockingbird*, starring Gregory Peck. She watches it on video at least once a week, but she'd love to see it at the Century Theater.

Reading Strategy: Breaking Down Confusing Sentences (p. 3)

Sample Answers:

1. Fortunato, like his countrymen, was a quack in painting and gemmary.

2. I encountered my friend at about dusk one evening during the supreme madness of the carnival season.

3. Fortunato possessed himself of my arm, and I, after putting on a mask of black silk and drawing a roquelaure closely about my person, suffered him to hurry me to my palazzo.

4. He had reached the extremity of the niche in an instant and stood stupidly bewildered, finding his progress arrested by the rock.

5. I hearkened in vain for a reply to these words.

Literary Analysis: Mood (p. 4)

1. Descriptive details: long and winding staircase; be cautious; damp ground of the catacombs. Mood: suspense, unease

2. Descriptive details: low arches; descended; descending again; deep crypt; foulness of the air caused our flambeaux rather to glow than flame. Mood: suspense

3. Descriptive details: very damp; implore you to return; positively leave you. Mood: chilling, horror

4. Descriptive details: loud and shrill screams; bursting from the throat; chained form; thrust me violently back. Mood: fear, horror

"The Most Dangerous Game"
by Richard Connell

Build Vocabulary (p. 5)

A. 1. scruples; 2. scrupulous; 3. unscrupulous

B. 1. d 2. f 3. h 4. a 5. b 6. g 7. e 8. c

C. 1. bizarre; 2. scruples; 3. futile;
4. grotesque

Build Grammar Skills: Pronouns and Antecedents (p. 6)

A. 1. You, Whitney

2. you, Whitney

3. It, sound

4. his, man's; his, man's

5. he, Ivan

6. He, general

7. me, general; he, quarry; him, quarry; he, quarry

B. 1. they

2. he

3. his

4. they, their

5. their

"The Most Dangerous Game"
by Richard Connell *(continued)*

Reading Strategy: Using Context Clues (p. 7)

1. type of pipe—puffed
2. with determination—deliberate
3. high—towers plunging upward
4. stiff, unbending—statue
5. ability to shoot—shot
6. evades, avoids—quarry, wins the game
7. old—dusty
8. anxious, restless—sleep did not visit
9. held in—air burst hotly
10. soft, muddy substance—foot sank

Literary Analysis: Suspense (p. 8)

A. Suggestions include: the bush moving; straining his eyes; surged through the weeds; pulled forward by some unseen force; holding the pack

B. Details that should not be circled: in a small town in Pennsylvania, the place is called the Davenport Theater. Students' paragraphs should use the most suspenseful details from the list.

"Casey at the Bat"
by Ernest Lawrence Thayer

Build Vocabulary (p. 9)

A. Sample sentences:

1. The coach talked loudly enough to be heard over the *tumult*.
2. The pitcher was greeted by *tumultuous* applause when he walked out to the mound.

B. 1. c 2. c 3. b 4. a

C. 1. a 2. b 3. a 4. b

Build Grammar Skills: Possessive Nouns (p. 10)

A. 1. body's; bodies'
2. woman's; women's
3. fox's; foxes'
4. igloo's; igloos'
5. class's; classes'

B. 1. crowd's cheers
2. team's chances
3. fans' anticipation
4. pitcher's skill

Reading Strategy: Summarizing (p. 11)

A. 1. c 2. b 3. a

B. Suggested responses: 1. The crowd expects the two batters before Casey to make outs. 2. Casey stills the crowd as the excitement mounts and the count goes to two strikes.

Literary Analysis: Climax and Anticlimax (p. 12)

Sample chart responses:

Story/Program: *The Light in the Sky*

Author/Director: Sheila McFie

Plot Summary: In the year 2050, an eerie light in the sky is believed to signal a visit from aliens from outer space. The inhabitants of Earth prepare to make contact with visitors from other worlds for the first time. The impending visit leads to a great deal of excitement and a frenzied debate about what it will mean for the future.

Climax/Anticlimax: It turns out that the light in the sky was not an alien visitor but a comet undetected by astronomers.

Comparison to "Casey at the Bat": The story has an anticlimax, as "Casey at the Bat" does.

"The Birds" by Daphne du Maurier

Build Vocabulary (p. 13)

A. Sample sentences:

1. The children were *fretful* at the approach of the storm.
2. The snow in the fields was a *wonderful* sight.
3. The sheep ate the entire *bucketful* in minutes.

B. 1. c 2. f 3. a 4. b 5. h 6. d 7. g 8. e

Build Grammar Skills: Reflexive and Intensive Pronouns (p. 14)

A. 1. intensive
2. reflexive
3. intensive
4. reflexive

B. 1. The villagers prepared themselves for more bird attacks.
2. Nat wanted to finish the work himself.
3. Nat's wife tried to keep herself calm by doing routine tasks.

4. In order to reach people, the birds themselves would destroy the house.

5. Nat prepared himself for the worst.

Reading Strategy: Predicting (p. 15)

Sample responses:

Make a Prediction

The number of birds may create a problem.

A bird may have hurt a child.

The gulls will begin to attack.

Birds had attacked the farm, and the Triggs are dead.

Assess Your Prediction

The birds become hostile to human beings.

Birds have gotten into the children's room.

The gulls are preparing to attack but do not attack immediately.

Correct prediction.

Literary Analysis: Foreshadowing (p. 16)

A. Suggested responses:

1. Birds are tapping at the window again.

2. The birds will eventually learn how to do these things. The author has taken care to describe in detail what the birds can't do, which suggests she wants to put this idea into the readers' heads.

B. Possible details: ominous clouds on the horizon, high winds, strange behavior by sea birds, worried looks on the faces of ship personnel, overheard conversations about lack of life preservers, passengers noticing missing pieces of safety equipment.
Possible plot: ship sinks in the storm, but passengers work together to save lives until rescue helicopters arrive.

"The Red-headed League" by Sir Arthur Conan Doyle

Build Vocabulary (p. 17)

A. 1. spectacular
2. spectacle
3. inspector
4. spectator

B. 1. c 2. f 3. h 4. a 5. b 6. d 7. e 8. g

C. 1. a 2. d

Build Grammar Skills: Coordinate Adjectives (p. 18)

A. 1. coordinate
2. not coordinate
3. coordinate
4. coordinate

B. Possible responses:

1. The tracks on the wall posed an *eerie, puzzling* mystery

2. The *dark brown* tracks didn't belong to any animal we had ever seen.

3. We began to suspect we were the victims of a *cruel, elaborate* hoax.

4. The investigation soon uncovered a *clever, fiendish* scheme.

Reading Strategy: Using Key Details (p. 19)

Possible additional chart entries:

Who: Jabez Wilson

What: proprietor, pawnbroker's shop; job at Red-headed League; League is dissolved

Where: Coburg Square; away from the shop

When: ten to two; after eight weeks

Who: John Clay

What: murderer, thief, forger

Where: City and Suburban Bank; behind the pawn shop

Literary Analysis: The Mystery (p. 20)

Sample chart entries:

Crime: mystery of the stolen necklace

Crime-solver: Standish McKee, private detective

Suspects: Miles, the butler; Madam Robinson, houseguest; Arthur France, houseguest

Suspects' motives: Miles: needs the money; Madam Robinson: covets the necklace; France: no apparent motive

Suspects' alibis: Miles: was in the pantry when crime occurred; Madam Robinson: was with Mrs. Henry, owner of necklace; France: contends he was away from the estate—alibi corroborated by tavern keeper

Clues: tavern-keeper buys new coach; France resembles description of Giscaird, the famous jewel thief; no actual customers at tavern remember France being there

"The Listeners"
by Walter de la Mare
"Beware: Do Not Read This Poem"
by Ishmael Reed
"Echo" by Henriqueta Lisboa

Build Vocabulary (p. 21)

A. Suggested responses:
Floating from the stage, the ancient tune
Fluid flowingeverupward
Lush lovely lively violins envelop'd me
Then the piccolo staccato
Its ntes wre vry shrt

B. Using the Word Bank
1. b 2. a 3. d 4. c

C. Suggested responses:
1. parliament—a governing body; parliamentary—of or having the characteristics of a parliament
2. budget—the amount of money available or required for a specific use during a certain time period; budgetary—something that is related to or connected with a budget

Build Grammar Skills: Types of Adjectives
(p. 22)

A. 1. night, noun; his, pronoun
   2. unsuspecting, verb
   3. parrot, noun

B. Sample Answers:
1. He went into the kitchen to get his morning coffee.
2. The sound of the whispering trees frightened them.
3. We watched as the gymnast regained her balance.

Reading Strategy: Using Your Senses (p. 23)
Suggested responses:
"The Listeners"
Touch: Knocking; smote upon the door
Taste: champed the grasses
Smell: forest's ferny floor; empty hall
Hearing: words of Traveler throughout; Knocking; in the silence smote; quiet; air stirred and shaken; lonely Traveler's call; stillness answering his cry; smote . . . even/Louder every word . . ./ Fell echoing; silence surged softly; plunging hoofs

Sight: moonlit door; forest's ferny floor; leaf-fringed sill; host of phantom listeners; moonlight; moonbeams; dark stair; empty hall; starred and leafy sky; shadowiness

"Beware: Do Not Read This Poem"
Touch: it has drawn in yr feet; this poem has yr eyes; this poem has his head . . . arms . . . fingersfingertips
Taste: (none)
Smell: (none)
Hearing: nobody can hear you can they?; you cant call out frm this poem
Sight: ol woman; disappeared; little girl; young woman; young woman/s husband; from the waist down; eyes; head; arms; fingers; fingertips; a space

"Echo"
Touch: rained and rained
Taste: (none)
Smell: (none)
Hearing: shrill scream; in sudden/anger; great uproar; rock echoed; strafing; steely screams; Very piercing screams!
Sight: Green parrot; Rock; forest; Thousands of parrots; From all sides/strafing space

Literary Analysis: Imagery (p. 24)
Suggested responses:
1. The dark stair is wide and made of stone. The walls, the steps, and the air feel cool. The hall has no furnishings—and the Traveler's knock sounds hollow as it bounces against the empty walls.
2. The old woman is a shadowy figure. She moves among the mirrors silently.
3. The mirror threatens to engulf the reader. The mirror is "greedy" but not violent.
4. The uproar is not friendly; it "invades." It causes animals to scream and run. Even the ground seems to make noise or tremble in the uproar.
5. The uproar continues—sharp, exotic bird noises fill the air. They seem to fall down upon the listeners like gunfire from an airplane.

"Caucasian Mummies Mystify Chinese" by Keay Davidson

Build Vocabulary (p. 25)

A. 1. pharmacist
2. anarchist
3. scientist
4. novelist
5. economist

B. 1. c 2. f 3. e 4. a 5. d 6. b

C. 1. b 2. a

Build Grammar Skills: Proper and Compound Adjectives (p. 26)

A. 1. Caucasian
2. well-preserved; European
3. Bedrock High School; well-written
4. Davidson; far-reaching; Chinese

B. Sample Answers:

1. The United States team won a lot of medals at the Olympics.
2. The wind-blown laundry smelled fresh and clean when we brought it inside.
3. The actors performed a lighthearted spoof.
4. The Canadian radio station reported the story first.
5. We took a three-hour drive to the Glacier National Park.

Reading Strategy: Finding the Main Idea (p.27)

Suggested responses:

Who? Chinese archaeologist Wang Binghua, researcher Victor Mair, other researchers

What? the discovery of Chinese mummies with Caucasian features

When? 1978–1979

Where? China's Xinjiang Province

Why? to discover important information about how Chinese civilization developed and possibly interacted with other civilizations

How? DNA analysis

Literary Analysis: News Article (p. 28)

Responses will vary.

Unit 2:   Challenges and Choices

from *A Lincoln Preface* by Carl Sandburg

Build Vocabulary (p. 29)

A. 1. hero—a brave person
heroic—pertaining to bravery
2. calorie—a measurement of energy in a food
caloric—related to the measure of energy in a food
3. optimist—a person who has a positive outlook
optimistic—having a positive outlook
4. sulfur—a yellow chemical element
sulfuric—like sulfur
5. athlete—a person physically trained in sports
athletic—related to an athlete

B. 1. d 2. g 3. b 4. e 5. f 6. c 7. a

Build Grammar Skills: Transitive and Intransitive Verbs (p. 30)

A. 1. T 2. T 3. I 4. T 5. I

B. 1. Lincoln won an election for the first time.
2. The politicians argued their positions for a week.
3. He chose his allies carefully.
4. President Lincoln wrote his speeches on his own

Reading Strategy: Establishing a Purpose for Reading (p. 31)

Sample Answers:

1. newspaper article: for information about current local, national, or international events; for a social-studies assignment
2. short story: for pleasure; for a language-arts assignment
3. comic strip: for pleasure
4. biography: to learn about a particular person's life

from *A Lincoln Preface*
by Carl Sandburg *(continued)*

5. a "how-to" book: to learn a new sport, to learn how to assemble a piece of furniture

6. a children's picture book: to entertain a young friend

Literary Analysis: Anecdotes (p. 32)

A. Suggested responses:

1. Although Lincoln valued democratic processes, he still believed that his decisions and beliefs ultimately were the most important.

2. Lincoln enjoyed the public perception of himself as an independent, sometimes unconventional, leader.

3. Lincoln's leadership abilities were so remarkable that they were praised by friends and enemies alike.

B. Suggested responses:

1. An anecdote would work well in a letter to a friend. It could reveal a personal interest or serve to recall a common experience.

2. An anecdote would not work well in a business letter, whose main purpose is to inform or request information.

3. A news report about flood victims could include an anecdote to illustrate the victims' resilience.

4. An anecdote probably does not belong in a report for biology class. Such a report establishes and explains facts.

"I Have a Dream"
by Martin Luther King, Jr.
from *Rosa Parks: My Story*
by Rosa Parks with Jim Haskins
"There Is a Longing . . ."
by Chief Dan George
"I Hear America Singing"
by Walt Whitman

Build Vocabulary (p. 33)

A. Suggested responses:

1. credence: making something believable

2. credit: entrusting something or being entrusted

3. incredible: not believable

4. credential: something that causes belief or trust

B. 1. g 2. h 3. f 4. b 5. a 6. i 7. d
8. j 9. e 10. c

Build Grammar Skills: Action Verbs and Linking Verbs (p. 34)

A. 1. have, action

2. is, linking

3. is, linking

4. was, linking

5. saw, action; took, action

B. Sample Answers:

1. Martin Luther King, Jr. felt concerned about freedom and civil rights.

2. Martin Luther King, Jr. describes his dream of all people walking together as brothers and sisters.

3. Rosa Parks was an early civil-rights activist.

4. The speaker is hopeful that he can help his people.

Reading Strategy: Responding (p. 35)

Suggested responses:

A. 1. He probably means that all people should be equal and should be able to pursue whatever they want to pursue.

2. Students may respond: acquire an education, be able to find a job, start a family, and not be restricted in what they want to do, as long as it doesn't hurt anybody.

3. He means judging people by "who" they are and how they act, not by what color they are.

4. Students may respond: I suppose I stereotype some people, especially some of the groups of people at school, by what they look like and who they hang around with. I recognize that I should judge people on an individual basis.

B. 1. hope, faith, freedom

2. Those words bring out strong feelings about the goodness of people and the possibility of all people living together peacefully.

C. 1. The audience probably felt very hopeful and energized, ready and eager to carry on the struggle for social and political justice.

2. Students may respond: The closing paragraph makes Dr. King's hopes and dreams seem possible.

Literary Analysis: Author's Purpose (p. 36)

Suggested responses:

1. The young people of the author's nation are restless; they want to be able to take a purposeful place in American society.

2. He establishes himself as a chief, then asks to have the courage of the "olden Chiefs."

3. The prayer format makes the section seem especially earnest and sincere.

4. The feeling is serious because the author is writing about the wants and needs of people who are left out of society and who want to resume a place in that society.

5. Students may respond: I think Chief Dan George's purpose was to point out how Native Americans feel about their place in society. They want to change their circumstances, but changes will have to be made by "fighting a war" with words.

"The Golden Kite, the Silver Wind" by Ray Bradbury

Build Vocabulary (p. 37)

A. 1. reclaim: to call out again

2. proclaim: to call out before or in front of

3. exclaim: to cry out or call out

B. 1. b 2. a 3. b 4. c 5. c 6. a

Build Grammar Skills: Compound Verbs (p. 38)

A. 1. groaned, wept

2. go, change

3. will quench, put

4. ran, built

5. will beautify, carry

B. 1. The Mandarin heard about the neighboring town's wall and worried about its shape.

2. The Mandarin's daughter listened to her father's concerns and suggested a solution.

3. One Mandarin saw the other's new wall and rebuilt his own.

4. The people couldn't hunt or fish anymore.

5. The two Mandarins could work together or grow even weaker.

Reading Strategy: Predicting Consequences Based on Actions (p. 39)

Suggested responses:

1. Mandarin is angered; club

Prediction: Perhaps Kwan-Si will build something to beat the club.

2. Mandarin builds city wall in shape of lake; Kwan-Si builds wall in shape of mouth

Prediction: Perhaps Kwan-Si will shape the walls to bend the needle.

3. Kwan-Si builds wall in shape of sword; Sickness spreads

Prediction: Perhaps the "winner" will be decided by the city whose population lasts the longest. Maybe it will all stop because the people just can't build anymore.

4. City grinds to a halt; Kwan-Si is carried to Mandarin's courtroom

Prediction: Mandarins might talk and come to some agreement.

5. Mandarins eat, embrace, and depart; Walls are built

Prediction: Perhaps this will be the end of the rivalry.

Literary Analysis: Fable (p. 40)

A. Suggested responses:

1. The walls get rebuilt over and over. The people begin to neglect their work. Sickness spreads. Funerals begin. The city grinds to a halt.

2. The daughter gives her father ideas for rebuilding the walls. Finally, she advises him to call Kwan-Si and propose the resolution to the problem.

3. The walls of Kwan-Si's town get rebuilt many times. The population suffers, just as the first Mandarin's people do.

4. This is the first step in the resolution of the conflict. It has only positive consequences.

5. The daughter's plan helps the two mandarins see that the towns can co-exist peacefully. They can benefit and support each other without having to "one up" each other.

"The Golden Kite, the Silver Wind"
by Ray Bradbury *(continued)*

B. Suggested responses:

1. The consequences of the Mandarin's actions are all negative until he finally begins to talk to Kwan-Si. Those negative consequences are extensive—all of the townspeople suffer.

2. The consequences of Kwan-Si's actions are negative and damaging until he talks to the first Mandarin. These negative consequences are as far-reaching as those that occurred in the first Mandarin's town.

3. At first, when she is advising her father, the consequences of her actions are negative. If she hadn't given her father any ideas, maybe the rivalry would not have gotten out of control. When she cries out for Kwan-Si to be called, the consequences are positive. This action is what brings about the rest of the resolution.

4. The negative consequences of the characters' actions are destructive behavior. The positive consequences of the characters' actions lead to cooperative behavior. These conclusions suggest the moral that people must learn to work cooperatively, or else they will perish.

"The Road Not Taken"
by Robert Frost
"New Directions" by Maya Angelou
"To be of use" by Marge Piercy

Build Vocabulary (p. 41)

A. 1. repeatedly—in a frequent, repetitious manner

2. savagely—in a savage, wild, untamed manner

3. habitually—in a regular, recurrent manner

4. excessively—in an extreme manner

B. 1. e 2. i 3. h 4. g 5. a 6. c 7. b 8. d 9. f

Build Grammar Skills: Regular Verbs (p. 42)

A. 1. present participle

2. past participle

3. past

4. present participle

5. present

B. Sample answers:

1. I poured the juice into a glass.

2. The dog chewed on the bone.

3. We amble home after school.

4. They are whispering secrets to each other.

Reading Strategy: Generating Questions From Text (p. 43)

Suggested Responses:

"The Road Not Taken"

1. The speaker must decide which path to take.

2. The speaker feels sorry that he cannot take both paths.

3. The speaker does not have an overwhelming reason for choosing one path over the other, but feels sad that he will never know what was on the other path.

"New Directions"

1. Annie does not want to be a "domestic," and she cannot work at the cotton gin or the lumber mill.

2. The job as a "domestic" will take her away from her children, and the jobs at the cotton gin and lumber mill are "off limits" because she is a woman.

3. Workers at the cotton gin and the lumber mill buy her food. People depend on Annie's business, and she is eventually able to open up her own store.

"To be of use"

1. The speaker loves people who "jump into work head first."

2. The speaker loves these people because they are productive and hardworking.

3. The speaker describes oxen pulling carts, straining in the mud; people moving in a common rhythm; and mud that is turned into useful pottery.

Literary Analysis: Figurative Language (p. 44)

Suggested responses:

1. **Concrete image:** The image of the road in the woods that the speaker chose not to take.

   Comparison: The road the speaker does not take is compared to the choices a person does not make in life, and the fact that people can never go back and make certain decisions over again.

2. **Concrete image:** The negative image of mud smearing the hands and turning to dust and the positive image of mud, like clay, being turned into something useful—shaped into pottery

   Comparison: The speaker compares dirty, useless mud and mud that can be turned into something useful to the different ways people can choose to live their lives. Work can be either useless or useful and satisfying.

3. **Concrete image:** A woman stepping off the road that she is on to cut a new path

   Comparison: The narrator compares stepping off a road to cut a new path to the idea that she refuses to conform to the old well-worn patterns and instead wants to try something different.

"Old Man of the Temple"
by R. K. Narayan

Build Vocabulary (p. 45)

A. Suggested answers:

1. The brutality of the king's laws caused great suffering, especially for people who were falsely accused.
2. The old man attributed his longevity to daily doses of milk, friendship, and laughter.
3. Known for her selfless generosity, the volunteer sparked in others the willingness to give.
4. To assure his sobriety, the designated driver drank only soft drinks or water.
5. Serena expresses her individuality by wearing purple clothes and writing poetry.
6. The severity of the winter created austere living conditions for the poor farmers.

B. 1. e 2. f 3. a 4. c 5. b 6. d

Build Grammar Skills: Adverbs (p. 46)

A. 1. always, arrow to *mystified*
2. brightly, arrow to *sparkled*
3. anxiously, arrow to *looked*
4. uncontrollably, arrow to *coughed*
5. ever, arrow to *come*
6. constantly, arrow to *interrupted*; deeply, arrow to *considered*

7. up, arrow to *drew*; forward, arrow to *dash*; down, arrow to *fell*
8. violently, arrow to *banged*

B. 1. The distance between Kumbum and Malgudi was too far to walk.
2. The driver drove the taxi smoothly.
3. It was very dark outside, but Doss was quite certain that he saw someone.
4. Doss's hands trembled uncontrollably, and he spoke in an unusually high voice.
5. The man had been violently attacked by robbers.
6. The people in the cottage had often heard knocking, but never found anyone at the door.

Reading Strategy: Distinguishing Fantasy From Reality (p. 47)

Suggested responses:

1. The doors at the temple are shut and sealed.
2. Doss insists that he saw the old man open the temple door.
3. The narrator and Doss return to the taxi.
4. Doss claims that the old man is sitting next to him and asks the narrator if the old man is permitted to come with them.
5. Doss admits he feels out of sorts and closes his eyes to rest.
6. Doss sits up suddenly and speaks in a voice that sounds like someone else's.
7. The narrator grows concerned and asks Doss what has come over him.
8. Doss claims he is eighty, complains about the "new chariots," talks about the king Vishnu Varma, and says his name is Krishna Battar.
9. The narrator bangs on the door of a nearby cottage, seeking help.
10. Krishna Battar sees Seetha and leaves Doss's body in a heap on the ground.

Literary Analysis: Fantasy (p. 48)

Suggested Responses:

1. Doss has actually been transformed into an old man.

"Old Man of the Temple"
by R. K. Narayan *(continued)*

2. The narrator knows the man is dead. The old man, ironically, finds the present situation impossible. The narrator assures the old man that he is dead but can't explain the present situation.

3. The old man is moving from his state as a ghost inhabiting Doss's body to a state of spirit that can move into the realm of the dead. The conversation is "real" but the transformation is fantasy.

4. The mysterious *it* was the old man looking for a place to rest. It had disturbed the villagers and the bullocks for a long time. The *it* disappears when the old man leaves.

"Perseus" by Edith Hamilton

Build Vocabulary (p. 49)

A. 1. mortuary: place where bodies are kept prior to burial
2. mortal wound: injury that causes death
3. immortal legend: story of enduring fame

B. 1. despair; 2. deity; 3. mortified; 4. wavering; 5. kindred; 6. revelry; 7. reconciled

Build Grammar Skills: Active and Passive Voice (p. 50)

A. 1. P; 2. A; 3. P; 4. A; 5. P; 6. P

B. 1. Danaë filled her days in the underground house with watching clouds.
2. The chest was tossed, rolled, and lifted by the wild sea.
3. Hermes and Pallas Athena helped Perseus slay the monster Medusa.
4. Perseus' flying discus fatally wounded King Acrisius.
5. The Gorgons will probably remember the day Perseus stole their shared eye.

Reading Strategy: Predicting (p. 51)

Suggested responses:

Situation: Danaë and Perseus locked in chest

Possible Outcomes: gods come to help; found by someone

Reasons for Prediction: Perseus is Zeus' son; anyone could find them

Actual Outcome: washed ashore and taken in by islanders

Situation: needs means to battle Gorgons

Possible Outcomes: uses conventional weapons and bravery; gods could assist

Reasons for Prediction: Perseus is heroic and brave; gods often help him

Actual Outcome: sword from Hermes, sandals, cap, and wallet from Hyperboreans

Situation: attack on the Gorgons

Possible Outcomes: defeats Gorgons; tricks Gorgons in some way

Reasons for Prediction: Perseus is the hero and will likely succeed

Actual Outcome: defeats Gorgons, kills Medusa

Situation: wants to rescue Andromeda

Possible Outcomes: saves her using divine aid; uses own strength

Reasons for Prediction: gods have helped Perseus; he is heroic and brave

Actual Outcome: slays monster himself

Situation: wants to rescue mother from Polydectes

Possible Outcomes: Perseus kills Polydectes; Polydectes flees in fear

Reasons for Prediction: Perseus is strong and helped by gods; Polydectes could recognize that Perseus is gods' favorite

Actual Outcome: Polydectes and his warriors turn to stone by viewing Medusa's head

Situation: returning to Acrisius

Possible Outcomes: Perseus and Acrisius reconcile; Perseus kills Acrisius from vengeance; Acrisius killed some other way to fulfill prophecy

Reasons for Prediction: story needs happy ending; Perseus has a right to be angry with Acrisius; Apollo's oracle is always right

Actual Outcome: Perseus kills Acrisius accidentally in discus contest

Literary Analysis: Hero in a Myth (p. 52)

Suggested responses:

Perseus

Natural: helpless infant; young hero; loves mother; embarrassed by poverty; sense of justice; has ambition; can fall in love

Supernatural: Zeus' son; aided by gods; invisibility; can fly with magic sandals

Other characters

Natural: Danaë; Acrisius; Polydectes; Dictys and his wife, Andromeda, Hyperboreans; Cassiopeia and Cepheus

Supernatural: Danaë; Zeus; Hermes; Athena; Gray Women; Hyperboreans; Gorgons; Medusa; sea serpent

Events

Natural: Acrisius' fear of prophecy; Danaë's love for her son; Perseus' love for his mother; Dictys' kindness; Polydectes' desire for Danaë; Perseus' embarrassment at poverty; Perseus' ambition; Perseus' attraction to Andromeda; accidental killing of Acrisius

Supernatural: Perseus conceived by Zeus; existence of Gorgons; Hermes' offer of assistance; Athena's assistance; journey to the Gray Women; flying; invisibility; battle with Medusa; slaying of sea monster; Polydectes' turning to stone

"Slam, Dunk, & Hook"
by Yusef Komunyakaa
"The Spearthrower"
by Lillian Morrison
"Shoulders" by Naomi Shihab Nye

Build Vocabulary (p. 53)

A. Suggested responses:

1. sidelined; football/soccer; made an observer
2. strike out: baseball; fail to accomplish a task
3. Monday-morning quarterback: football; hindsight
4. game plan: sports; strategy
5. get in gear: automotive; set in motion
6. aced the exam: tennis; executed perfectly

B. 1. d   2. c   3. a   4. b

Build Grammar Skills: Irregular Verbs (p. 54)

A. 1. has spun
2. knew
3. ran
4. flew
5. has said
6. have fallen

B. Sample responses:

1. The show has begun.
2. The receiver caught the football.
3. We found the lost kitten.
4. Spring is coming.
5. They have gone to the movies.

Reading Strategy: Forming Mental Images (p. 55)

Suggested responses:

1. soft breathing, warm breath on neck, heaviness from carrying child, fluttering eyelids, heartbeat
2. running, strong legs, heavy breathing, rattle of falling pole, heel ticking the bar, *whumpf* of jumper landing on the mat
3. singer's high note, ball arcing, hanging in the air, blue sky, thump and bounce as it hits the rim, suspended time
4. boys not yet men, long arms and legs, graceful, clumsy

Literary Analysis: Theme in Poetry (p. 56)

A. Suggested responses:

1. footwork/of bad angels; raises issue of good and bad
2. metaphysical; contrasts with physical nature of sport
3. When Sonny Boy's mama died; subject of death
4. Trouble was there; basketball played amidst difficulties of surroundings
5. beautiful and dangerous; playing as the players do defines entire identity

B. Suggested responses:

1. javelin of light; light versus darkness
2. singing song/her signed song; singing and song connote self-expression
3. the sprinter surge; implies growing power
4. clear the highest bar; indicates accomplishment
5. as the great crowds cry/to their heroines/Come on!; crowd exhorts and cheers success

Unit 3:   Moments of Discovery

"Children in the Woods"
by Barry Lopez

Build Vocabulary (p. 57)

A. 1. sensory; extrasensory—being outside or beyond the senses

2. ordinary; extraordinary—being outside or beyond the ordinary

3. legal; extralegal—outside of or not regulated by law

B. 1. insidious; 2. elucidate; 3. ineffable; 4. acutely; 5. extrapolation; 6. effervesce; 7. charged; 8. myriad; 9. detritus

Build Grammar Skills: Prepositions (p. 58)

A. 1. of, from, into
2. of
3. into
4. in
5. of, in
6. by
7. with, in
8. on, beside

B. *Possible answer:* Barry Lopez knows a lot about nature in the Oregon forests. He enjoys taking curious children on nature walks into the woods and talking with them about the things they find there. As he wanders through the woods, Lopez's curiosity probably leads him to inspect everything beside the streams and among the leaves.

Reading Strategy: Relating Generalizations and Evidence (p. 59)

Generalization (possible answers):

Barry Lopez has noticed details all his life.

Barry Lopez enjoys finding relationships among the things he encounters in nature.

Evidence (possible answers):

1. He states that he feels a sense of responsibility toward children.

2. Lopez takes time to take children on discovery walks in the forest.

3. Lopez helps a child carefully examine every aspect of a raccoon's jaw bone.

Literary Analysis: Reflective Essay (p. 60)

Answers should include details from the story that identify both an experience or incident and the author's reaction to or reflection on the experience. Possible examples might include

Experience: woman's comment about children noticing things

Reflection: sense of responsibility toward children, realizing how much he was affected by an adult's words

Experience: talked too much at first

Reflection: realized that children learned more when they discovered things themselves

Experience: found raccoon jaw

Reflection: thought about the relationships between things in the forest

"Rules of the Game" by Amy Tan

Build Vocabulary (p. 61)

A. 1. restaurant—French
2. alley—Middle French, from Old French
3. trace—Middle French
4. pungent—Latin
5. torture—French
6. sign—Old French
7. costume—French
8. menu—French

B. 1. c 2. e 3. a 4. f 5. d 6. b
C. 1. d 2. b

Build Grammar Skills: Prepositional Phrases (p. 62)

A. 1. of invisible (strength)
2. down the (street)
3. from this (door;) at (night)
4. during Christmas (week)
5. in a cardboard (box;) with rubber (bands)
6. with (surprise) at the (box;) under my (arm)
7. down the (sidewalk)

B. Sample responses:

1. before the storm

   It was calm before the storm.

2. until starting time

They sat nervously on the bench until starting time.

3. at the bike shop

There was a sale at the bike shop.

4. during dinner

The phone rang during dinner.

5. according to the weather report

According to the weather report, a hurricane was approaching.

Reading Strategy: Contrasting Characters (p. 63)

Students may mention some of the following:

1. Waverly was born and raised in the United States; Mrs. Jong was born and raised in China.

2. Their similarities more than their differences cause Meimei and her mother to clash. Both characters are strong-willed, proud, and stubborn, and neither is readily willing to give in to the other. Meimei is clever and determined, but Mrs. Jong is equally confident of her ideas.

3. Waverly enjoys the opportunity to mingle with the outside world as much as she enjoys winning. She is proud of her accomplishments but embarrassed by her mother's bragging. Mrs. Jong displays pride in Waverly's chess playing, makes concessions to allow Waverly to practice, and becomes angry when Waverly tells her to "stop using me to show off."

4. Waverly hopes to be a good chess player, but even more she hopes to blend in and to be "American." Mrs. Jong hopes Waverly will succeed but she disapproves of certain American standards of behavior—namely, outward displays of emotion and self-promotion. She counsels Waverly to display "invisible strength."

Literary Analysis: Generational Conflict (p. 64)

Suggested responses:

1. **Generational:** Mrs. Jong wants her children to do better, but the children don't think they are poor. **Cultural:** Mrs. Jong wants her children to know Chinese "truths."

2. **Generational:** Meimei is being wicked in an effort to belittle her mother. **Cultural:** Meimei is rebelling against her Chinese heritage.

3. **Generational:** Mrs. Jong wants the best for her daughter, and Meimei tolerates this gesture. **Cultural:** The red jade tablet is a Chinese good luck piece that Meimei does not see as important.

4. **Generational:** Mrs. Jong, as a mother, thinks she knows best and tries to advise her daughter, but, unlike her mother, Meimei understands the rules of chess. **Cultural:** Mrs. Jong continues to give daily truths.

5. **Generational:** She does not want her mother watching over her as if she were a small child. **Cultural:** Meimei's mother feels she is losing control, so she retreats to the kitchen.

"Checkouts" by Cynthia Rylant
"Fifteen" by William Stafford

Build Vocabulary (p. 65)

A. 1. bereave; to deprive, to leave in a sad state; the condition of grief because of loss

2. atone; to make amends; satisfaction given for wrongdoing

B. 1. c 2. b 3. a 4. d 5. c 6. a

Build Grammar Skills: Prepositional Phrases as Modifiers (p. 66)

A. 1. of mayonnaise; arrow to *jar*

2. through the door; arrow to *came*

3. with the orange bow; arrow to *girl*

4. blood on his hand; arrow to *blood*

5. walk to his machine; arrow to *walk*

B. Sample responses:

1. in her room
2. in the checkout line
3. about each other
4. with their dates
5. near the road
6. over the rail

Reading Strategy: Relating to Personal Experience (p. 67)

Suggested responses:

South of the Bridge on Seventeenth; bridge in local town

a motorcycle with engine running; friend or relative's motorcycle

pulsing gleam, shiny flanks, demure headlights; image of big motorcycle, possibly from film or television

indulged a forward feeling, a tremble; mechanical vibration from any machine

"Checkouts" by Cynthia Rylant
"Fifteen" by William Stafford *(continued)*

blood on his hand, was pale; recollection of victim of similar accident

called me a good man, roared away; encounter with intimidating but friendly stranger

Literary Analysis: Irony (p. 68)

1. I; She is not really suffering much, and "art" indicates pretended quality of her actions.
2. N; This is straight description. Nothing indicates exaggeration.
3. I; The house is not "perfectly beautiful" to her. She hates it.
4. N; This sentence is just an expression of motive for the boy and the girl.
5. N; This sentence is merely a sensual description of the motorcycle.
6. I; At fifteen, the indecisive boy is not yet a man, and he feels that acutely when the gruff rider, though grateful, calls him one.

"Sympathy"
by Paul Laurence Dunbar
"Caged Bird" by Maya Angelou
"We never know how high we are"
by Emily Dickinson
from *In My Place*
by Charlayne Hunter-Gault

Build Vocabulary (p. 69)

A. Possible responses:

1. The use of elevated diction can persuade readers of the author's intelligence and dedication.
2. The use of words such as *bruised, sore,* and *beats* creates a mood of oppression and defeat.

B. 1. effigies; epithets; 2. imbued; 3. keener; 4. warp; 5. perpetuated; 6. disperse

Build Grammar Skills: Preposition or Adverb? (p. 70)

A. 1. preposition
2. adverb
3. adverb, preposition
4. preposition
5. preposition, adverb

B. Sample responses:

1. <u>behind</u> the green truck
2. <u>under</u> the bed
3. <u>along</u> the side of the road
4. <u>over</u> the bridge
5. <u>in</u> the evening
6. <u>down</u> the garden path

Reading Strategy: Drawing Conclusions (p. 71)

Suggested responses:

1. You can conclude that the speaker thinks a caged bird is unhappy and longs to fly freely.
2. The speaker identifies with the caged bird—what it feels, why it beats its wing, why it sings.
3. *But* is a transition that signals a change in idea or focus.
4. The speaker feels that dreaming is essential for us to achieve all we can be.

Literary Analysis: Symbol (p. 72)

A. 1. f 2. e 3. a 4. c 5. d 6. b

B. Possible responses:

1. scales: definition—device for weighing things; symbolic—justice, balance
2. fog: definition—wet weather condition; symbolic—unclear thinking or blurred vision
3. hourglass: definition—instrument that uses flowing sand to measure time; symbolic—the passing of time
4. fire: definition—flames, heat, and light produced by burning; symbolic—passion or desire; intensity; destruction

"The Interlopers"
by Saki (H. H. Munro)

Build Vocabulary (p. 73)

A. Suggested responses:

1. doleful—full of sadness
2. dolor—grief
3. dolorous—sad
4. indolent—avoiding pain; lazy

B. 1. c 2. f 3. b 4. e 5. a 6. d

Build Grammar Skills: Different Kinds of Conjunctions (p. 74)

A. 1. and/coordinating; as though/subordinating; and/coordinating

2. not . . . but/correlative

3. and/coordinating; and/coordinating

4. when/subordinating

B. Writing Application (sample answers):

1. I'm going to the bookstore <u>because</u> I need something to read.

2. <u>Either</u> a book on history <u>or</u> a book on science interests me.

3. The store sells paperback books and hardcover books.

Reading Strategy: Identifying Causes and Effects (p. 75)

Suggested responses:

Cause: feud between families

Effect: hatred between Georg and Ulrich

Cause: strong wind

Effect: fallen beech tree

Cause: fallen beech tree

Effect: entrapment of Georg and Ulrich

Cause: being in a life-threatening situation

Effect: desire to end feud and be friends

Cause: shouts for help

Effect: pack of wolves

Literary Analysis: Conflict (p. 76)

A. 1. Ulrich and Georg patrol the land on a stormy night. A tree falls and pins both men to the ground. Attracted by the men's shouts for help, a pack of wolves races toward the men.

2. Two neighboring families have been feuding over some land for three generations. Ulrich and Georg have become personal enemies, each wishing to harm the other.

3. Despite his hatred for Georg, Ulrich is eventually moved to pity the injured man's pain. Georg silently thinks over Ulrich's offer of friendship and finally concludes that everyone would benefit if the two were to end their feud.

B. Students should identify the central conflict between person and person, for it is the senseless feud between the two families that drives the plot and forms the basis for the irony of the ending.

"The Rug Merchant"
by James A. Michener

Build Vocabulary (p. 77)

A. 1. vista; 2. visionary; 3. visit; 4. visible

B. 1. d 2. e 3. a 4. c 5. b

C. 1. d 2. c

Build Grammar Skills: Interjections (p. 78)

A. Sample responses:

1. impatience

2. admiration, wonder

3. resignation, fatigue, curiosity

4. disappointment, regret, sadness

B. Sample responses:

1. Ouch! That pan is hot!

2. Wow! You did a great job!

3. Oops! I didn't mean to do it that way.

4. Ugh! That looks awful.

Reading Strategy: Making Inferences About Characters (p. 79)

Suggested responses:

Students should list such details as leaving the rugs on Michener's floor, Zaqir's constant smile, Zaqir's willingness to sell the rugs and wait for money, Zaqir's use of Michener's check for five years to sell more rugs.

Literary Analysis: Characterization in Essays (p. 80)

Suggested responses:

1. Zaqir is a successful, friendly, and persistent salesperson.

2. Words such as, "No necessity to buy. I leave here. You study, you learn to like" show Zaqir's friendly and persistent manner. His actions are as persistent as his words. For example, Zaqir sits with Michener in the evenings, then returns the next morning for bargaining. Zaqir is constantly trying to find ways to get the rugs to Michener.

3. Michener is drawn to Zaqir because he is endearing, and in his persistence, he is never rude.

4. Zaqir is a trusting character. He is also aware enough of human nature to know who is trustworthy.

5. Michener is sharply observant and appreciative of human nature.

"Combing" by Gladys Cardiff
"Women" by Alice Walker
"maggie and milly and molly and may" by E. E. Cummings
"Astonishment" by Wisława Szymborska

Build Vocabulary (p. 81)

A. 1. fashion; The word *fashion* means "stylish dress" as well as "way," and implies extravagance as well as expense.

2. sharp; The word *sharp* carries a connotation of intensity consistent with interrogation.

3. performed; The word *performed* suggests acting in a show, whether true or not.

4. stand; The word *stand* also means resistance, lending drama to the sentence.

B. 1. c 2. d 3. a 4. b

Build Grammar Skills: Parenthetical Expression (p. 82)

A. 1. Gladys Cardiff—a poet whose work I enjoy—wrote "Combing."

2. It was this poem, not that one, that I liked better.

3. The women in these poems (they remind me of people I know) seem strong.

4. Alice Walker, by the way, writes a lot about the strong women who influenced her.

5. E. E. Cummings (his poetry is always interesting) is famous for his creative misuse of grammar conventions.

6. Wisława Szymborska, however, uses questions to catch the reader's attention.

B. Sample responses:

1. Poetry, in my opinion, is more interesting than short stories.

2. Otherwise, the car may skid on the ice.

3. It was this player—not that one—who scored the goal.

4. I've been thinking of doing some volunteer work (there are certainly a lot of opportunities) during the summer break.

Reading Strategy: Interpreting Meaning (p. 83)

Suggested responses:

From "Combing": Wet and fragrant; daughter's hair after shampoo; memory of self as child

From "Women": And ironed/starched white shirts; worked hard at domestic jobs; amount of effort necessary to support family as well as pursue goals

From "maggie and milly and molly and may": befriended a stranded star; found a starfish; someone known who was gentle and kind to animals

From "Astonishment": not in a nest; why human and not a bird; wonder, perhaps as child, at other forms of life

Literary Analysis: Moment of Insight (p. 84)

Suggested responses:

maggie: found a seashell and was content to listen to it

milly: found a starfish and liked it

molly: ran away from a crab

may: brought home a smooth stone

Insight: We see the world according to what kind of people we are.

maggie: sweet, looks for ease, escape, easily distracted

milly: loves nature, curious about starfish, open, gentle

molly: fears nature, finds differences "horrible," flees life

may: thoughtful, philosophical, curious, symbolic (keeps stone)

"The Secret Life of Walter Mitty"
by James Thurber

Build Vocabulary (p. 85)

A. 1. b   2. d   3. a   4. c

B. 1. The people waiting at the emergency veterinary clinic all looked <u>distraught</u>.

2. Crowds outside the government building chanted <u>derisive</u> slogans.

3. On occasion, Ms. Mason gave <u>inscrutable</u> answers to our questions.

4. The meteorite was <u>hurtling</u> through space toward Earth.

5. Last night's <u>cannonading</u> took its toll on the factories on the edge of town.

6. The <u>insolent</u> way in which the child looked at me made me uncomfortable.

7. She always wore her hats <u>rakishly</u>, as if she hadn't a care in the world.

8. The fact that she looked at me <u>insinuatingly</u> made me angry.

Build Grammar Skills: Complete Subjects and Predicates (p. 86)

A. Practice

1. Walter Mitty | has a lively imagination.

2. Mitty | faces a tense situation in each of his daydreams.

3. Mrs. Mitty | wonders why her husband is so absentminded.

4. Mitty | tried to take his tire chains off.

5. One daydream | occurs in a hospital waiting room

6. Dr. Remington and Dr. Pritchard-Mitford | recognize Walter Mitty as a famous surgeon.

7. Some passersby | were amused at Mitty's comment.

8. He | can't remember things on his shopping list.

9. An old magazine | triggers another daydream.

10. His wife | wants to take his temperature.

B. Writing Application

Possible responses:

1. My favorite vacation spot is on an island off the Florida coast.

2. The most interesting school club is the Herpetological Society.

3. My friend likes to sky dive.

4. Sam's sister set a new record in the long jump.

5. The two old friends went out to dinner.

Reading Strategy: Reading Back and Reading Ahead (p. 87)

Possible responses:

"Reading-Back Details":

• Mitty sat down in a big leather chair while waiting for his wife.

• He started reading a magazine article about air warfare.

• He looked at the pictures of bombers.

"Reading-Ahead Details":

• Walter Mitty imagines that he goes on a bombing mission.

• Mrs. Mitty finally finds him in the chair and taps him on the shoulder

1. *Cannonading* is an extended artillery attack.

2. The magazine story about war triggers Mitty's daydream.

3. Mrs. Mitty's tap on his shoulder rouses him from the daydream.

Literary Analysis: Point of View (p. 88)

Suggested responses:

1. The woman on the sidewalk overhears Mitty talking to himself about puppy biscuits, a comment she finds comical. If the story were written from her point of view, Mitty would be seen primarily as an odd but not troublesome person; the cause of his behavior would not be known.

2. The parking-lot attendant stops Mitty from crashing his car into another car and then humiliates him by insisting on taking Mitty's car keys. If the episode were written from the attendant's point of view, Mitty would be seen primarily as a poor driver—not only an incompetent person, but a dangerous one as well. His distracting daydreams, and the possible reasons for them, would not be explained.

"The Secret Life of Walter Mitty"
by James Thurber *(continued)*

3. Mrs. Mitty views Walter as an aging bumbling fool. She acts as though he needs to be overseen and controlled at all times, like an unruly child. Mitty's dream life would not be revealed or understood.

"The Inspector-General"
by Anton Chekhov

Build Vocabulary (p. 89)

A. Suggested responses:

1. *Synonym* means having similar meaning.
2. *Pseudonym* means a fictitious name.
3. *Patronymic* means a name formed or derived from the father's name.

B. 1. d 2. c 3. a 4. e 5. b

C. 1. a 2. c

Build Grammar Skills: Compound Verbs and Compound Subjects (p. 90)

A. Practice

1. eats, drinks
2. questions, answers
3. plots, plans
4. driver, friends
5. shouts, gestures

B. Writing Application

Possible responses:

1. The noisy neighborhood children ran and played before dinner.
2. The elephants and the hippos snuffled in their cages.
3. The linebackers blocked and tackled well.
4. My brother and his friend lifted the heavy table.
5. The sleek racing boats sliced and slammed through the waves.

Reading Strategy: Reading Between the Lines (p. 91)

Suggested responses:

1. <u>Evidence</u>: The traveler asks the driver, "Know anything about him?" and "Any good, is he?" <u>Evidence suggests</u>: The traveler is fishing for information, trying to find out how much is known about the new inspector-general.

2. <u>Evidence</u>: The driver describes the inspector's way of talking as "wheezing," to which the traveler responds, "That's not wheezing! That's the way he talks! So I gather." <u>Evidence suggests</u>: The traveler knows how the inspector-general talks but is pretending that he knows less than he does.

3. <u>Evidence</u>: The traveler is upset and offended by the driver's description of the inspector's drinking habits and asks, "How do you know all this, may I ask?" <u>Evidence suggests</u>: The traveler wants to know how information about the inspector's personal habits is leaking out to the public.

4. <u>Evidence</u>: The traveler says about the inspector, "Very cunning." <u>Evidence suggests</u>: The traveler/inspector still believes the inspector's methods are sly and undetected.

5. <u>Evidence</u>: The traveler shouts to the driver "Turn around!" <u>Evidence suggests</u>: The traveler/inspector realizes that his identity is known by all and that his surprise visit is not a surprise at all.

6. The traveler is the new inspector-general.

7. He travels incognito because he wishes to "pounce" upon the unsuspecting townspeople with a surprise inspection.

8. The traveler/inspector takes his work seriously.

9. The traveler/inspector expects his disguise and surprise inspection to be a success.

10. The traveler/inspector is an earnest man who has little idea of how matters in his life really work, such as the revelation regarding his valet and housekeeper.

Literary Analysis: Irony (p. 92)

Suggested responses:

1. <u>Type</u>: verbal irony

   <u>Contrast</u>: A contradiction occurs between the meaning of the word *good* and the driver's intended meaning.

2. <u>Type</u>: dramatic irony

   <u>Contrast</u>: There is a direct contradiction between the inspector's belief that his identity is well-hidden and the reality that everyone knows who he is.

3. Type: verbal irony

   Contrast: The traveler earnestly describes the inspector as "cunning," which is in sharp contrast to the reality of his ineffectiveness.

4. Type: dramatic irony

   Contrast: The traveler/inspector believes the townspeople will be surprised, which contradicts the fact that it is the inspector who will be surprised.

5. Type: irony of situation

   Contrast: The actual outcome directly contradicts the inspector's expectations for the success of his disguise and surprise visit.

"Go Deep to the Sewer"
by Bill Cosby
"Fly Away" by Ralph Helfer

Build Vocabulary (p. 93)

A. 1. differed from the expected; from a type of baseball pitch

2. near the end of a project or endeavor; from horse racing—the last lap of the track

3. spoke too soon; from the starting pistol in track and field

B. 1. d 2. b 3. c 4. a

Build Grammar Skills: Direct Objects (p. 94)

A. Practice

1. position
2. pattern
3. ball
4. man
5. play
6. thousands
7. friend
8. swarms
9. door
10. flies

B. Writing Application

Possible responses:

1. My dog chewed the bone happily.
2. The carpenter built a beautiful desk.
3. My brother washed the dinner dishes.

Reading Strategy: Recognizing Situational Humor (p. 95)

Suggested responses:

1. Cosby running on asphalt fields; street; Cosby, playing in street; craziness of boys unconcerned about danger

2. Taking a handoff and running a sweep; street, using cars for blockers; Cosby, prancing like a player on TV; incongruity of street instead of field, and dancing over dog dung

3. Junior diagramming plays in trash; street; Junior and other players taking it as seriously as a real championship; garbage as prop, seriousness of players in comic situation, and dialogue

4. Trying to catch football in dark; night in Philadelphia; all the players "staggering" in dark; comic attempt to catch football blindly, and enthusiasm of boys at play in silly situation.

Literary Analysis: Humorous Remembrance (p. 96)

Suggested responses:

1. Probably the entire account is more or less true. The dialogue is invented, and Cosby's details exaggerate for effect, but the boys doubtless played these games.

2. The setting brings up the serious issue of the difficult circumstances of the boys' youth, and the lack of a safe place to play.

3. They are probably real people, or based on real people. Dialogue and characteristics may be exaggerated for effect.

4. Childhood is a time of play, wherever it occurs. Children often ignore grown-up concerns, and these boys were making the best of what they had. Cosby is remembering childhood, not poverty.

5. Helfer may exaggerate some of his conversations (although he may not). Other than that, the account seems likely to be true.

6. The flies have to perform as required. We do not know whether they will do it or not until the rest of the crew does. Suspense builds until the actual moment.

7. The tale is memorable because of the unusual nature of the animals' "training" and the suspenseful nature of Helfer's account of it.

"An Entomological Study of Apartment 4A" by Patricia Volk

Build Vocabulary (p. 97)

A. 1. microfilm

2. microorganisms

3. microcomputer

4. microscopic

5. microwaves

B. 1. d 2. b 3. c 4. a 5. d

Build Grammar Skills: Indirect Objects (p. 98)

A. Practice

1. him

2. her

3. us

4. people

5. author

B. Writing Application

Possible responses:

1. She threw her teammate the pass to score.

2. Mike wrote Michelle a letter from camp.

3. I bought my brother a new video game.

4. He told his grandfather a story.

5. The class asked the teacher a question about the assignment.

Reading Strategy: Establishing a Purpose for Reading (p. 99)

Suggested responses:

Purpose: To learn about insects

Items that will help me to achieve my purpose: entomologist's facts about insects; narrator's descriptions of insects in her apartment.

Details students might list in their charts include:

• Roaches have a three-stage metamorphosis.

• German cockroaches are also called Belgian cockroaches, steam-bugs, shiners, and Yankee settlers.

• House centipedes have their front legs modified to inject venom. They live on roaches and spiders and probably other centipedes.

• Two species of certain follicle mites live around the nose and forehead of most people.

• A belostomadid, or true water bug, tastes like Gorgonzola cheese. Grubs taste like bacon.

• Centipedes don't really have a hundred legs; they have one pair per segment, and twenty to thirty segments is normal.

Literary Analysis: Feature Article (p. 100)

Suggested responses:

1. The main subject of the article is the complicated world of insects.

2. The article presents detailed information about insects during the discussions between Louis Sorkin and the narrator.

3. The article becomes a human interest story when the narrator shares her own thoughts and concerns about her insect dilemma. She also associates some of her human experiences and emotions with some of the insects.

4. The writer is trying to get readers to look at insects from a different perspective and see the insect world as a small version of the human world.

5. The article does not present straight, unbiased facts as a news article or research report would. The article focuses on the narrator's view of insects.

"Macavity: The Mystery Cat" by T. S. Eliot
"Problems With Hurricanes" by Victor Hernández Cruz
"Jabberwocky" by Lewis Carroll

Build Vocabulary (p. 101)

A. 1. frabjous

2. chortled

3. burbled

4. vorpal

B. 1. e 2. d 3. h 4. g 5. c 6. a 7. f 8. b

Build Grammar Skills: Predicate Adjectives (p. 102)

A. Practice

1. orange/color

2. respectable, crafty/Macavity

3. dishonest/cat

4. loud, furious/wind

5. beautiful, sweet/mangoes

B. Writing Application

Possible responses:

1. The early sunset was red and orange.
2. The writer's new novel is suspenseful.
3. Her tennis games are fast and skillful.
4. The snow was very heavy and wet.

Reading Strategy: Contrasting the Serious and the Ridiculous (p. 103)

Suggested responses:

"Jabberwocky"

Serious—the boy being warned by his father; the boy resting by the trees planning his adventure; the boy slaying the mighty monster

Ridiculous—invented words and creatures such as *mimsy, Jubjub bird, frumious, Tulgey, burbled,* and *galumphing.*

"Macavity: The Mystery Cat"

Serious—references to Scotland Yard and the Flying Squad; references to crime

Ridiculous—physical descriptions of Macavity; descriptions of some of Macavity's behavior, such as cheating at cards, stealing milk and jewels, and "resting, or a-licking of his thumbs,/or engaged in complicated long-division sums"; references to Macavity as the "Napoleon of Crime"

"Problems With Hurricanes"

Serious—descriptions of the wind, the noise, and the water of a hurricane

Ridiculous—references to flying bananas, mangoes, avocados, and green plantains.

Literary Analysis: Humorous Diction (p. 104)

Suggested responses:

1. The following words and phrases make the passage light and humorous: vorpal blade; the phrase *snicker-snack;* the boy "galumphing" back with the monster's head.
2. The description of Macavity cheating at cards and the description of a Peke, a dog, being stifled by Macavity create humor.
3. Humor is created by the images of destructive mangoes and plantains, and the idea that being hit by flying fruit is the "ultimate disgrace."

"Talk" by Harold Courlander and George Herzog

Build Vocabulary (p. 105)

A. Suggested responses:

1. *Recite* means "to tell again."
2. *Recall* means "to bring back from memory."
3. *Reappear* means "to show up again."
4. *Reflect* means "to throw back or mirror."

B. scowling; ford; refrain

C. 1. b 2. c 3. a

Build Grammar Skills: Predicate Nominatives (p. 106)

A. Practice

1. The storyteller is a <u>comedian</u>.
2. The inanimate objects are big <u>talkers</u>.
3. The farmer may be a <u>coward</u>.
4. The chief was a good <u>listener</u>.
5. The neighborhood men were <u>victims</u> in this amusing folk tale.

B. Writing Application

Possible responses:

1. My uncle is an actor.
2. Thomas wants to be a musician or a scientist.
3. Last year, she finally became an astronaut.
4. Samantha's grandmother was a teacher.
5. I think Peter will become a teacher.

Reading Strategy: Recognizing Illogical Situations (p. 107)

Suggested responses:

Farmer: yam, dog, palm tree, stone all talk back; animals and inanimate objects can't talk; establish fantasy element, highlight the farmer's anger at losing control of his "possessions"

Fisherman: fish trap talks; inanimate objects can't talk; increases humor, highlights fisherman's arrogance

Weaver: bundle talks; inanimate objects can't talk; further adds to absurdity

Bather: river talks; elements of nature can't talk; adds to fantasy and humor

Chief: stool talks; inanimate objects can't speak; caps humor of story, underscores the arrogance of human characters

Literary Analysis: Humorous Folk Tales
(p. 108)

Suggested responses:

1. The yam complains that the farmer never weeded it but now comes around with his digging stick. He tells the farmer to go away and leave the yam alone.

2. The yam resents the farmer, who seems to think only of his own needs and not the yam's.

3. The yam, dog, tree, and stone all use a resentful and disdainful tone with the farmer.

4. Initially, the words anger the farmer, but he eventually becomes frightened and runs away.

5. The other men first respond by acting unimpressed, as if such a situation were entirely possible and not worthy of such panic.

6. They immediately become frightened and run away from the talking object.

7. The chief tells the men they are disturbing the peace and sends them away. When the men are gone, the chief's stool comments that a talking yam is "fantastic."

8. People rarely believe anything until they experience it themselves.

"One Ordinary Day, With Peanuts"
by Shirley Jackson

Build Vocabulary (p. 109)

A. repair—to fix; irreparable—unable to be fixed

omit—to leave out; omission—something that is left out

compare—to represent as similar; incomparable—something that cannot be compared to anything else

judge—to form an opinion about, to determine or estimate; judicious—having or characterized by sound judgment or opinions

B. 1. g 2. e 3. a 4. f 5. h 6. c 7. b 8. d

Build Grammar Skills: Direct Object or Object of a Preposition? (p. 110)

A. Practice

1. door/direct object; him/object of a preposition

2. shop/object of a preposition; carnation/direct object; buttonhole/object of a preposition

3. steps/object of a preposition

4. card/direct object; name/direct object; back/object of a preposition

5. job/direct object

B. Writing Application

Sample response:

The soccer player kicked the ball into the goal.

ball/direct object; goal/object of a preposition

Reading Strategy: Questioning Characters' Actions (p. 111)

Suggested responses:

1. gives flower to young child; is trying to be friendly; mother and child happen to be in Mr. Johnson's path; yes, still apparently friendly to everyone

2. watches boy while mother supervises movers; Mr. Johnson is trying to be helpful; mother appears stressed; yes, seems to like children particularly

3. detains young woman who bumps into him; thinks she would be happier if she relaxed; woman seems rushed and uptight, displays ill humor; yes, though this action seems more bold or intrusive than previous actions

4. finds a young man to introduce to woman; thinks both would be happier if they relaxed and got acquainted; young woman's stress gave him the idea, but she did not suggest it; a still bolder action, but intentions seem kind and friendly

5. gives peanut and dollar bill to man; kindness; man asks for a dime; yes, he has been generous to others as well

Literary Analysis: Surprise Ending (p. 112)

1. Choosing a side street "at random" and pursuing an "eventful way in wide detours" does not sound like someone who goes to the same office each day. Also, the simile referring to a puppy gives a hint, since Mr. Johnson's wanderings do turn out to be similar to a curious puppy's path.

2. If he were going to a workplace where he goes every day, he wouldn't need to "decide" to go on uptown, it would just be part of his routine.

3. At this point in the story, readers believe that Johnson *is* responsible, truthful, and respectable. At the end of the story, they learn otherwise.

4. Jackson tells us that Mr. Johnson can move very quickly when he wants to. Thus far, readers haven't seen anything about Mr. Johnson that would indicate that he would ever need or want to move quickly. Also, his quick movements indicate that he is confident of the outcome of his actions.

Unit 5: Visions of the Future

from *The Road Ahead* by Bill Gates

Build Vocabulary (p. 113)

A. Suggested responses:

1. The actor simulated a fall down a hill by half rolling and half tumbling across the stage.

2. The simultaneity of my question about Mary's whereabouts and her entrance into the room was funny because they both happened at once, answering my question.

3. During the simulator portion of driver's education, we were able to learn what it feels like to be behind the wheel controlling the vehicle without actually being in a car.

B. 1. d   2. a   3. e   4. c   5. b

C. 1. c   2. c   3. a

Build Grammar Skills: Main and Subordinate Clauses (p. 114)

A. Practice

1. S   2. M   3. M   4. S   5. S   6. M   7. M   8. S

B. Writing Application

Possible responses:

1. Because I wouldn't be home in time to watch the debate, I taped it.

2. I finished my math, which is a difficult subject for me.

3. After the big thunderstorm, we saw several trees that had fallen.

Reading Strategy: Recognizing a Writer's Motives and Bias (p. 115)

Possible responses:

1. His priorities seem to include control, speed, and flexibility.

2. These priorities would bias him in favor of the new technology.

3. He may hope to generate his readers'enthusiasm so they eventually will buy the technology from him.

Literary Analysis: Expository Writing (p.116)

Suggested responses:

Facts

1. Ed Sullivan was on television at eight o'clock on Sunday nights.

2. Conventional television allows us to decide what we watch but not when we watch it.

3. In the early 1980s, the videocassette recorder gave us more flexibility.

4. Even people who rarely record television programs routinely rent movies. . . .

5. Many corporate networks already have enough bandwidth, but even in the U.S. most homes will have to make do for some time . . . with narrowband and midband access.

Personal Details

1. watching *The Ed Sullivan Show*

2. That's how I watched *The Ed Sullivan Show* thirty years ago. (i.e., synchronously)

3. I'm writing these words at home on a summer evening.

"The Machine That Won the War" by Isaac Asimov

Build Vocabulary (p. 117)

A. 1. turning around

2. walking around

3. around the pole

4. flowing around

5. talking around, as in evading

"The Machine That Won the War"
by Isaac Asimov (continued)

B. 1. e 2. g 3. a 4. f 5. c 6. d 7. b

Build Grammar Skills: Adverb Clauses and Noun Clauses (p. 118)

A. Practice

1. When he discovered the data was corrupt; adverb clause

2. that any data Multivac provided; noun clause

3. until each revealed his secrets; adverb clause

4. as if the computer had made the decisions; adverb clause

5. Whatever Swift's coin toss decided; noun clause

B. Writing Application

1. He typed his essay when the word processor was fixed.

2. Whenever it rains, the basement floods.

3. Jennifer plans to stay until the project is finished.

Reading Strategy: Identifying Relevant Details (p. 119)

Suggested responses:

1. "when we weren't at war with Deneb"; S; event that's occurred; War with Deneb is over.

2. "he was conscious only of his weight of guilt"; C; Henderson; He feels guilty about something.

3. "on the Moon, on Mars, even on Titan"; S; range of Earth's territory; interplanetary settlement achieved

4. "if I told you the data was unreliable"; A; information in Multivac; Multivac's conclusions are questionable.

5. "What made you think Multivac was in working order?"; A; Multivac's reliability; Not only was data wrong, the machine was probably not working.

Literary Analysis: Science Fiction (p. 120)

Suggested responses:

Students' summaries should demonstrate an understanding that science fiction is a type of literature that considers the effect of scientific possibilities on people.

"All Watched Over by Machines of Loving Grace" by Richard Brautigan
"Fire and Ice" by Robert Frost
"The Horses" by Edwin Muir
"There Will Come Soft Rains" by Sara Teasdale

Build Vocabulary (p. 121)

A. Suggested responses:

1. great insult or wrong or to anger or commit a wrong against; characterized by a great insult or wrong

2. an amazing or remarkable event; characterized by an amazing or remarkable event

3. belief generally held as irrational, or that cannot be proven by laws of science; full of beliefs that are irrational or that can't be proven

B. 1. e 2. d 3. g 4. a 5. c 6. b 7. f

Build Grammar Skills: Adjective Clauses (p. 122)

A. Practice

1. whose work we have just read; poets

2. who won four Pulitzer Prizes; writer

3. which are often about love; poems

4. that comes from the Orkney Islands; imagery

5. who was influenced by the beat and hippie generations; poet

B. Writing Application:

Sample responses:

1. We heard a rumbling in the distance that sounded like thunder.

2. Sandy, whose painting is almost finished, hopes to frame it next week.

3. There is the boy who found the lost necklace.

4. She found the blue jacket, which was hanging in the closet.

5. He was the candidate whom the voters elected to the Senate.

Reading Strategy: Recognizing a Poet's Purpose (p. 123)

Suggested responses:

1. For "Fire and Ice," students might write that the poet would prefer the world to end in fire because it is most like desire. These details reflect the author's purpose, which is to show cynicism toward the world by treating a seemingly serious subject lightly.

2. For "All Watched Over by Machines of Loving Grace," students might list details that illustrate the poet's vision of a future "cybernetic" world. Students should realize that these details show how the speaker views the coexistence of nature and computer technology.

3. For "There Will Come Soft Rains," students might list details related to the peacefulness of nature despite the destruction caused by people. They should recognize that these details demonstrate nature's indifference to the affairs of people, and the fact that the natural world will go on without them.

4. For "The Horses," students might list details related to the postwar society and to the arrival of the horses. Students should relate these details to the speaker's purpose of showing how people are forced to revert to a simpler existence after they succeed in destroying themselves with technology.

Literary Analysis: Alliteration (p. 124)

Suggested responses:

1. favor fire; Alliteration continues to give the poem's serious subject a whimsical tone.

2. forest filled; peacefully past; Alliteration again gives the poem a musical quality, which reflects the scene the poet is trying to create.

3. feathery fire; whistling, whims, wire; Alliteration gives the line a light, musical tone, which shows that nature is unaffected by the outcome of the war.

4. Spring, she, scarcely; Alliteration again emphasizes the peaceful, lighthearted tone of the natural world.

5. deepening drumming; Alliteration gives readers a sense of the sound made by the horses arriving into the silent, dreary world.

"If I Forget Thee, Oh Earth . . ." by Arthur C. Clarke
from *Silent Spring* by Rachel Carson
"To the Residents of A.D. 2029" by Bryan Woolley

Build Vocabulary (p. 125)

A. 1. annals—a record of events arranged in yearly sequence

2. anniversary—the marking of a notable event each year

3. annuity—an amount of money to be paid yearly

4. biennial—occurring every two years or lasting for two years

B. 1. b 2. h 3. d 4. f 5. a 6. c 7. e 8. g

C. 1. b 2. a 3. c

Build Grammar Skills: Compound and Complex Sentences (p. 126)

A. Practice

1. CX 2. C 3. CX 4. C 5. CX

B. Writing Application

Sample responses:

1. Rachel Carson is a writer who writes about the environment.

2. In Carson's fictional town, birds were plentiful, and fish swam in the streams.

3. When Marvin began his journey home, he did not look back at Earth.

4. The narrator is worried about the future, but he is optimistic.

Reading Strategy: Distinguishing Between Fact and Opinion (p. 127)

Suggested responses:

"If I Forget Thee, Oh Earth . . ."

Facts: 1. People need a source of oxygen to survive on the surface of the moon. 2. The outlines of Earth's continents and clouds in Earth's atmosphere can be seen from the moon.

Opinions: 1. The view of the earth was "beautiful." 2. If people didn't have a goal, they would lose the will to live.

from *Silent Spring*

Facts: 1. Oak, maple, and birch trees "set up a blaze of color" in the autumn. 2. Without bees there is no pollination, and without pollination there can be no fruit development.

Opinions: 1. People are solely responsible for the potential destruction that she describes. 2. The consequences of the use of pesticides (Carson's "grim specter") has "crept upon us almost unnoticed."

"If I Forget Thee, Oh Earth . . ."
by Arthur C. Clarke
from *Silent Spring* by Rachel Carson
"To the Residents of A.D. 2029"
by Bryan Woolley *(continued)*

"To the Residents of A.D. 2029"

Facts: 1. We continue to depend on unrenewable resources—petroleum, natural gas, and coal—for most of the fuel that heats and cools our homes. . . . 2. Without usable land, air, water, and fuel, food production would be impossible.

Opinions: 1. When "doing" becomes necessary, we invent a means of doing, especially when we are in danger. 2. Most of the problems about which we worry will seem quaint in the year 2029.

"If I Forget Thee, Oh Earth . . .": Grim details of the view of Earth and of the quality of life ("exile") on the moon persuade us not to destroy life on Earth through nuclear war.

from *Silent Spring:* Though Carson sets up a hypothetical town, her list of disasters and her statement that these things have all happened in one place or another are sufficiently impressive to persuade readers that something is wrong and needs to be stopped.

"To the Residents of A.D. 2029": Just enough facts, along with statements about wastefulness, make the essay persuasive. Though light in tone, the essay points out the need to change our behavior if we are to leave any kind of a positive legacy for those residents of 2029.

Literary Analysis: Persuasive Appeal
(p. 128)

Suggested responses:

"If I Forget Thee, Oh Earth" . . .

1. Let's not allow ourselves to destroy Earth through nuclear war; the consequences are beyond our comprehension.
2. implied
3. ". . . the glow of dying atoms was still visible, a perennial reminder of the ruinous past." "He would never walk beside the rivers of that lost and legendary world, or listen to the thunder raging above its softly rounded hills."

from *Silent Spring*

1. Pesticides are killing us as well as animals and we need to be aware of it and do something about it.
2. implied;
3. "The people had done it themselves." "Yet every one of these disasters has actually happened somewhere. . . ." "What has already silenced the voices of spring in countless towns in America?"

"To the Residents of A.D. 2029"

1. We need to learn to respect the natural world.
2. stated;
3. "A healing of the schism between man and the rest of nature. Our present disrespect for the natural world is our most serious stupidity to date. We must realize that man can't long outlive the other living creatures."

"Gifts" by Shu Ting
"Glory and Hope" by Nelson Mandela

Build Vocabulary (p. 129)

A. 1. b 2. c 3. a

B. 1. Most of us consider maintaining our dignity as a right that is *inalienable*.
2. Mandela views black and white South Africans as separated by *chasms*.
3. The *hieroglyphics* on the cave wall were a mystery at first.
4. Nelson Mandela hopes to *confer* to South Africans a sense of freedom.
5. Mandela hopes to build a *covenant* among the people of South Africa.
6. The *ideology* of South Africa has changed greatly.
7. Mandela views apartheid as a *pernicious* system.
8. The *pinions* are attached to the bird's wing.

Build Grammar Skills: Parallelism: Clauses
(p. 130)

A. Practice

Parallel clauses occur in the first three lines.

B. Writing Application

Students' sentences should be similar in grammatical structure.

Reading Strategy: Evaluating the Writer's Message (p. 131)

Suggested responses:

Nelson Mandela

1. There is hope for South Africa. South Africans have secured their "first democratic elections"; they have achieved "political emancipation"; they are committed to a "just and lasting peace"; they have entered into a covenant that will ensure the inalienable rights of both blacks and whites.

2. As a speaker, Mandela could have emphasized important words, such as *democracy, justice, freedom, liberty*, by raising his voice or by pronouncing them especially clearly. He could have paused frequently to let the crowd react. He could have slowed down to give emphasis to important points in the speech.

Shu Ting

1. She feels a connectedness to the earth. She expresses that connectedness by using the images of the pond, sunlight, and birds. Also, in the last two lines she credits the earth for being responsible for all that she is.

2. She wants to leave a message for others. Lines 11–13: "I will leave shining words/In the pupils of children's eyes/Igniting golden flames." Lines 21–24: "There my blood-stained pinions/Will scratch hiero-glyphics/On every human heart/For every year to come."

Literary Analysis: Tone (p. 132)

Suggested responses:

"Glory and Hope"

"a common victory for justice"—patriotic, unifying

"chasms that divide us"—serious, dramatic

"rainbow nation"—all-encompassing

"Gifts"

Guidelines for student response: Students may label the tones of the first three stanzas, in general, as wistful, celebratory, and hopeful, respectively. Overall, students will probably conclude that the poem has a fairly positive tone, such as hopeful or thankful.

Unit 6: Short Stories

"The Gift of the Magi" by O. Henry

Build Vocabulary (p.133)

A. 1. c   2. a   3. b

B. 1. Della's *cascade* of brown hair shimmered in the firelight.

2. Hardly *meretricious*, the combs were pure tortoise shell, rimmed with jewels.

3. For Della the upcoming Christmas holiday *instigates* the desire to give Jim a special gift.

4. To hide the worn leather strap, Jim took a *discreet* glance at his watch.

5. Della chose the platinum fob chain because of its simple *chaste* design.

6. So that Jim would not be startled by the *ravages* of her haircut, Della curled her short hair.

7. The beauty of Della's hair was so great that it could *depreciate* even the Queen's jewels.

Build Grammar Skills: Adverb Phrases (p. 134)

A. Practice

1. to her cheeks; with the powder rag

2. from the window; before the glass

3. below her knee

4. for Jim's present

5. off the table; for him

B. Writing Application

Sample responses:

1. Sara returned to New York after the party.

2. She started to laugh during the film.

3. Jared pulled into the garage and then turned off the ignition.

4. At the skating rink, music blared from the stereo speakers.

5. I put the brownies on the table so they could cool off.

© Prentice-Hall, Inc.

Answers **263**

6. My mom walks around the lake three times every morning.

7. The pile of papers sitting near the desk is the one I want.

Reading Strategy: Asking Questions
(p. 135)

Sample responses:

3. What does the word *appertaining* mean?

4. Who is Mr. James Dillingham Young?

7. Why did she suddenly whirl and look at herself in the glass?

8. Why did her face lose its color so quickly?

Literary Analysis: Plot (p. 136)

Suggested responses:

Exposition: introduction of a young couple named Della and Jim; the day before Christmas and very little money to spend on gifts; two prized possessions: Della's hair and Jim's watch

Rising Action: Della sells her hair; Della goes to the pawnshop and buys the watch chain; Della returns home and readies herself for Jim's arrival; Jim's arrival and shock at Della's haircut

Climax: exchange of gifts

Falling Action: dismay at the uselessness of each other's gifts

Resolution: The couple put their gifts away for a later date. Their selfless gestures prove their love; the gifts themselves are merely material possessions.

"Sonata for Harp and Bicycle"
by Joan Aiken

Build Vocabulary (p.137)

A. 1. *Jovial* means "happy" or "jolly." The word comes from the name of the Roman god Jove. Those born under the sign of Jove were thought to lead lucky and happy lives.

2. *Hector* means "to harass or heckle." In Homer's *Iliad,* Hector was the greatest Trojan, killed by Greek hero Achilles. In later drama, Hector was often portrayed as a bully; hence the meaning "to browbeat."

3. The name for the fifth day of the week comes from Norse mythology. The day is named for Thor, god of war and strength, son of Odin.

4. A *volcano* is a vent, usually a conical hill or mountain, in the earth's crust, which ejects lava, gases, ash, and steam from the planet's interior. The structure is named for Vulcan, the Roman god of fire and smelting.

5. *Siren* may mean an "alluring entity, especially female," "an alarm," or less commonly, "a species of eel-shaped salamanders." All meanings owe their origin to any of several Greek and Roman myths of sea nymphs luring sailors to doom with beautiful songs. The alarm used by emergency vehicles was so named because its precursor was a musical instrument that played sweetly.

B. 1. f   2. h   3. d   4. j   5. i   6. a   7. g   8. c   9. b   10. e

Build Grammar Skills: Participial Phrases
(p. 138)

A. Practice

1. shaking her head

2. Walking as softly as an Indian

3. beckoning him like a pair of dividers

4. tucking the bottle of Médoc in his jacket pocket

5. falling over her face

6. forbidding

B. Writing Application

Possible responses:

1. Peter carried the new cello strapped inside the case.

2. Walking to school, Jane saw an antique car.

3. Lucy watched the trapeze artist dangling from a high wire.

Reading Strategy: Predicting (p. 139)

Suggested responses (for **Outcome**):

1. Workers must leave because those who see the ghost of Heron will die.

2. Ashgrove sees the ghost, then pries the secret from Miss Golden.

3. Jason wrests himself from the grasp of the ghost and escapes.

4. The first lovers to meet in the room, Miss Bell and Heron, are reunited by the second, Miss Golden and Ashgrove.

5. Jason's plan reunites the spirits and wins Miss Golden.

6. Each couple, alive or dead, gets a bottle and a bouquet. The canvas bag contains a parachute so Jason can leap and live.

Literary Analysis: Rising Action (p. 140)
Suggested responses:

1. The Grimes Buildings empty daily.

2. Golden tells Ashgrove he can't know the secret until he's on the Established Staff.

3. Ashgrove remains to learn the secret, and he sees the ghost.

4. Ashgrove learns the mystery and resolves to "remedy the situation."

5. The dead lovers unite in Room 492.

6. Jason and Berenice parachute into their future.

"The Scarlet Ibis" by James Hurst

Build Vocabulary (p. 141)
A. 1. codices
   2. cortices, cortexes
   3. vertices, vertexes
B. 1. a 2. d 3. e 4. g 5. b 6. c 7. f
C. 1. d 2. b 3. a

Build Grammar Skills: Gerund Phrases (p. 142)
A. Practice

1. Renaming my brother

2. Crawling backward

3. listening to what he said

4. his coming with me

5. the going

B. Writing Application
Sample responses:

1. The narrator passed time by giving Doodle swimming lessons.

2. Standing on his own was a great accomplishment for Doodle.

3. The narrator believed he was good at climbing the vines in the swamp.

4. Thinking about the past fills the narrator with sadness.

5. The narrator and Doodle loved telling lies to pass the time.

Reading Strategy: Identifying With a Character (p. 143)
Suggested responses:

Event: Doodle smiles **Reaction:** pure joy **Event:** Doodle crawls **Reaction:** names him Doodle **Event:** takes him to Old Woman Swamp **Reaction:** glad to have playmate **Event:** shows Doodle the casket **Reaction:** remorse **Event:** starts to teach him to walk **Reaction:** persistence **Event:** Doodle takes a step **Reaction:** delight **Event:** Doodle falls ill **Reaction:** concern **Event:** Ibis arrives and dies **Reaction:** sadness **Event:** Boys walk home in rain—Doodle can't keep up **Reaction:** remorse at leaving him behind **Event:** holds Doodle in his arms **Reaction:** despair

Literary Analysis: Point of View (p. 144)
Suggested responses:

1. Instead of relating only the brother's frustrations, the scene would include the thoughts and feelings of Doodle. He would have been fearful, exhausted, weak, determined to please his brother, frustrated, and so on. We can only speculate about what Doodle was thinking during the walking lessons since we are not told Doodle's thoughts in Hurst's story.

2. A third-person omniscient narrator would likely have described more fully each person's reaction to Doodle's walking. The parents' incredulity, the conviction behind Aunt Nicey's "thanks praying," and Doodle's own feelings of pride and accomplishment would all be worthy of mention.

3. Students must choose *one* character from whose point of view they want to write. The details they include in the paragraph must be consistent with that character's point of view.

"Blues Ain't No Mockin Bird" by Toni Cade Bambara
"Uncle Marcos" by Isabel Allende

Build Vocabulary (p.145)
A. 1. disadvantage—without advantage
   2. disarm—to remove arms, or to be without armaments
   3. disable—to remove ability, or to be without ability

"Blues Ain't No Mockin Bird"
by Toni Cade Bambara
"Uncle Marcos" by Isabel Allende (continued)

B. Suggested responses:

1. Calling Myrtle by her plain first name showed a lack of formality because it went against established rules or customs.

2. It seemed as if the cameraman had his camera lassoed to him because its strap was wrapped around his shoulder.

3. Uncle Marcos's affection for Cousin Antonieta was unrequited because she did not return the feelings of affection.

4. In addition to the fetid smoke from experiments, the animals in jars of formaldehyde probably also smelled rank or rancid.

5. Severo assumed that Marcos was a vanquished hero because he did not return.

6. The fact that Nivea wept disconsolately indicates that she was very unhappy about her brother's disappearance.

7. As it turned out, Cousin Antonieta was impassive because she showed no emotion toward Marcos.

8. When Clara says the plastic angels were pallid, she means that they were pale.

Build Grammar Skills: Infinitive Phrases
(p. 146)

A. Practice

1. to have another word to say
2. to take my turn
3. to go for him
4. to do
5. to hand him the camera
6. to stay forever
7. to see the sight
8. to watch the sky

B. Writing Application

Possible responses:

1. Granny didn't want to speak with the photographers.

2. To ask questions was the men's job.

3. Cathy's dream is to write a story about it.

4. Clara did not need the aid of a picture to describe her uncle.

Reading Strategy: Making Inferences About Characters (p.147)

Suggested responses:

Cathy in "Blues Ain't No Mockin Bird"

Cathy says something about the twins in a "grown-up" way; Cathy is older than the twins.

"Me standin there wonderin how Cathy knew it was 'of course' when I didn't and it was my grandmother."; Cathy appears to be wise and to understand Granny—or at least she acts as if she does.

Cathy sounds "like Granny teacher"; Cathy acts like Granny, which indicates that she apparently respects Granny.

Cathy is described as "Cathy actress" and "Cathy dreamer"; Cathy's personality has different sides that come out in different ways as she talks about different things.

Clara in "Uncle Marcos"

Clara, in particular, likes Uncle Marcos's visits; Uncle Marcos's different-ness appeals to Clara, perhaps because she herself is different from the rest of the family.

Clara continues to "peer at the horizon" even after Uncle Marcos's remains have apparently been found; perhaps because of her fondness for Uncle Marcos, she refuses to believe that he has died.

Clara had "prophesying powers" at age seven; Clara was an intuitive child, perhaps due to the innocence of youth and perhaps due to some special gift.

Clara learned to read from Marcos's books, could relate Marcos's stories, and could recite tales and "unpronounceable names of the flora and fauna" her uncle had seen; Clara was a very bright child who could pick up and remember details that interested her.

Literary Analysis: Direct and Indirect Characterization (p.148)

1. D   2. I   3. I   4. D   5. D   6. I   7. D

"The Man to Send Rain Clouds"
by Leslie Marmon Silko
"The Invalid's Story" by Mark Twain

Build Vocabulary (p.149)

A. Suggested response:

Being a *gracious* man, the narrator of "The Invalid's Story" took on the *ambitious* task of delivering his friend's remains to the man's family in Wisconsin. The narrator boarded the train to Wisconsin without realizing that an *outrageous* mistake had been made, and instead of his friend he was delivering a box of guns and *odorous* cheese. The *hideous* smell of the cheese makes the narrator's train ride uncomfortable and leads to a *humorous* story.

B. 1. f 2. g 3. e 4. i 5. b 6. c 7. a
      8. d 9. h

Build Grammar Skills: Infinitive or Prepositional Phrase? (p. 150)

A. Practice

1. PP 2. PP 3. I 4. I 5. I 6. I 7. PP 8. I
9. PP 10. I

B. Writing Application

Sample responses:

1. She almost started to laugh during the workshop. (I)

2. The sprinter flew to the finish line. (PP)

3. His coach had warned the runner not to stumble. (I)

4. Barry walked quickly to his class. (PP)

5. Everyone thought it was time to relax after skiing all day. (I)

Reading Strategy: Using Your Senses (p. 151)

Suggested responses:

"The Man to Send Rain Clouds"

Touch: heat of the sun; cold evening air and cold dry wind; feel of hands in the pockets of Leon's green army jacket; corn meal dust on the hands; stiff fingers twisting the lid off the holy water

Taste: hot coffee; beans with hot bread; cold air

Smell: coffee; beans and hot bread; cold, night air; candles

Hearing: truck; conversations of characters; church bells; wind; sprinkling of the holy water

Sight: Teofilo under the cottonwood tree; face paint; setting sun; Teofilo's small body; dining room windows of the cloister; pile of jackets, gloves, and scarves in the yellow, dry tumbleweeds; people standing close together; clouds of steam; dark spots on blanket from the holy water; highway full of headlights

"The Invalid's Story"

Touch: comfortable seat on a bale of buckets; rumble of the train; hot stove in the train car; swallowing; gripping the box; freezing, thawing, and stifling

Taste: sandwich; cigar; smoke

Smell: cheese; cigar smoke; carbolic acid; burning chicken feathers, dried apples, leaf tobacco; shoes, sulfur, and asafetida

Hearing: moving train; humming; conversation

Sight: dark, driving snowstorm; the expressman's simple, honest, good-natured face; white-pine boxes; chicken feathers, dried apples, leaf tobacco; shoes, sulfur, and asafetida piled on sheet iron

Literary Analysis: Setting (p. 152)

Suggested responses:

"The Man to Send Rain Clouds"

Physical surroundings: dry desert; cottonwood trees; high blue mountains covered in snow; highway

Era: pickup truck; black iron stove; presence of missionary priest; highway

Culture: feather; face paint; sprinkling of corn meal; candles; medicine bags; ceremonial dance; holy water; cloistered nuns; priest

Importance: The blending of two religions in a small desert community is at the heart of the story.

"The Invalid's Story"

Physical surroundings: stifling express car on a moving train

Era: wood stove in the train; the way in which the body is transported; the expressman; typhoid fever

"The Man to Send Rain Clouds"
by Leslie Marmon Silko

"The Invalid's Story" by Mark Twain
(continued)

Culture: song the expressman hums; dialect of the characters; use of the words "general" and "commander"; cigars

Importance: The conflict and the humor in the story are created by the fact that the men are trapped in a small, hot train car with what they think is a decomposing body.

"The Necklace"
by Guy de Maupassant
"The Harvest" by Tomás Rivera

Build Vocabulary (p. 153)

A. Suggested responses:

1. a denial of acceptance
2. forced to endure
3. interrupted

B. 1. d 2. g 3. a 4. f 5. e 6. b 7. c

Build Grammar Skills: Appositive Phrases
(p. 154)

A. Practice

1. a famous short story writer
2. a strand of worthless diamonds
3. a very wealthy woman
4. a seemingly colossal debt
5. a mountain of dirty dishes

B. Writing Application

Sample responses:

1. Autumn, the best time of year, marks the end of the harvest.
2. Don Trine, a migrant worker, confuses the townspeople with his strange behavior.

3. All alone, Don Trine takes walks, long strolls in the afternoon.
4. Rumors, speculations that Don Trine had a lot of money, began to circulate throughout the town.
5. The boys came upon a mystery, odd holes in the ground that they could not explain.

Reading Strategy: Drawing Conclusions
(p. 155)

Suggested response:

"The Necklace": *Character's Action:* Madame Loisel borrows necklace *Related Character Trait:* vanity *Reasons for Actions:* wants to make an impression *Suggests About Theme:* character places high value on material possessions and appearances

"The Harvest" *Character's Action:* Don Trine takes a walk by himself *Related Character Trait:* Enjoys solitude *Reasons for Action:* Likes to feel the earth *Suggests About Theme:* Love for the land

Literary Analysis: Theme (p.156)

Suggested responses:

1. This passage shows the importance society places on wealth and social status. This passage relates to the story's theme of people attaching too much importance to money.

2. The passage reveals how the townspeople jump to conclusions about Don Trine. They believe money or buried treasure are the only things that could drive someone to behave in such a way, even though this explanation could not be further from the truth. This passage relates to the theme that most people are too caught up in their human concerns to appreciate what Don Trine is doing, or to appreciate the earth in the way that he does.

Unit 7:   Nonfiction

"Single Room, Earth View"
by Sally Ride

Build Vocabulary (p.157)

A. 1. novelty; 2. renovated; 3. novice;

B. 1. i 2. g 3. c 4. d 5. b 6. j 7. a
8. h 9. e 10. f

C. 1. d 2. b

Build Grammar Skills: Subject -Verb Agreement (p. 158)

A. Practice

1. subject, space shuttle; verb, orbits
2. subject, activities; verb, harm
3. subject, storm; verb, is
4. subject, moonlight; verb, creates

5. subject, wake *and* contrails; verb, are

6. subject, description; verb, inspires

B. Writing Application

Possible responses:

1. Sally Ride's description of her space flights is enjoyable to read.

2. As they look at the earth, astronauts see many beautiful sights.

3. Pollution in the rain forests appears on infrared film carried in the space shuttle.

4. From space, city lights and stars are sometimes indistinguishable.

Reading Strategy: Varying Your Reading Rate (p. 159)

Possible responses:

1. Ride was flying over Africa. I scanned the passage quickly for specific information.

2. A dust storm obscured Ride's view. I scanned the passage quickly for specific information.

3. Scientists have discovered huge circular and spiral eddies and standing waves. I read this material slowly because it was unfamiliar.

4. The passage suggests that understanding the oceans is easier when they are observed from above. I read slowly so I would understand the passage as a whole.

Literary Analysis: Observation (p. 160)

Suggested response:

Most students will realize that Ride's observations are active rather than passive and are fresh and full of novelty. They will also see that a key aspect of her ability to observe is her skill at posing the right questions.

"The Washwoman"
by Isaac Bashevis Singer
"On Summer" by Lorraine Hansberry
"A Celebration of Grandfathers"
by Rudolfo Anaya

Build Vocabulary (p.161)

A. 1. foretold; 2. forestall; 3. forecast; 4. foresight

B. 1. a   2. c   3. d   4. c   5. b   6. a   7. a   8. c

Build Grammar Skills: Consistency of Verb Tenses (p. 162)

A. Practice

1. is, present

2. started, past; was, past

3. will live, future

4. have retained, present perfect

5. will live, future

6. had covered, past perfect

B. Writing Application

1. When the washwoman didn't return, the family thought that she had died.

2. After she delivered the laundry, the washwoman never came back.

3. The author remembered some significant summers in her life, so she decided to write about them.

4. While she was in Maine, Hansberry met a woman who bravely battled cancer.

5. As child, the author learned to greet his grandfather respectfully.

6. I wonder if the author will live in New Mexico when he is an old man.

Reading Strategy: Identifying the Author's Attitude (p.163)

Suggested responses:

1. **Attitude:** The writer feels that the washwoman is an extraordinary person. **Words and phrases:** calling her a holy soul; saying that he cannot imagine paradise without her; saying that she deserves a reward for her efforts

2. **Attitude:** The writer has come to appreciate summer. **Words and phrases:** comparing summer to the other seasons; calling summer a gift; saying that summer is an assertion of "life at the apex"

3. **Attitude:** The writer finds comfort in his grandfather's views of aging. He feels this attitude is more accepting and respectful toward the process of aging. He recognizes that in the modern world, people try to hide signs of aging. **Words and phrases:** saying that the aging process, though painful, is something to be faced; reference to the "always young image of the Hollywood star"

"**The Washwoman**"
by Isaac Bashevis Singer
"**On Summer**" by Lorraine Hansberry
"**A Celebration of Grandfathers**"
by Rudolfo Anaya *(continued)*

Literary Analysis: Essay (p.164)

Suggested responses:

1. Students might list her physical strength and stamina, her honesty, and her loyalty.

2. Students might say that Singer is trying to give the washwoman the credit she is due and the respect she never received from her own son. He also wants to show that there is a place in the world for hard work and honesty.

3. She presents the opinion that summer is a special season.

4. Hansberry describes her childhood memories of summer, describes the courageous woman who wanted to live to see one more summer, and then compares summer to the other seasons.

5. Anaya reflects on elderly people and his respect for his ancestors.

6. His reflections reveal that he believes people have a great deal to learn from the older generation.

from *A White House Diary*
by Lady Bird Johnson
"Arthur Ashe Remembered"
by John McPhee
"Georgia O'Keeffe" by Joan Didion

Build Vocabulary (p. 165)

A. Suggested responses:

1. a feeling or perception
2. able to be perceived
3. a state of feeling excessively emotional

B. 1. e 2. h 3. j 4. a 5. i 6. b 7. c
8. d 9. g 10. f

C. 1. c 2. b

Build Grammar Skills: Subject-Verb Agreement: Confusing Subjects (p. 166)
A. Practice

1. I; was
2. C
3. I; are

4. I; were
5. C

B. Writing Application

In this article about Arthur Ashe, there are several stories about the tennis player's inner strength. Here are some examples. Ashe did not let the other players know what he was feeling. There was always a sense of control about him. Among his strengths was unpredictability. He often tried high-risk shots. Does the author admire Ashe? There is no doubt about it!

Reading Strategy: Finding Writer's Main Points and Support (p. 167)

Suggested responses:

1. a. "I heard a Secret Service man say in the most desolate voice—and I hurt for him: 'We never lost a President in the Service.'"

   b. "I looked up at a building and there, already, was a flag at half-mast. I think that was when the enormity of what had happened first struck me."

2. a. description of Ashe's aggressive playing style when faced with defeat

   b. direct quotation of Ashe's words about his demeanor

3. a. From a young age, O'Keeffe knew she wanted to be an artist.

   b. O'Keeffe persevered in her desire to paint, despite discouragement and criticism from instructors.

Literary Analysis: Biographical and Autobiographical Writing (p. 168)

Suggested responses:

1. Supports include direct quotation from Ashe and detailed description of Ashe's actions.

2. It reveals Johnson's private response to a public event and allows readers to connect their own experience of the event to hers.

3. Didion believes O'Keeffe's main motivation was challenging the male establishment.

4. She reveals compassion, sensitivity, and personal strength.

5. McPhee uses direct quotations from family members and from Ashe, anecdotes, and detailed descriptions of the actions and reactions of Ashe and other people.

"Understanding Comics"
by Scott McCloud

Build Vocabulary (p. 169)

A. 1. My station was the water table at the halfway point of the race.

2. As impressive as Kathy's stature was, her teammate Lou was even taller.

3. We set the thermostat at a moderate level to keep the house warm without wasting energy.

B. 1. Because Scott McCloud really was obsessed with comics, he probably had them on his mind all the time.

2. McCloud's argument is that there *is* aesthetic value in comics, meaning that comics do contain something artistic.

3. The first draft of the definition seems arbitrary because the words were randomly chosen without reason.

Build Grammar Skills: Varieties of English: Standard, Nonstandard (p. 170)

A. Practice

1. N 2. N 3. S 4. N 5. S 6. N

B. Writing Application

Sample responses:

1. Please give me that pencil.

2. How are you?

3. She enjoyed the concert very much.

4. These directions are very confusing.

5. I telephoned and asked him to come quickly.

Reading Strategy: Using Visuals as a Key to Meaning (p. 171)

Suggested responses:

Pictures That Add Humor

Frame—the "too narrow" illustration: As the speaker defends his chosen career, he finds himself in danger of being squashed by the "narrow definitions" he is speaking of.

Frame—the "I failed miserably" illustration: The speaker's straightforward, serious statement is amplified by a picture of "failing"—actually being laughed at by someone to whom he is trying to explain the worth of comics.

Pictures That Add Details

Frame—the "World of Comics" illustration: The picture adds details through the dozens of comic characters that appear on the globe, which is much more interesting and effective than listing the characters.

Frame—the "sequential art" illustration: Simply showing the sun sinking to the horizon or the hands of a clock advancing, for example, is much more effective than describing the passage of time with words.

Pictures That Signal Flashbacks or Fantasies

Frame—the "practice, practice, practice" illustration: The speaker shows himself as a boy working hard with a pen.

Frame—any of several frames with a "starry sky" background: The starry sky represents the speaker's imagination.

Literary Analysis: Visual Essay (p.172)

Suggested responses:

Logical/emotional appeals: McCloud seeks a "proper definition" to show that comics are "limitless and exciting" (logical); the "I was hooked" frame may serve as an emotional appeal to others who have been hooked on comics.

Opinions supported by reasons and evidence: McCloud shows the "world of comics" to support his statement that comics are "limitless and exciting"; other media receive this kind of attention, so comics should, too.

Facts, statistics, examples, anecdotes: childhood experiences (anecdotes); common definition of comics as "crude, poorly drawn, semiliterate, cheap, disposable kiddie fare" ("negative" example); Eisner's definition (fact)

Expert opinions: Will Eisner, master comics artist

Identifies opposing positions: "I failed miserably" frame (a humorous look at opposition); other opposition takes the form of several of the suggestions from the audience toward the end of the essay.

"Earhart Redux"
by Alex Chadwick
In These Girls, Hope Is a Muscle
by Madeleine Blais,
a book review by Steve Gietschier
In These Girls, Hope Is a Muscle
by Madeleine Blais, book jacket

Build Vocabulary (p. 173)

A. Suggested responses:

1. *Dynamic* means "forceful and energetic." One who is dynamic possesses energy or power.

2. Dynamite is a powerful explosive.

B. Student responses should indicate understanding of the meaning of the Word Bank word. Sample responses:

1. Aerodynamics affect flight performance, so airplanes today compared to those in the 1930s are more streamlined in order to move through the air better.

2. Because modern aircraft, unlike Earhart's and Finch's, use hydraulic systems, their controls are power-assisted by pressurized fluid in tubes.

3. To pursue financial success might be enough for some, but Finch has also chosen to seek to finish Earhart's lost flight.

4. It is improbable that we will ever know for certain what happened to Amelia Earhart because we are unlikely to find conclusive evidence of her fate.

5. When author Blais derides the town of Amherst, she mocks it.

6. The legacy of success of the girls' team in Amherst had been passed down from previous teams.

7. The book blurb says In These Girls, Hope Is a Muscle is riveting because it holds readers' attention.

8. Another way to say that the girls' team was ruminative would be to say that the girls were thoughtful and contemplative.

9. Adept at capturing the life of an American town, writer Madeleine Blais skillfully gives us an account of the team's year.

10. One would consider this account of a championship season compelling because one can't wait to see what happens on the next page.

Build Grammar Skills: Usage: There, They're, and Their (p. 174)

A. Practice

1. there
2. their
3. their
4. they're
5. They're, their
6. There

B. Writing Application

1. Astronomers think there will be an eclipse of the moon next week.
2. correct
3. They're hoping to see a full eclipse.
4. The children are studying astronomy in their classes.

Reading Strategy: Determining Author's Purpose (p.175)

Suggested responses:

"Earhart Redux"

General Purpose: to inform listeners about Finch's attempt to recreate Amelia Earhart's flight

Detail(s); Impression(s):

Begins with hangar opening; dramatic

Finch is "rare herself"; focus on individual

Airplane facts; task is to re-create Earhart's plane exactly

What does your family think?; focus on personal life

Particular Purpose: to dramatize the personal quest of Linda Finch as a woman accomplishing things, and to compare it all these years later to Earhart's attempt to do the same thing.

Review: *In These Girls, Hope Is a Muscle*

General Purpose: to explain what the book is about and comment on how good it is or isn't

Detail(s); Impression(s):

Feel the passion of women's athletics; writer agrees with book author

Beautifully written; writer has positive opinion

Amherst unusual setting for basketball book; story more interesting because atypical

Pains of adolescence and families broken up; not just about sports

Particular Purpose: to explain why this book is so good, not just as a sports story, but as a human story with an important point to make about women's athletics

Book Blurb: *In These Girls, Hope Is a Muscle*

General Purpose: to interest readers in the book and persuade them to buy it

Detail(s); Impression(s):

Opens with quotes from reviewers; others liked the book

Compares to other books; these were good books

"One season all that changed"; dramatic summary of the plot adds interest

"compelling, funny, and touching"; emotions and pleasures

Particular Purpose: to persuade readers that this book has depth, compares well with others of its type, and offers pleasurable and rewarding reading

Literary Analysis: Career Writing (p.176)

Suggested responses:

1. Human resource manager needs to communicate effectively with employees; union negotiator needs skills for effective bargaining; public relations executive needs to write well to represent clients; car mechanic needs to write a summary of repairs made; lawyer needs to write briefs, appeals, etc.

2. A letter to a friend on a personal topic is not career writing.

3. (Some variation acceptable)

   __3__ Understanding what your audience knows

   __6__ Using a large and impressive vocabulary

   __5__ The capability of writing long documents

   __4__ Knowledge of business terminology

   __2__ The ability to get to the point quickly

   __1__ An aptitude for clear and concise language

Unit 8:   Drama

The Dancers by Horton Foote

Build Vocabulary (p. 177)

A. Suggested responses:

1. the bottom of the foot
2. only
3. the front section of a boat
4. to bend downward

B. 1. Elizabeth Crews is *mortified* by her daughter's refusal to go to the dance with Horace.

2. Herman Stanley voices his *defiance* to his wife's plan for Horace's visit.

3. Emily makes an effort to *console* her mother when she is crying.

4. Neither Elizabeth Crews nor Inez Stanley is as *genteel* as she pretends to be.

Build Grammar Skills: Pronoun Case (p. 178)

A. Practice

1. I/nominative; him/objective
2. she/nominative; you/nominative
3. me/objective; you/nominative
4. He/nominative; his/possessive
5. they/nominative; it/objective

B. Writing Application

1. Horace looked thin to her.
2. They are very close friends.
3. She has planned a busy schedule for him.
4. It will be a new experience for them.
5. She enjoys his company.

Reading Strategy: Picturing the Action (p. 179)

Suggested responses:

1. Emily's unhappiness is probably expressed with a frown, slouch or poor posture, and crossed arms.

2. Horace's embarrassment is probably expressed by his reddened or blushing face. Perhaps he stands with his hands in his pockets and looks down at the floor.

3. Herman probably sits in an easy chair, resting his feet on an ottoman and reading the paper.

Answers   **273**

The Dancers by Horton Foote *(continued)*

4. Inez probably paces back and forth, quickening her pace as she warms to her story.
5. As she enters the room, Inez possibly shows her disgust by slamming the door or throwing a coat over an armchair, frowning, and slumping down into a nearby chair.

Literary Analysis: Staging (p. 180)

Suggested responses:

1. Living room of Inez and Herman Stanley: radio or stereo, overstuffed reading chair with matching ottoman, oval floor rug. Living room of Elizabeth Crews: elegant couch and lamp. Yard and living room of Mary Catherine Davis: one blooming tree, such as a magnolia; radio, plain couch, and coffee table. Drugstore: counter and three stools.
2. Elizabeth Crews's living room is more refined and elegant.
3. The action of the play is intended to "flow continuously from one area to the other."
4. The lighting illuminates the specific area of the stage where the action is taking place.
5. The waitress is probably dressed in a pale pink uniform with a white apron. Perhaps she has a waitress hat pinned on her head. Inez Stanley is most probably wearing a dress with a tight-fitting bodice and flaring, belted skirt.

The Tragedy of Romeo and Juliet, Act I, by William Shakespeare

Build Vocabulary (p. 181)

A. Suggested responses:

1. A transient visitor is one who passes through and stays only briefly.
2. A transatlantic traveler is one who crosses the Atlantic.
3. A transfusion is the process of injecting the blood or plasma of one person into a vein or artery of another.
4. A transfer ticket allows you to cross from one bus or train to another.
5. The transcontinental railroad takes people from coast to coast.

B. 1. e 2. a 3. d 4. b 5. c
C. 1. b 2. c 3. a 4. a 5. b

Build Grammar Skills: Pronoun Case in Elliptical Clauses (p. 182)

A. Practice

1. they
2. her
3. he
4. they
5. him
6. I
7. we

B. Writing Application

Possible answers

1. I
2. they
3. her
4. he
5. she

Reading Strategy: Using Text Aids (p. 183)

Suggested responses:

1. Two Verona families, both of high social rank, hold an old grudge against each other. Violence has broken out yet again as a result of this grudge. Some citizens (i.e., members of the two families) have killed each other.
2. Let us make sure the law is on our side. Let them (the Montague servants) begin (the fight) so that *they* will be responsible and we (Sampson and Gregory) will be the victims.
3. I hope that by staying you are lucky enough to hear Romeo tell or confess what's bothering him.
4. Look over Paris' face as if it were a book. See the handsomeness there. Study every harmonious feature and see how one complements the other. What you can't tell by his face alone, look for it in his eyes, as if looking for notes in the margin of a book.
5. I am uneasy. I feel something unhappy is about to happen as a result of tonight's party. This unhappy thing will cause an early death for me.

Literary Analysis: Character (p. 184)

Suggested responses:

Capulet

Sampson, flat; Gregory, flat; Tybalt, round: hot tempered, extremely loyal to his family's grudge; Capulet, round: jovial, hospitable, essentially peace loving; Lady Capulet, round:

dislikes violence of the street brawl, eager for daughter to "make a good match" and thinks Paris is the man; Paris, flat; Nurse, round: fond of Juliet, loyal, somewhat crude or uneducated; Juliet, round: happy to stay a child and not have to think about marriage

Montague

Abram, flat; Balthasar, flat; Benvolio, round: strong enough to try to keep the peace, fun-loving, loyal to Romeo; Montague, round: would have joined brawl if his honor had been questioned, loving father; Lady Montague, round: dislikes violence at brawl, concerned about her son; Romeo, round: concerned about love, moody, Capulet says he is a "virtuous and well-governed youth"; Mercutio, round: gently mocking of Romeo's mood, relatively easygoing

The Tragedy of Romeo and Juliet, Act II, by William Shakespeare

Build Vocabulary (p. 185)

A. 1. interact—to carry on between two or more people, chemicals, etc.

2. intercrop—to plant one crop between the rows of another crop

3. interglacial—occurring between glacial epochs

4. intermission—an interval of time between acts

5. intersect—to cut or divide by passing through or across

B. 1. c 2. g 3. i 4. f 5. e 6. b 7. a 8. d 9. h

Build Grammar Skills: Using the Possessive Case of Personal Pronouns (p. 186)

A. Practice

1. their
2. his
3. my
4. ours
5. mine, hers, hers, mine
6. your
7. our

B. Writing Application

Possible answers:

1. their
2. my

3. his
4. hers
5. our

Reading Strategy: Reading Blank Verse (p. 187)

A. Suggested responses:

1. Who are you, who has heard me speaking my secret thoughts?

2. The orchard walls are high and hard to climb, and given who you are, this place means death for you if any of my family find you here.

3. And what love can do, that is what love dares to attempt.

Literary Analysis: Blank Verse (p. 188)

JULIET. Thĕ clŏck strŭck niṅe whĕn Ì dĭd sènd thĕ nùrse;

Iṅ half aṅ hoùr shĕ prŏmĭsed tò rĕturṅ.

Pĕrchaṅce shĕ cànnŏt meèt hìm. Thàt's ṅot sò.

Ŏ, she ĭs laṁe! Loṽe's herălds shoùld bĕ thoùghts,

Whĭch tèn tiṁes fàstĕr glide thăn thĕ sŭn's beaṁs

Drĭvin̄g băck shàdŏws oveř low'riṅg hìlls.

Thĕrefòre dŏ niṁblĕ-pìnioṅed doṽes dřaw Loṽe,

Aṅd thèrefore hàth the winḍ-swift Cùpĭd wiṅgs.

Nŏw ĭs the sùn upòṅ the highmŏst hìll

Ŏf thĭs dăy's jouřnĕy, aṅd frŏm niṅe tĭll tweĺve

Ĭs three loṅg hoùřs; yèt she ĭs ṅot còme.

Hăd she affèctiŏns aṅd wărm youthfŭl bloòd,

She woùld bĕ ăs swift iṅ mŏtiòn ăs ă ball;

Mў woŕds woùld bàndȳ hèr tŏ my sweet loṽe,

Aṅd his tŏ ṁe.

Bùt òld foĺks, màñy feiṅ ăs thèy wĕre deàd—

Uñwiеlḍy, sloẁ, heăvȳ aṅd pałe ăs leàd.

1. The word *hours* needs to be treated as a two-syllable word.

2. Line 13: She would be as swift in motion as a ball; The extra syllable adds a little bounce at the end of the line, as is appropriate given the words.

3. Line 15; The four syllables of this line call attention to Juliet's fervent, anxious wish to hear any news of Romeo.

The Tragedy of Romeo and Juliet, Act III, by William Shakespeare

Build Vocabulary (p. 189)

A. 1. **arachnid:** In Greek mythology, the weaver Arachne was turned into a spider by Athene so that the proud girl would weave and spin forever. Arachnid is the name of a class of animals into which spiders fall.

2. **panic:** Pan was the Greek god of shepherds and hunters and the inventor of the panpipe. A panic is the emotional state induced by the god Pan, i.e., fear, confusion.

3. **museum:** A museum is a "place of the muses." The muses were nine sisters in Greek mythology who fostered or inspired song, poetry, and arts and sciences.

4. **jovial:** Jove, or Jupiter, was the chief god of the Romans. He was regarded as a fair god who sometimes showed a sense of humor. *Jovial* has come to mean good-humored.

5. **saturnine:** Saturn was a Roman god, the father of Jupiter, Juno, Neptune, and Pluto. To be saturnine is to be like Saturn, i.e., cold, gloomy, or surly in mood or disposition.

6. **calliope:** Kalliope was the Greek muse of heroic poetry. Poetry, when recited in Ancient Greece, was always accompanied by music. We know a calliope as an organlike musical instrument.

B. 1. c 2. a 3. e 4. f 5. d 6. b

Build Grammar Skills: *Who* and *Whom* (p. 190)

A. 1. who—S
   2. who—S
   3. whom—OP
   4. who—S
   5. whom—OP
   6. whom—OV

B. Suggested responses:

1. Capulet, who is fond of Paris, believes Juliet will be pleased.

2. Juliet deceives her mother by speaking about Romeo as if he were the man whom she hates.

3. Nurse, for whom Juliet has great affection, abandons Juliet at the end of the act.

Reading Strategy: Paraphrasing (p. 191)

Suggested responses:

1. Romeo, I have so little affection for you that I can only say this: You are a villain.

2. Because of your fighting, my kinsman lies here wounded. But I will punish you with so strong a fine that you shall all regret my kinsman's death.

3. This day is so long and tiresome, just like the night before a festival when an eager child has new clothes to wear but must wait to put them on until the time for the festival.

Literary Analysis: Soliloquy, Aside, and Monologue (p. 192)

Suggested responses:

1. Juliet's aside takes the audience into her confidence about her little secret and serves as a signal that the rest of the conversation will be full of double meanings. The audience needs only the one aside to figure out what is happening.

2. The close of Scene v is a soliloquy because Juliet is alone on stage and addresses her remarks to the audience.

3. Juliet reveals that she feels betrayed by Nurse and will never again trust her. She says she will go to the friar, not to be absolved for displeasing her father but to get help. If there is no help, she can take her own life.

4. Capulet's words are a monologue because they make up a lengthy speech that is directed to other characters, and most specifically Juliet.

5. Juliet, Lady Capulet, and Nurse need to see the extent of Capulet's resolve on the match with Paris. The threat to disown Juliet is not a light one.

The Tragedy of Romeo and Juliet, Act IV, by William Shakespeare

Build Vocabulary (p. 193)

A. 1. Romeo travels eastward to the rising sun.

2. Homeward bound after the party, Benvolio wonders where Romeo is.

B. 1. b 2. a 3. d 4. a 5. c 6. c 7. b

Build Grammar Skills: Degrees of Comparison, (p. 194)

A. Practice

1. more—comparative

2. hideous, madly—positive

3. most lamentable, most woeful—superlative

4. better—comparative

B. Writing Application

1. Juliet knows she will be **happier** with Romeo than with Paris.

2. Of everyone around Juliet, the nurse is the **most understanding.**

3. Paris is **more eager** than Juliet for their wedding day to arrive.

4. Juliet contemplates that **horrible** things await her in the tomb.

Reading Strategy: Predicting (p. 195)

Suggested responses in Outcome column:

1. Juliet avoids the wedding by feigning death.

2. Juliet, though anxious, takes the risk.

3. Wedding plans go forward, but fail when Juliet is discovered apparently dead.

4. Lawrence's intentions are true. The potion works as planned, but in Act V, the weakness of the strategy appears.

5. The plan works as far as fooling the Capulets and Paris. In Act V, though, chance foils the plan.

Literary Analysis: Dramatic Irony (p. 196)

Suggested responses:

1. Paris does indeed "disturb devotion," that of Juliet to Romeo, and as we learn later in the act, no one will "rouse" Juliet on Thursday.

2. The irony is that Juliet is of course not "reclaimed" to Capulet's wishes, even though she appears that way to him. His lightness is doomed.

3. The "state tomorrow" that Juliet will be in and the necessities culled are not those that Lady Capulet might have in mind.

The Tragedy of Romeo and Juliet, Act V, by William Shakespeare

Build Vocabulary (p. 197)

Suggested responses:

A. 1. My ambidextrous sister writes as beautifully with her left hand as with her right.

2. She was ambivalent about the movie and couldn't decide whether to go or stay home.

B. 1. d 2. a 3. f 4. c 5. e 6. b

C. 1. a 2. c 3. a

Build Grammar Skills: Agreement With Indefinite Pronouns (p. 198)

A. Practice

1. was

2. was

3. were

4. is

5. offers

B. Writing Application

1. Each of the actors **has** learned the lines perfectly.

2. correct

3. Either the stage manager or the director **helps** us with the lighting.

4. correct

5. Most of the girls have started reading **their** lines for tomorrow's rehearsal.

Reading Strategy: Identifying Causes and Effects (p. 199)

Suggested responses:

Scene i

Balthasar arrives in Mantua. → Romeo learns of Juliet's "death." → Romeo buys poison.

Scene ii

Friar Lawrence's message has not been delivered. → Friar Lawrence heads to churchyard.

Scene iii (first half)

Paris arrives at churchyard. → Romeo arrives at churchyard. → Paris and Romeo fight. → Paris is killed. → Romeo enters tomb. → Romeo drinks poison. → Romeo dies.

The Tragedy of Romeo and Juliet, Act V,
by William Shakespeare *(continued)*

Scene iii (second half)

Friar Lawrence arrives at churchyard. → Friar sees Romeo and Paris. → Tries to lead Juliet away → Juliet will not leave; kills herself. → Montague and Capulet make peace.

Literary Analysis: Tragedy (p. 200)

Suggested responses:

1. Romeo fits the description because he is basically good, though not utterly virtuous, and he is not a villain. He does not fit the description in the sense that he does not possess a great character flaw that causes his downfall. His behavior may occasionally be rash or impetuous, but that does not constitute a frailty. What causes his downfall is an abundance of bad timing and rotten luck. The Prologue to Act I prepares us for this: Juliet and Romeo are "star-crossed"—ill-fated.

2. The whole tragic situation is not recognized until it is too late in *Romeo and Juliet.* It is Capulet, then Montague, who see it in all its awfulness. They see that it is their feud that has caused the tragedy.

Unit 9: Poetry

"I Wandered Lonely as a Cloud"
by William Wordsworth

Build Vocabulary (p. 201)

A. Suggested responses:

Whene're (Whenever); 'Twill (It will); ne'er (never)

B. 1. b 2. d 3. c 4. a

Build Grammar Skills: Semicolons and Colons (p. 202)

A. Practice

1. first; he
2. daffodils; that
3. things: dancing
4. lake; however
5. read: poetry

B. Writing Application

Sample response:

Last weekend I walked near Lake Michigan. The temperature was below freezing; waves had frozen on the sand. I could see a few seagulls in the distance; however, I couldn't hear them. Two things stand out in my memory: how cold it was and how peacefully quiet.

Reading Strategy: Using Your Senses (p. 203)

Suggested responses:

1. beside the lake, beneath the trees
2. fluttering, dancing
3. breeze
4. danced, sparkling
5. glee

Literary Analysis: Rhyme Scheme (p. 204)

Suggested responses:

1. *abccab cdd*
2. The last two lines of the poem share the same end rhyme. The rhyme of these last two lines does not appear anywhere else in the poem.
3. The last two lines of the poem express the author's main idea—that he wishes to go through life in a state of childlike wonder and fascination with the natural world.
4. Important lines such as "A rainbow in the sky," "So was it when my life began;/So is it now I am a man," and "Or let me die!" are reinforced by rhyme.
5. The rhyme scheme of "I Wandered Lonely as a Cloud" is different because its overall pattern is *ababcc dedeff ghghii jkjkll.* The rhyme schemes of the two poems are similar in that the final two lines of each stanza in "I Wandered Lonely as a Cloud" are set off with a unique end rhyme, and the final two lines in "My Heart Leaps Up" are set off in the same way.

"The Eagle" by Alfred, Lord Tennyson
"'Hope' is the thing with feathers—"
by Emily Dickinson
"Dream Deferred" and "Dreams"
by Langston Hughes

Build Vocabulary (p. 205)

A. 1. The beach was bathed in the amber light of sunset.

2. Indigo waves broke on the rocky shore.

3. The blazing crimson sun sank slowly beneath the horizon.

B. 1. c 2. e 3. f 4. d 5. a 6. b

C. 1. b 2. d

Build Grammar Skills: Dashes (p. 206)

A. Practice

1. I saw an eagle once in the wild—what an amazing sight!

2. Megan gave a report on Emily Dickinson—she has read all of the poet's work—and we learned a lot.

3. Langston Hughes drew on many life experiences—teacher, farmer, cook, and sailor—to write his poetry.

B. Writing Application

Possible responses:

1. The dash makes the reader stop abruptly so that the image of rotten, crusted meat is especially strong. Then the next line becomes even more unpleasant to imagine.

2. By using dashes often, the poet forces the reader to stop and consider each line carefully. The phrase "at all" becomes especially strong because it is surrounded by dashes.

Reading Strategy: Paraphrasing (p. 207)

Suggested responses:

1. Real hope has an immediate effect. It makes people feel more powerful and respected.

2. Everyone needs to have dreams.

3. I'm poor, so my dreams are all I have. I've let you know what my dreams are. Please be careful not to crush my dreams.

4. Hope is essential to people who are separated from society.

5. Not being able to hope leads to sadness.

6. It is reasonable to hope that people will do the right thing in the end.

Literary Analysis: Figurative Language (p. 208)

A. 1. S 2. P 3. M 4. M 5. S 6. S 7. P 8. M

B. Suggested responses:

1. A cat darted by like an arrow.

2. The wind sounded like a wounded animal.

3. Gym class is a boot camp.

4. These flowers are as delicate as cobwebs.

5. A snow day is a surprise party.

C. 1. Groaning about his age, the ancient oak slowly stretched his stiff arms.

2. The mosquito had drawn up his battle plans, and I was his next target.

3. The night before my audition, nervousness paid me an unwelcome visit.

"Blackberry Eating"
by Galway Kinnell
"Memory" by Margaret Walker
"Woman's Work" by Julia Alvarez
"Meciendo" by Gabriela Mistral
"Eulogy for a Hermit Crab"
by Pattiann Rogers

Build Vocabulary (p. 209)

A. Suggested responses:

1. I used a primer to prepare the walls for painting.

2. Jenn was a prima donna who always had to have things her way.

B. 1. The candidate was primed for the campaign.

2. Dark streets on a rainy night may appear to be sinister.

3. To nature lovers, the ocean's shore might be a divine place.

4. We were glad that the children had returned unbidden.

5. The server meticulously brushed the crumbs from her apron.

Build Grammar Skills: Ellipses (p. 210)

A. Practice

1. C 2. I 3. I 4. C 5. C

B. Writing Application

Sample responses:

1. When the countdown reached ten, nine, eight, seven . . . , we looked expectantly at the sky.

"Blackberry Eating"
by Galway Kinnell
"Memory" by Margaret Walker
"Woman's Work" by Julia Alvarez
"Meciendo" by Gabriela Mistral
"Eulogy for a Hermit Crab"
by Pattiann Rogers *(continued)*

2. John needed an idea for his composition, so he thought and thought . . . until he had an inspiration.

3. The basket overflowed with colorful fruit: apples, oranges, lemons . . . we used each in the centerpiece.

Reading Strategy: Picturing the Imagery
(p. 211)

Suggested responses:

1. taste, touch
2. touch
3. hearing
4. smell
5. sight
6. sight
7. sight, taste
8. sight

Literary Analysis: Imagery (p. 212)

Suggested responses:

1. The words *fat, overripe,* and *black* are all very visual. I can see the bulging berries hanging on the bushes, and I imagine my fingers stained with blackberry juice. The word *icy* appeals to the senses of touch, taste, and sight. I can see the sun glinting off the little sections of the black blackberries.

2. This is a very visual image. The poet says "heads under" instead of "people wearing" or "people carrying," so one imagines people almost hidden from view under their hats and parasols, as everything drips from a drenching rain. Their shoulders are hunched, so one can feel the discomfort caused by the rain or by their "sharp concern."

3. I can see the sun slanting through a window—maybe through blinds—creating an irregular shape on a wooden floor. The sun accentuates the dust, making it all the harder to sweep "till she was satisfied."

4. I can feel and smell and hear a late summer night (it must be late summer if the wheat is up). The crickets are singing and a breeze is causing the wheat to wave gently and to rustle as its ripe heads come into contact with one another.

5. First, I can see the white foam and roiled water as they roll up on the beach or among some rocks. The water splashes back upon itself as each wave recedes. Then I can hear the rhythmic roaring and the crash of the "pistol-shot collisions"—the sound overtakes everything.

"Uphill" by Christina Rossetti
"Summer" by Walter Dean Myers
Ecclesiastes 3:1–8,
The King James Bible
"The Bells" by Edgar Allan Poe

Build Vocabulary (p. 213)

A. Suggested responses:

1. *Monogamy* means "being married to one person."
2. *Monochrome* means "one color."
3. *Monologue* means "a performance or speech by one person."
4. *Monosyllabic* means "having one syllable."

B. 1. true
2. false
3. true
4. false
5. false

C. 1. b 2. d

Build Grammar Skills: End Punctuation
(p. 214)

A. Suggested responses:

1. distress
2. resignation
3. excitement
4. disbelief
5. intensity
6. resignation

B. Suggested responses:

1. I've been looking forward to it for weeks!
2. But didn't you get a ticket for me?
3. You never said any such thing!
4. Good, I was worried for a moment.

Reading Strategy: Listen (p. 215)

Suggested responses:

1. The rhythm is short and regular; the short lines and simple words create a rolling rhythm.
2. The rhythm encourages the reader to read at a lively pace.
3. The lively rhythm reinforces the poem's happy and spirited ideas of summer.
4. Rhythm, rhyme, and alliteration combine to re-create the sound of fire alarm bells.
5. Rhyme and rhythm underscore the frightening feel of the alarm bells. Reading the lines aloud, the reader can almost hear the bells clanging.

Literary Analysis: Lyric Poetry and Sound Devices (p. 216)

Suggested responses:

"Uphill": Rhythm: varying patterns of three and four beats per line; Alliteration: none; Rhyme: end words in question lines rhyme and end words in answer lines rhyme; Onomatopoeia: none

"Summer": Rhythm: pattern of two, three, and four beats; Alliteration: bugs buzzin, Running and ripping; Rhyme: end rhymes (dripping and ripping) and rhymes within lines (beaming and dreaming); Onomatopoeia: buzzin, peeping

Ecclesiastes 3:1–8: Rhythm: fairly regular pattern of equal stress within pairs of opposites; Alliteration: repetition of initial *t* in *time;* Rhyme: none; Onomatopoeia: none

"The Bells": Rhythm: varying beats and stresses mimic sound of bells and create tone; Alliteration: repetition of soft sounds (merriment their melody foretells) and harsh sounds (the clamor and the clangor); Rhyme: lots of end rhymes; Onomatopoeia: tinkle, twinkle, twanging, clanging

"The Raven" by Edgar Allan Poe
"The Seven Ages of Man" by William Shakespeare

Build Vocabulary (p. 217)

A. Suggested responses:

1. a dramatic speech in which a character speaks to himself or herself

2. alone, single
3. single performer

B. 1. a 2. c 3. d 4. b 5. c 6. a 7. c

Build Grammar Skills: Punctuation With Quotation Marks (p. 218)

A. Practice

1. I 2. C 3. C 4. I

B. Writing Application

Last night, I heard a strange noise, and I said to myself, "It's probably the wind"; however, when it got louder, I asked in a trembling voice, "Who's there?" When my cat wandered into the room, I sighed, "Oh, it was only Goldie."

Reading Strategy: Drawing Inferences About the Speaker (p. 219)

Suggested responses:

"The Raven"

1. He is gloomy and depressed. Word clues: *dreary, weak,* and *weary*
2. He is mourning the death of his beloved Lenore.

"The Seven Ages of Man"

1. He is a cynic who thinks life is of little serious consequence.
2. He finds them ridiculous and completely obsessed with love.

Literary Analysis: Narrative and Dramatic Poetry (p. 220)

Suggested responses:

"The Raven"

1. The speaker is a gloomy, depressed young man.
2. Other characters include the mourned Lenore and a raven.
3. The poem takes place late at night during a bleak, dreary December.
4. The poem tells the story of a depressed man who, in despair over the loss of his beloved Lenore, is haunted by thoughts of death.
5. The speaker desperately wants the raven to tell him whether there is life after death.

"The Seven Ages of Man"

1. He is a cynic or bitter realist who does not think matters of life are of serious consequence.

"The Raven" by Edgar Allan Poe
"The Seven Ages of Man"
by William Shakespeare (continued)

2. Perhaps the speaker is an old man who looks back bitterly, or a young man whose cynical nature forms his attitude.

3. He describes his view of the seven ages of man, from infancy to death. He views each of the seven ages with contempt.

4. Perhaps he feels as he does toward "the lover" because he has never been loved.

5. We do not know the "developing situation" within the play in which this speech is made. The experience of reading the dramatic monologue would be enhanced by knowing the situation within the play, the characters to whom the speaker is responding, and the events to which he is responding.

"On the Grasshopper and the Cricket" by John Keats
Sonnet 30 by William Shakespeare
Three Haiku by Bashō and Chiyojo
"Hokku Poems" by Richard Wright

Build Vocabulary (p. 221)

A. 1. b 2. c 3. a 4. d

B. Suggested responses:

1. The sculptor *wrought* a delicate metal dragonfly.

2. The poet expressed a feeling of *woe* over the lost friendship.

3. Listening to a cricket's chirping might lead to *drowsiness.*

4. The *ceasing* of the temple bells and the fragrance of the blossoms signal a "perfect evening."

C. 1. b 2. c

Build Grammar Skills: Hyphens (p. 222)

A. Practice

1. greenish-brown
2. never-ceasing
3. twenty-five
4. well-known
5. president-elect

B. Writing Application

Sample response:

In "On the Grasshopper and the Cricket," the poet calls the sounds of the insects "poetry of earth." The creatures' well-sung songs comfort those who hear them.

Reading Strategy: Reading in Sentences (p. 223)

Suggested responses:

1. Reading until the first long pause indicated by the dash in line 5 helps you understand that these lines express a single idea—the grasshopper's voice runs about the meadow.

2. The longest pauses or stops occur at the end of line 1, within lines 5 and 6, and at the end of line 8. They are indicated by a colon, dashes, and a period.

3. That is the grasshopper's. He takes the lead in summer luxury. He has never done with his delights, for when tired out with fun he rests at ease beneath some pleasant weed.

Literary Analysis: Sonnets and Haiku (p. 224)

Suggested responses:

1. *cdecde*

2. They are a sestet, not a quatrain and a couplet. They present one unified idea.

3. fading temple bells and fragrant blossoms

4. The contrasting images create a peaceful, relaxed impression.

Unit 10:   The Epic

The *Odyssey,* Part 1 by Homer

Build Vocabulary (p. 225)

A. 1. helium; 2. Trojan horse; 3. calypso; 4. titanic

B. 1. e 2. f 3. d 4. b 5. h 6. i 7. c 8. a 9. g

C. 1. d 2. a

Build Grammar Skills: Usage: *Like* and *As If* (p. 226)

A. Practice

1. As
2. like
3. as if
4. like

5. As
6. as
7. as

B. Writing Application

Sample response:

Reading about Odysseus' adventures is like watching an adventure film. Homer describes the events as if he were there. As Odysseus confronts each crisis, he really acts like a hero.

Reading Strategy: Reading in Sentences (p. 227)

Suggested responses:

1. Sirens weaving a haunting song over the sea we are to shun, she said, and their green shore all sweet with clover.
2. Dear friends, Circe told me what she foresaw for us, and I think I should share her words with you. If we're going to die, we should at least go into the situation prepared.
3. 1) Tie me up tightly; 2) Lash me to the mast; 3) If I shout and beg to be untied, wrap more rope around me.

Literary Analysis: The Epic Hero (p. 228)

1. **Physical:** He rounds up some of his men and ties them on board to keep them from the Lotus-Eaters. **Intellectual:** He resolves to resist the temptations of the Lotus-Eaters.
2. **Physical:** He leads his men in attacking the Cyclops at just the right time—after he has gotten the Cyclops drunk. **Intellectual:** He devises the plan to fool the Cyclops and escape, using the name "Nobody" as the key.
3. **Physical:** He endures being tied to the mast and steels himself to bear the song that all others find irresistible. **Intellectual:** He works out a plan to escape the lure of the Sirens, stopping the ears of his crew with beeswax.
4. **Physical:** Never yielding, he leads his men in attempting to overcome the hazards of the monster and of the whirlpool. **Intellectual:** His strategy enables the crew to avoid panic, minimize their losses, and at last escape.

The *Odyssey*, Part 2 by Homer

Build Vocabulary (p. 229)

A. Suggested responses:

1. A traveler wants to find a town *equidistant* from his home and his destination in which to spend the night. That town will be halfway, or an equal distance, from both his home and his destination.
2. If you were a careful fruit vendor who sells fruit by the pound, you would likely *equilibrate*, or balance/make equal, your scales regularly.
3. Because you are a very nervous person, your friends recommend that you strive for some *equanimity*, or evenness of mind, in your life.
4. As an architect studying weight-bearing structures, you are particularly interested in constructions that include *equilateral*, or equal-sided, triangles.

B. 1. b 2. c 3. f 4. a 5. g 6. h 7. d 8. e

C. 1. c 2. b 3. c

Build Grammar Skills: Usage: *Among* and *Between* (p. 230)

A. Practice

1. between
2. among
3. between
4. between
5. between
6. between

B. Writing Application

Sample responses:

1. In ancient Greece, stories were passed around among many people.
2. In the *Odyssey*, there is a big fight between Odysseus and Cyclops.
3. There is a strong relationship between Odysseus and his crew.
4. Penelope has grown very weary of living among the many suitors.

The *Odyssey*, Part 2
by Homer *(continued)*

Reading Strategy: Summarizing (p. 231)

Suggested responses:

Odysseus' Return to Ithaca—Odysseus, on Athena's advice, reveals his identity to his son Telemachus. Telemachus informs Odysseus of the behavior and number of suitors. Odysseus devises a way for him and Telemachus to overcome the suitors. In the meantime, Odysseus will remain in Athena's disguise as he enters his own house.

Argus—An old dog, Argus, whom Odysseus had trained before he set sail for Troy, recognizes his master's voice. Odysseus sees how he is neglected and wipes away a tear. The neglected old dog dies, satisfied at having seen his master once more.

The Suitors—Upon entering his home disguised as a beggar, Odysseus is challenged by the suitor Antinous. They exchange words and Antinous angrily hurls a stool at the "beggar." Telemachus sits by, barely containing his anger. Penelope hears of the beggar's treatment and has him summoned to see if he knows anything about Odysseus.

Penelope—Penelope questions the disguised Odysseus. Penelope tells of her difficulties, her ruse of weaving now having failed. Odysseus, in turn, makes up a story and declares that he knows Penelope's husband will arrive soon.

The Challenge—Penelope devises a difficult contest, saying that she will marry the winner. The suitors all try and fail to shoot an arrow through twelve axhandle sockets. The disguised Odysseus gets a turn. He readies his own familiar bow carefully and shoots his arrow cleanly through the axhandles. Telemachus, at his father's sign, straps on his sword and steps to his father's side.

Odysseus' Revenge—Odysseus reveals his true identity to everyone present. He immediately kills Antinous and has the suitors' attention. The suitor Eurymachus tries to soothe Odysseus with payment in oxen and with gifts. Odysseus will accept only their deaths in payment. The suitors swarm to overpower Odysseus, but Odysseus, with the help of Telemachus, Eumaeus, and another herdsman, is able to kill all the suitors.

Penelope's Test—Penelope instructs a servant to make up Odysseus' bed for him outside of her bedchamber. Odysseus angrily replies that no one could possibly have moved their bed, since he had built it himself into the trunk of an old olive tree. Penelope then knows that this really is Odysseus, because no one except herself, one servant, and Odysseus had ever laid eyes on the bed. They embrace and weep.

Literary Analysis: Epic Simile (p. 232)

A. 1. c 2. b

B. 1. d 2. b

"An Ancient Gesture" by Edna St. Vincent Millay
"Siren Song" by Margaret Atwood
"Prologue" and "Epilogue" from *The Odyssey* by Derek Walcott
"Ithaca" by Constantine Cavafy

Build Vocabulary (p. 233)

A. Suggested response:

1. frighteningly gross; The grotesque mask made us shiver.

2. tall, like a statue; We admired the statuesque horse.

3. related to Roman culture; We studied Romanesque art.

B. 1. d 2. a 3. e 4. f 5. b 6. c

Build Grammar Skills: Varying Sentence Lengths (p. 234)

Practice:

Sample responses:

1. When the Sirens sing their irresistible song, it always forces me to leap overboard.

2. Odysseus hoped to travel safely home from Troy. He and his crew had many difficult adventures, but many of them survived the journey.

3. Their difficult journey to Ithaca was worthwhile because it presented challenging and valuable experiences. Odysseus and his men confronted Cyclops and Poseidon, and they saw lots of seaports and Egyptian cities.

Reading Strategy: Comparing and Contrasting (p. 235)

Suggested responses:

Students should be aware of the details taken directly from Homer as well as the details found in each modern interpretation.

Literary Analysis: Contemporary Interpretations (p. 236)

1. a 2. b 3. d 4. b 5. a